Robin Koffler MBA FCIM | Jason Yate

CW00799095

the **power protection** *guide*

The design, installation and operation
of uninterruptible power supplies

UK First Edition

Riello UPS Manufacturing srl

First published in the UK in 2007 for:

Riello UPS Manufacturing srl
Viale Europa, 7 ZAI
37048 S. Pietro di Legnago
Verona, Italy
www.riello-ups.com

entiveon Publishing
3 Wychwood Court
Cotswold Business Village
London Road
Moreton-in-Marsh
GL56 0JQ United Kingdom
www.entiveon.com

Cover design by Laura Dines
Edited by entiveon Publishing - www.entiveon.com
Design and layout by Laura Dines
Printed and Bound in the UK by Artisan Print & Design Ltd - www.artisanlitho.co.uk

Contents

3. UPS Sizing and Selection 49

8. Alarm Monitoring and Remote Control

10. Warranties, Maintenance and Services   207

Appendices 215

Indexes 270

Forward

Securing a source of power has become an essential part of everyday life and a fundamental aspect of any continuity plan.

The demands for services such as banking, utilities, broadcast, global manufacturing, supply chains and information resources, rely on complex computer and communication technologies with voracious appetites for electricity. In the last two decades, global commerce has grown at an unprecedented rate in the same timeframe as consumption of electricity has risen by a staggering 30%.

This need for power - and increase in its consumption - is unlikely to diminish. Add to this the growing risk to power continuity and threats of the modern era, such as unusual weather phenomena and terrorism, and it soon becomes obvious the world is on the brink of an energy crisis. We have already witnessed high-profile power cuts in many capital cities such as New York and London. Existing power infrastructures and supply networks cannot cope with the current level of demand and in some countries governments have already begun to implement energy rationing measures. This situation demands a radical new approach to power continuity from commerce, industry and governments alike. Security operations, defence ministries and emergency services, the world over, are not exempt either. All of them are having to recognise responsibility in terms of securing and ensuring power protection. Businesses are now also realising they are at the mercy of suppliers, including electricity providers, and in order to comply with regulations and ensure continuity of trade, they need to take steps to implement their own power protection measures. One such measure is the installation and usage of uninterruptible power supplies (UPS) and standby power systems.

Today's business environments particularly telecommunications, where convergence between voice and data processing technologies is rife, are also striving for the highest availability for their services and systems. UPS can perform a vital role in attaining this but the reliability of any installation is dependent upon a number of key factors: the choice of UPS topology and its fault tolerance; battery run-time; standby power arrangements; environmental conditions and, within the installation itself, the management of any single-points-of-failure.

UPS is a complex subject and requires fundamental and in-depth knowledge if costly pitfalls are to be avoided. The Power Protection Guide has been produced for this purpose and is born out of the knowledge and expertise obtained from installing thousands of Riello UPS systems globally over many years. We hope you find it both useful and informative.

Roberto Facci
Commercial Director - Riello UPS Manufacturing srl

About The Power Protection Guide

This guide is intended to provide a generic overview of the design, installation and operation of secure power protection systems for a wide readership including:

- computer, telecoms and data centre managers
- consultants and specifiers
- facilities managers, electrical engineers and contractors
- project managers
- power protection resellers and consultants

Each chapter covers a specific topic area and can be read in isolation. As a whole, the guide represents best practice in power protection and how to achieve the highest levels of resilience and power continuity. All ratings and data given are to be considered typically representative of the technologies currently available and supporting appendices provide additional information. When comparing information between UPS suppliers, we recommend you ensure a common basis for analysis.

Blog

This guide is supported by a blog at www.power-protection.co.uk

Contacts

Riello UPS operates a Technical Energy Consultant (TEC) team from its manufacturing base in Italy and within each of its subsidiaries in Europe and Asia. For more information visit: www.riello-ups.com

Riello UPS subsidiary contact details can be found on page 290 at the end of this guide.

Acknowledgements

Robin Koffler and Jason Yates from Riello UPS Ltd, the UK subsidiary of Riello UPS Manufacturing srl, have written The Power Protection Guide with help, advice and support from: Bill Knight (independent consultant), Leo Craig (Riello UPS Ltd), Riello UPS Manufacturing (Massimo Zampieri, Stefano Sinigallia) and Riello Onduleurs (Raymond Ritter). The input from the Riello UPS Manufacturing Research & Development teams headed by Alessandro Policante and Maurizio Scarpone, is also acknowledged. Without their innovation and world class designs, Riello UPS would not be in the position it is today at the forefront of the power protection industry. Copy and editorial advice was provided by Alison Campbell of entiveon Publishing and design and layout by Laura Dines.

1. Power Quality, Problems and Solutions

In this chapter:

- Understanding how electricity is generated.
- Explaining power problems and their effect on sensitive loads.
- Power Continuity Plans and Uninterruptible Power Supplies (UPS).
- Alternative power protection solutions.

Introduction

Most organisations are now wholly dependent on their data and voice processing systems. They have become a fundamental part of everyday infrastructure and a partial or total failure can have catastrophic consequences including financial impact and loss of Business Continuity.

The more central these computer and telecommunications systems to product and service delivery, the more they can be classified as *Critical Loads*. For most organisations, two further classes of load can also be identified, known as *Essential* and *Non-essential*.

Critical loads directly affect the ability of an organisation to operate and must either be kept running when their mains power supply fails or be powered down in an orderly manner to prevent system crashes, data corruption and life shortening hardware damage. Their routine operation can also be interrupted when the mains power supply is polluted.

Essential loads provide secondary support services and may be required for health & safety reasons or to maintain ambient temperature levels. Whilst requiring a form of back-up in case of mains power supply failure, they do not require uninterruptible power and can be allowed to fail or ride through the time it takes for a generator or alternative back-up systems to start-up. Examples of essential loads include air-conditioning, heating and emergency lighting.

Non-essential loads are those that an organisation can afford to lose when the mains power supply fails, for example, general lighting and some print services.

Power problems are by their very nature unpredictable and power quality varies across the world. Within developed nations, mains power supply failures are becoming more frequent due to rapidly expanding demands for electricity and aging generation and distribution infrastructures. In terms of power quality today, a major European capital like London can expect up to 30 power quality events per annum and this is forecast to rise. In the UK, electricity consumption is increasing by roughly 20% each decade and it is forecast that the country will only be able to generate 80% of its power needs by 2012.

The country will become more dependent on imported gas supplies, nuclear power and investments in alternative energy sources such as wind, wave and solar power, which will further complicate supply issues.

Outside of Europe, the USA experienced the largest power failure in history in 2003 when a single incident led to 21 power stations failing within three minutes leaving over 55 million people - commercial, industrial, government, military, emergency services and domestic users - without mains power. In California, electricity supply has already been rationed at peak times, as it has in Brazil and China. Emerging economic areas like China and India are also experiencing the problems associated with rapid modernisation, including huge demands for electrical power.

Across the world, business continuity is a fundamental concern for most organisations. Reliable power is just one aspect that can affect routine operations and this can be achieved through the implementation of a *Power Continuity Plan*.

1.1 Electricity Generation and Distribution

Electricity is produced in a number of ways; at a coal, gas-fired or nuclear generating station, or through some form of renewable technology such as wind, wave or solar power. The actual phenomenon used to generate electricity is known as *Electro-Magnetic Induction* the output of which is an *alternating current (ac)* waveform. The process is one where magnets on a shaft are rotated near three windings into which electric current is induced (referred to as *Electro-Motive Force*). The difference between the various energy generation types is the fuel used to make the shaft spin. The windings within a generator are separated by 120° of rotation to create a three-phase waveform, comprising of phase 1 (P1), phase 2 (P2) and phase 3 (P3) components.

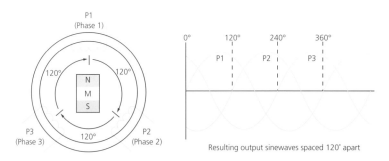

Diagram 1.1 – Three-phase supply generation and output waveform

In the UK, electricity is generated typically at 25kV and then stepped up to 275/400kV before distribution as a three-phase 50Hz supply. This high voltage helps to overcome distribution network resistance and transmission losses. As electricity moves through the network to its point of use, the voltage is reduced. On the outskirts of major cities and towns, substations lower the voltage to 132kV. To these are connected 33kV and 11kV substations found within the area or very close to the point of delivery.

Typically, at the substation a neutral and earth reference are added. The substation then supplies a 400Vac three-phase plus neutral and earth (TP+N+E) supply to the *incomer* of a site or building, known as the *Point of Common Coupling (PCC)*. A single-phase 230Vac supply can be derived from the same substation (or incomer), by drawing on any one phase and neutral. In this way, the earth and neutral reference points are connected all the way back along the distribution network to the substation.

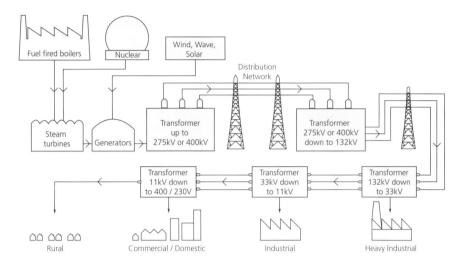

Diagram 1.2 – Typical electricity distribution schematic showing voltage reduction

Electricity generation and distribution is governed by a number of country specific Grid, Transmission and Distribution codes. These stipulate, in particular, the minimum and maximum voltage and frequency values allowed. For any site, the quality of power received through its incomer is directly affected by the performance of the electrical distribution network upstream. Today this can be intercontinental and across a range of political environments. Within a distribution network power problems can result from:

- normal network operation, grid switching, auto re-closers and fault tracing
- network hardware failure including transformer and breaker malfunctions
- power shortages during peak demand periods when supply is restricted
- accidental severing of supply cables during construction or street works
- acts of terrorism, vandalism or deliberate sabotage
- environmental conditions such as lightning activity, heat, rain, snow, ice, wind or wildlife

On any site, a stable and clean electrical supply can be affected by local overloading, simple switchgear faults and the operation of industrial or commercial equipment and fittings including: mechanical presses, welding equipment, lifts, escalators, air-conditioners, photocopiers and fluorescent lights. All can induce power problems into a mains power supply that was reasonably stable and clean beforehand.

1.2 Power Problems

A general definition of poor power quality is: any variation in electrical power resulting in malfunction or equipment failure. In terms of power protection, knowing which power problems are most prevalent, their magnitude and frequency, will affect the choice of power solution selected.

Power failures are the most obvious power problem and evidence points to more frequent, short breaks in supply. In the UK, the *Ofgem Electricity Distribution Quality of Supply Report* statistics for 2004/05 show the average number of minutes customers were off supply in 2004/05 across Great Britain was 94.3, an increase of 13.2 from 2003/04. This statistic relates to failures of three minutes or longer which is all that the electricity suppliers (*Network Operating Companies - NOCs*) are obliged to record.

The *Computer and Business Equipment Manufacturers Association (CBEMA)* curve, *diagram 1.3*, provides a graphical representation of the power quality required by critical loads and their *Power Supply Units (PSUs)*. The graph shows a typical PSU input tolerance envelope (input voltage window) and how it is affected by momentary breaks and changes in mains power supply voltage.

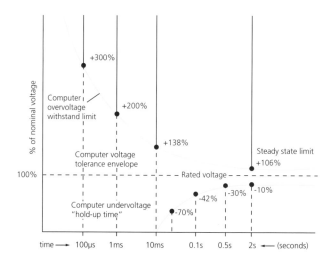

Diagram 1.3 – The Computer and Business Equipment Manufacturers Association Curve

The *Information Technology Industry Council (ITIC) curve* in *diagram 1.4,* developed this further to identify areas where equipment will malfunction and/or be damaged when subjected to the same levels of voltage fluctuations and breaks in supply.

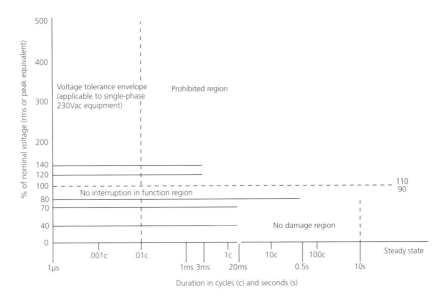

Diagram 1.4 – The Information Technology Industry Council Curve

In Europe, existing power quality is itself becoming more of an issue today with regulations to govern permissible *Harmonics* and *Electro-Magnetic Compatibility (EMC)* levels. Poor power quality can be as dangerous to critical loads as a partial or complete mains power supply failure leading to intermittent data corruption, and over long periods, hardware failure. The quality of a mains power supply is measured in terms of its waveform, voltage and frequency and the presence or not of a variety of power problems.

1.2.1 Sags

Sags are short duration voltage reductions below the nominal mains power supply level, typically lasting for several cycles. They are one of the more common forms of disturbance. When sag voltages fall below an expected input voltage window, data and voice processing hardware, for example, can lock-up, fail or re-boot. Sags can also result in more current being drawn by their PSUs as they strive to deliver the power required, resulting in component stress and heat build up. Possible causes include: switching heavy loads such as air-conditioners, motors, industrial machinery and other types of high in-rush loads, into or out of the local supply circuit.

Diagram 1.5 – Sag waveform

1.2.2 Brownouts

Brownouts are long-term reductions in the mains power supply voltage which can last up to several days and produce the same effects as sags. The term 'Brownout' comes from the effect seen in New York where heavy demand by air-conditioners on the local supply network lowers lighting levels within office and other environments.

1.2.3 Surges

Surges are short duration voltage increases above the nominal mains power supply level, which generally last for several cycles. When surge voltages rise above the input voltage window of a PSU, built-in cut-out protection will typically activate to protect the unit itself, resulting in a system crash. High surge voltages can lead to increased component wear-and-tear and general degradation over the long-term. This may not be noticed until failure, though 'hot-spots' are good indicators of future problems. Possible causes are the same as for sags.

Diagram 1.6 – Surge waveform

1.2.4 Spikes and Transients

Spikes and *Transients* are fast-moving, high-energy bursts (some in excess of 6kV or higher) lasting only a few milliseconds, superimposed onto the normal mains power supply. Their energy can cause board and processor damage, memory loss and data corruption. Possible causes include: nearby lightning strikes, electrical storms, local load shedding, fluorescent lights, relay-based thermostats and inductive motor loads such as lifts, escalators, fridges and freezers.

Diagram 1.7 – Spike or transient waveform

1.2.5 Electrical Noise

Electrical Noise is a high-frequency noise classed as either *Common* or *Normal Mode*. Common Mode is a disturbance that occurs between the supply lines and earth (phase-to-earth or neutral-to-earth). Normal Mode occurs between phase and neutral. Electrical noise can disrupt the operation of circuits and equipment and potentially damage them. Possible causes include: lighting (flickering), cable and switchgear faults and sometimes electronic equipment such as radio transmitters.

Diagram 1.8 – Electrical noise waveform

1.2.6 Harmonics

Harmonics are voltage or current waveforms the frequencies of which are multiples of the fundamental. In Europe the fundamental frequency is 50Hz (50 cycles per second) and the multiples are ordered into a specific sequence. For example, the 2nd harmonic is 100Hz (2x50Hz), 3rd harmonic 150Hz (3x50Hz) and 4th harmonic 200Hz (4x50Hz) and so on.

Diagram 1.9 – Distorted voltage waveform due to harmonics

The problems associated with harmonics include: distortion of the mains power supply voltage, overheating of building wiring circuits, neutral conductors, supply transformers and switchgear, and the nuisance tripping of breakers. Harmonics can also cause disruption to equipment on the same supply and lead to random failures.

Harmonic pollution is a growing problem. Within the UK, the subject is addressed by *Engineering Recommendation G5/4-1*, published by *The Energy Networks Association*. This is a guideline document, concerned with aggregate harmonic levels on mains power supplies within the voltage range 230V-400kVac, and particularly at the PCC and incomer of a building. In the UK, under the terms of their supply contract with a local electricity provider, all users are responsible for the total harmonic values generated at their PCC when new installations are made. When specific harmonic levels cannot be met, special approval may be required from the electricity supplier before connection.

Chapter 4 discusses the two main types of On-Line UPS, *transformer-based* and *transformerless*, and how they can be configured to achieve the lowest possible levels of total harmonic distortion. *Chapter 9* discusses the G5/4-1 assessment process in more detail from an electrical installation viewpoint and its relevance to the type of UPS installed.

Harmonics are an issue, in part, due to the high number of *Switch Mode Power Supply (SMPS)* loads being connected to electrical distribution networks. These are the most common form of PSU in use today and as a *non-linear* load they draw their power in regular, modulated pulses of current from a mains power supply rather than as continuous *linear* supply.

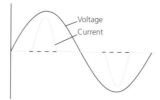

Diagram 1.10 – Typical current waveform drawn by an SMPS

This action can lead to an SMPS generating high levels of harmonics (especially when a large number are supplied from a three-phase mains power supply) including potentially damaging *Triple-Ns* or *Triplens* whose harmonic order numbers are multiples of three and include the 3rd, 9th and 15th. *Diagram 1.11* shows the 3rd harmonic, which is potentially the most serious in terms of neutral conductor loading (within a three-phase system).

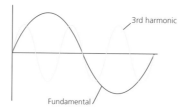

Diagram 1.11 – 3rd harmonic waveform superimposed on the fundamental sinewave

Diagram 1.12 shows the summing effects within the neutral conductor of the 3rd harmonics produced by the individual phases of a three-phase mains power supply. As these harmonics are multiples of three, they are all in phase with one another and therefore their magnitudes are added together. Other harmonic orders, not in phase with one another, simply cancel each other out. The summing effect of Triplen harmonics greatly increases the current flowing within the neutral, which can potentially overload conductors and switchgear.

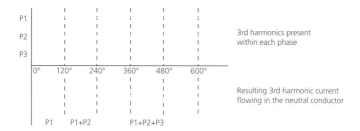

Diagram 1.12 – Cumulative effect of the Triplen harmonics

Even where the load is balanced across the phases, Triplens can generate neutral currents up to 1.73 (√3) times the average phase currents. The additional loading and heat generated can degrade upstream neutral conductors or transformer winding insulation and potentially lead to a fire hazard. Other sources of harmonics include: rectifiers, variable speed drives, discharge lamps, fluorescent lighting, mercury and sodium lamps.

1.2.7 Frequency Variations

Frequency variations are typically caused by poorly maintained standby power generators and can upset critical load operation. Especially where the zero-crossing (commutation point) of the supply sinewave is used as a timing or measurement reference.

Diagram 1.13 – Frequency variation waveform

1.2.8 Blackouts and Mains Power Supply Failures

A *Blackout* (also known as an *Outage*) is a complete mains power supply failure. This can last from milliseconds to several hours or more. Momentary breaks in the mains power supply can typically be long enough to 'crash', lock or re-boot the hardware within a data or voice processing network, including: PCs, terminals, consoles, servers, PBXs, printers, modems, hubs and routers.

Diagram 1.14 – Blackout and momentary break waveform

Power monitoring (or mains monitoring) is a service used to asses power quality. This service is generally provided by specialist companies and involves the connection of a portable monitoring device to a three-phase or single-phase mains power supply to record disturbances over a specified time period.

Power monitors can also be used to identify installation problems where electrical and protection devices are failing prematurely or not performing to specification. This is extremely rare and usually results from interaction with other hardware on site. Most monitors provide wave trace print-outs and digital data for analysis, showing the times and duration of any excursion outside set tolerances. Such units are available on a rental basis or can be purchased to become a permanent site fixture.

1.3 Power Continuity Plans and Uninterruptible Power Supplies

The purpose of a *Power Continuity Plan* is to provide a power protection system with the highest possible levels of *reliability* and *resilience* (fault tolerance). The plan design must allow for the continuous operation of critical loads irrespective of the quality or availability of a local mains power supply.

1.3.1 Critical, Essential and Non-Essential Loads

The first stage focuses on identifying the systems which could be affected by power problems. These will typically include:

- PCs, work stations, terminals, servers, hubs, routers and tape drives
- telecoms PBXs, Power-over-Ethernet (PoE) and Voice-over-IP (VoIP) devices
- Point-of-Sale (PoS) terminals, cash machines, kiosks and retail web servers
- instrumentation and Programmable Logic Controllers (PLCs)
- medical operating theatres and life support systems
- scientific experiments and measurement systems
- lighting, including tungsten, fluorescent and high-pressure discharge lamps
- access and security alarm systems including surveillance systems
- motor driven loads: lifts, escalators, air-conditioners, heating and ventilation systems

The aim is to group the loads into one of the three types: critical, essential or non-essential by considering their importance to the organisation in terms of:

- financial penalties, lost business and customer service
- service provision, transportation and emergency services
- lost production, scrapped materials, manufacturing moulds and furnaces
- quality, health & safety, and environmental systems
- security breaches and loss of control
- organisation reputation and stakeholder confidence

1.3.2 Power Quality Review

Stage two reviews each of the three groups in terms of:

- the quality of mains power available and any historical power problems
- the quality of power required in terms of its voltage, frequency and current
- future demands and power supply reliability
- alternative power sources on site
- priority-based load shedding and shutdown

Where the power quality of a particular site is suspect, direct data can be gathered from the power monitoring service already described. Alternatively, IT system event logs and electrical system maintenance records can provide useful information on which to base assumptions. An IT event log could record, for example, the date and time of specific system hardware failures, data corruptions and system lock-ups. Electrical system maintenance records could record incidents of sudden circuit-breaker tripping, fuse ruptures, relay chattering, or simply the dimming or flickering of overhead lights.

The load itself may vary considerably in type and size. Each load will have its own demands in terms of the current drawn (*Amps*), power consumed and voltage and frequency of supply required. Within Europe most loads generally draw either a single-phase 230Vac or three-phase 400Vac supply at 50Hz.

Computer and telecommunications loads can range from single desktop computers and keyphone systems to fully integrated data centres using the latest software-based PBX technologies, Blade and Edge servers. Each piece of hardware should be assessed to establish both the in-rush (switch-on) and normal running current levels of their PSUs, which will generally be SMPS-based.

An SMPS converts the *ac* voltage of its mains power supply into the *direct current (dc)* required for the various voltage rails needed to power internal assemblies such as processor and memory boards. The typical modern SMPS is designed for mass distribution and can be operated on either a 230Vac 50Hz or 120Vac 60Hz mains power supply. The corresponding input voltage windows will be around 180-264Vac and 90-130Vac respectively, with specialist wider voltage ranges available.

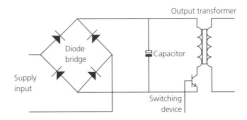

Diagram 1.15 – Basic SMPS input stage design

At switch-on, most SMPS have a high in-rush current (as internal capacitors and inductors are charged), which then reduces down to a normal running current. Through internal capacitance, an SMPS can provide a 'hold-up' time of around 10-30ms or longer and this allows it to ride through short duration interruptions in mains power. The actual time is dependent upon the design of the SMPS, energy stored at the time of the interruption and the load characteristics. For critical military applications, *MIL-STD-704A* specifies a hold-up time of 50ms.

Small, older SMPS designs tend to have a poor *Power Factor (pF)* of typically 0.55 to 0.65. This represents how far the current waveform drawn by a load is out of phase with the voltage waveform from its mains power supply. The nearer the power factor is to *unity* (1) the closer the two waveforms are in phase with one another, and the more efficiently the device uses the power drawn. For example, an SMPS with a power factor of 0.55 will have to draw more current to achieve the same output power characteristics as an SMPS with a power factor of 0.9. Loads with poor power factors place extra current demands on supply connections including cabling, conductors, transformers and distribution boards.

Most modern SMPS now incorporate either passive or active *Power Factor Correction (PFC)* to comply with European regulations. The aim is to make the input current drawn by the SMPS appear more linear and in phase with the voltage waveform available from the mains power supply. Within Europe, *EN/IEC 61000-3-2* stipulates that an SMPS above 75W must include a *passive* PFC to achieve 0.7 to 0.75pF. With an *active* PFC front-end, a PSU can achieve an input power factor of up to 0.99.

Linear loads draw their power in more regular sinusoidal waveforms and include heaters and lighting. Linear loads are generally classed as essential or non-essential dependent upon whether or not they have a vital role to perform.

This can be the case with air-conditioning within data centres where the typical hardware in use (a rack cabinet of Blade servers, for example) can generate a large amount of heat (up to 18kW) at any one time. Without sufficient air-conditioning, their reliable operation cannot be guaranteed.

However, air-conditioners can add a significant load to a power protection system. In addition, whilst most air-conditioners have soft-start features they can still have fairly high in-rush currents (up to five or six times that of their normal levels) which need to be factored into any sizing calculations.

Lighting is another load which may be classed as either essential or non-essential. For example, emergency lighting may be required for evacuation purposes on mains power supply failure but at reduced levels. There are also various forms of lighting, each with their own characteristics. A tungsten lamp, depending upon design, has an in-rush current of ten-to-15 times normal running current. This current is of a highly transient nature and may only be present for a matter of one to two cycles. A fluorescent lamp has an in-rush of two to three times nominal for approximately one to two seconds and can induce harmonics back onto the mains power supply.

High pressure discharge lamps usually have a fairly long run up time of two to five minutes, which can cause power factor and harmonic problems. These types of lamp are also sensitive to surges and transient voltages. A loss of power for more than one cycle can extinguish them, leading to a restart period of five minutes or more. This is because the lamps have an arc tube, running close to or slightly above atmospheric pressure, and they need to cool down and reduce internal pressure prior to re-striking.

The sensitivity of the loads to the range of potential power problems and supply waveforms should also be assessed. For example, instrumentation loads may use highly sensitive relays which can trip-out within half a cycle (10ms) of power loss. Most SMPS will work on either a sinewave, modified sinewave (step-wave) or square-wave supply. A sinewave is the waveform generated within the distribution network and is the most suitable for long-term operation. Step and square-waves are the most basic type of waveform and are generated, for example, by simple inverters. The peak voltages of these inferior waveforms are substantially lower than the peak voltages of a true sinewave and this can lead to component stress, wear-and-tear, and at worst, early failure of a PSU in its working life.

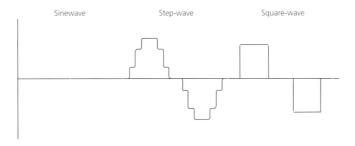

Sinewave   Step-wave   Square-wave

Diagram 1.16 – Types of inverter output waveforms

Whilst the loads are assessed in terms of their power draw, a safety margin should be added for system expansion within a two to five year period. This guideline factor is typically 25% of today's load and it can be achieved by over-sizing the power solution or providing the facility to install additional capacity at a later date.

An estimate of future power quality and availability should also be made. For example, within the London financial district of Canary Wharf, organisations now face potential supply issues in terms of power availability. This is due to growth rates far exceeding expectations and the supplies originally laid down for the area. Alternate on-site power sources to be used within the *Power Continuity Plan* should also be investigated. Large sites may already have on-site power generation in the form of local generators with spare capacity.

Once the loads have been identified they can be prioritised by their level of importance to an organisation, whether they must be kept running during a mains power supply failure and for how long. Some critical loads may only require sufficient back-up time for shutdown - a local file server, for example. Others may need to be kept running for as long as possible such as a telecommunications PBX supporting critical services. This aspect of the plan is known as *load shedding.*

1.3.3 UPS Selection

There are many types of power solution available and the selection process must be geared towards choosing the solution that achieves the highest level of resilience for the budget available. For data and voice processing systems, the most commonly implemented power solution is a UPS because of its ability to provide a clean and stable source of uninterruptible power. *EN/IEC 62040-3:* defines three generic Static (solid-state) UPS topologies and within each classifies a UPS based on its output waveform and dynamic performance:

- **VFI - Voltage and Frequency Independent:** more generally referred to as *On-Line* or *Double-Conversion* where the UPS output is independent of any fluctuations in *ac* supply voltage (for example, mains or generator) and frequency variations are maintained within the limits prescribed by EN/IEC 61000-2-2. The highest classification for an On-Line UPS is VFI-SS-111.

- **VI - Voltage Independent:** usually referred to as *Line Interactive*, where voltage fluctuations are stabilised and regulated to within an output specification by built-in passive (electronic) regulation devices. When a mains power supply is present the output frequency of the UPS tracks the input frequency of the mains.

- **VFD - Voltage and Frequency Dependent:** more commonly referred to as *Off-Line* or *Standby* where the output of the UPS tracks the mains power supply in terms of voltage and frequency variations.

Power Problem	On-Line (VFI)	Line Interactive (VI)	Off-Line (VFD)
Sags/Brownouts	yes	yes	-
Surges	yes	yes	-
Spikes/Transients	yes	yes	yes
Electrical Noise	yes	yes	yes
Harmonics	yes	-	-
Frequency Variations	yes	-	-
Mains Failures	yes	yes	yes

Table 1.1 – UPS topologies and performance

Each of the three Static UPS topologies provides varying degrees of power protection.

On-Line UPS are the preferred choice for critical data and voice processing systems because they provide superior electrical performance (whether on mains or battery power), a break-free supply on mains power supply failure (or restore) and an automatic system bypass for safe failure to mains if an overload or fault condition occurs.

On-Line UPS are typically used for a number of specialist applications where they can be modified using a range of accessories and small batch production techniques, including:

- Rail (unmanned signalling and telecoms) requiring runtimes up to 12 hours, batteries to BS 6290-4 and flame retardant, fast recharge and small cabinet footprints.
- Remote mobile telecommunications sites where there is a high risk of damage to the UPS itself from lightning strikes and high-energy transients.
- Industrial areas where a variety of dusts, powders, and oily atmospheres require specialised air filters to prevent ingress, corrosion and fire risks.
- Water treatment works requiring UPS with raised plinths and *Ingress Protection (IP)* ratings greater than 20.
- Scientific sites at altitude and tropical (with high humidity) or sub-zero temperature areas.
- Military applications requiring ruggedised assemblies for transportation and wide operating temperature ranges.
- Remote sites where wind, wave or solar energy are the only power sources, and a guaranteed uninterruptible power source is required.
- Medical applications (operating rooms, intensive care and cardiac areas) requiring an isolated supply, low earth leakage and power restoration within 0.5 seconds.

Most On-Line UPS can act as frequency converters providing 50/60Hz or 60/50Hz. Special application solutions exist for 400Hz systems. Voltage conversion (*ac*) is also possible using double-wound transformers to match the local electrical supply to that of the load. These transformers can be used either on the input or output of the UPS to step voltages up or down. Care has to be taken when sizing them. On the output side, the transformer must be matched to the rating of the UPS. On the input side, the transformer needs to be oversized to cater for input power factors, battery charging and any operating losses.

Chapter 2 discusses Static UPS topologies in more detail and identifies the levels of power protection that each approach provides, the size of application they can support, accessories, features and benefits. The chapter also provides a brief introduction to a fourth category of UPS, known as a *Rotary UPS*. These rely on Kinetic rather than stored electrical energy to support their loads and are considered only as an alternative to Static UPS systems for very large installations such as industrial complexes.

There are two approaches to Static *On-Line* UPS: transformer-based and transformerless. The features and benefits of both are discussed in *chapter 4*, whilst *chapter 5* discusses how to operate both types of UPS in parallel configurations to achieve scalable and more fault tolerant solutions.

1.3.4 Battery Sets, Flywheels and Fuel Cells

Battery performance is one of the most central features within a *Power Continuity Plan*. In a UPS, the battery set provides a source of power when the mains power supply fails. For a generator, they are an integral part of the automatic starter-circuit. *Chapter 6* discusses battery topologies, battery installation, life expectancy, testing and other aspects that can affect performance. The chapter concludes with an overview of alternative technologies including *dc* flywheels, fuel cells and super capacitors.

1.3.5 Generators

In a *Power Continuity Plan* generators provide a source of standby power when the mains power supply fails. On start-up, generators can take from five to 15 seconds before they can supply their rated output power and a suitable waveform. A UPS typically uses its battery set to cover this period and maintain power to the critical loads.

Generators can also be used to supply essential loads directly (for example, air-conditioners) as these are less susceptible to mains power disturbances and momentary interruptions. If placed on a UPS, such loads could also lead to dramatic and costly over sizing.

Chapter 7 provides an overview of generator design, sizing for UPS compatibility, and generator installation, operation, testing and maintenance. It concludes by introducing gas turbines and developments in this area.

1.3.6 Alarm Monitoring, Communication and Control

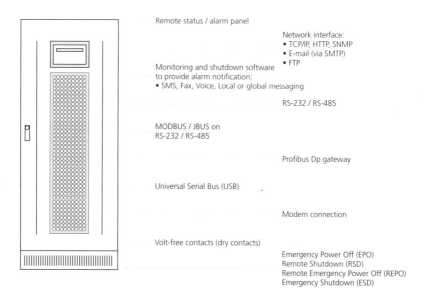

Diagram 1.17 – Typical remote monitoring methods

Most UPS and generators provide signals for alarm notification and interfaces for remote monitoring and control. How an organisation responds to such alarms and the actions taken when they arise needs to be considered, especially for remote and unmanned applications. *Chapter 8* explains in detail the levels and types of alarms that can be generated by a UPS and describes the software and hardware accessories available for remote monitoring.

1.3.7 Project Management, Logistics and Installation

The larger the UPS the more it may be part of a far wider project with specific time slots for installation and commissioning. *Chapter 9* provides an overview of UPS project management and discusses site surveys, electrical installation and power distribution.

1.3.8 Warranties, Maintenance and Service

Chapter 10 provides an overview of what a UPS manufacturer should provide in terms of warranties, maintenance support and pre and post sale services. UPS are supplied with standard 'return-to-base' or on-site warranties but for critical applications a maintenance plan with guaranteed response times should be considered. For customers requiring a two-hour response, *crash kits* (first line spares) may be held on-site with trained engineers available nearby.

1.4 Other Power Solutions

Other power solutions are available which provide varying degrees of protection. Some may be more expensive than an equivalently rated UPS at certain power levels. These alternative solutions are mentioned here briefly as their mode of operation may be discussed elsewhere in this *Power Protection Guide*. They can be grouped into those that provide standby back-up power and those that only provide some form of power protection when a mains power supply is present.

1.4.1 Standby Back-Up Power Solutions

a) Central Power Supply Systems (CPSS) For Emergency Applications

This product is similar in design and operation to that of an On-Line UPS but configured to meet EN 50171, the European standard for *Central Power Supply Systems for Emergency Applications*, including lighting, alarms and security applications. A typical CPSS has the following characteristics:

- extended battery runtimes (three hours - or one hour if there is a generator on-site)
- very short recharge times to 80% within 12 hours
- battery deep discharge protection
- high-level diagnostics, from a front mimic panel display
- remote interface, normally volt-free contacts or RS-232 communications
- high in-rush (short-circuit) current capability, especially for emergency lighting
- optional Galvanic isolation - a complete separation of the input and output supplies

Some of the On-Line UPS discussed within this guide can be configured to operate in the modes required from a CPSS device as defined by EN 50171.

b) Standby Power Systems (SPS)

Some telecoms loads are *dc* powered and rely on a *Standby Power System (SPS)* with a built-in rectifier to provide this source when the mains power supply is present (and charge a battery set). The battery set is sized to support the load when the mains power supply fails, for a duration of several minutes to many hours.

Within a *Power Continuity Plan*, an SPS can be left to run as a standalone device or be powered from a UPS or generator.

c) Inverters

Inverters provide either a continuous or standby source of *ac* power from a *dc* supply. They are typically used in remote and off-shore applications. The *dc* supply is most commonly a Sealed Lead-Acid battery or Photovoltaic Cell used as part of a solar panel array. The output from the inverter will typically be a sinewave, modified sinewave (step-wave) or square-wave supply and the battery will have a separate charger.

1.4.2 Mains Present Power Solutions

These solutions have no alternative sources of power such as a battery and only operate when mains power is present. They react to changes in the mains power supply and are suitable for specific power problems, with varying reaction times and approaches. They may neutralise a particular power problem or simply reduce its impact.

Power Problem	Power Conditioners	Automatic Voltage Stabilisers	Filters and Filter Strips	TVSS
Sags/Brownouts	some	yes	-	-
Surges	some	yes	-	-
Spikes/Transients	yes	limited	yes	yes
Electrical Noise	yes	limited	limited	-
Harmonics	-	-	-	-
Frequency Variations	-	-	-	-

Table 1.2 – Mains present power solution performance

a) Power Conditioners

Power conditioners *attenuate* spikes, transients and electrical noise voltages to very low levels and can be solid state electronic or transformer-based. They are typically used to protect sensitive loads where these types of power problems predominate, such as industrial environments. The term power conditioner is also sometimes used to refer to a superior version which can provide the additional benefits of voltage *stabilisation* over a wide input voltage window (typically +15/-20%) and output voltage *regulation* (typically ±5%). A typical example of this is a *Constant Voltage Transformer (CVT)* or *Ferroresonant* type design.

This type of transformer is inherently more reliable than a solid state electronic design and provides Galvanic isolation. The CVT was used in a popular UPS design from the 1980s known as a *Ferro* UPS which paired the CVT with a Line Interactive UPS design to achieve a 'no-break' output. The output relied on the capacitance and inductance of the CVT to provide energy to the load during the switch-on period of the inverter. Though highly reliable and robust, this type of UPS was only practical for single-phase installations and could not compete with the cost, noise, size and weight advantages of the transformerless UPS designs that emerged in the early 1990s.

b) Automatic Voltage Stabilisers (AVS)

AVS provide protection from sags, brownouts and surges. They may be electro-mechanical or solid state electronic-based devices and are sometimes referred to as *Automatic Voltage Regulators (AVRs)*. AVS typically have wide input voltage windows (+20/-40%). When presented with a low or high mains power supply voltage, a control circuit selects a transformer tap setting to *buck* (step-down) or *boost* (step-up) the output voltage to more acceptable levels. The output voltage generally tracks the input voltage window as there is typically no voltage regulation.

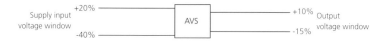

Diagram 1.18 – Typical AVS operational window

Some AVS may also incorporate a filter to provide both the load and AVS with protection (sometimes limited) from spikes, transients and electrical noise. AVS are typically used to protect hardware in remote areas where sags, surges and particularly brownouts are common. Typical use includes the protection of fridges and freezers, and domestic electrical and electronic goods.

c) Filters and Filter Strips

Filters provide power protection from spikes, transients and electrical noise. Rather than the attenuation performance achieved by a power conditioner they will 'clamp' peak voltages to pre-defined *let-through* levels and prevent damaging electrical noise from passing through.

Diagram 1.19 – Filter clamping levels

Filter performance varies considerably across the range of products available which runs from the types of filter (surge) strips commonly used within some IT environments for power distribution, to the more specialist filters used within scientific laboratories. Within any given situation, actual performance is dependent upon the filter circuit design ('clamping' level and speed of response) and the size of the disturbance it is faced with, which may be in excess of its ratings.

d) Transient Voltage Surge Suppressors (TVSS)

TVSS provide protection from transient voltages and high-energy spikes, especially those induced into a building's electrical supply by local lightning strikes. TVSS are rated in terms of the *Amps (A)* or *Joules (J)* they can dissipate. They are installed in parallel to the load and only react when presented with a transient or high-energy surge. When installed within a building, a 'Zoned Approach' is recommended. This places higher-rated devices before distribution boards rated at say 200kA and smaller-rated devices around 10kA within local offices. A TVSS device may be fitted upstream of a UPS or inside a bypass panel, generator AMF panel or distribution boards to provide protection from nearby lightning strikes.

TVSS designs tend to be based around the use of *Metal Oxide Varistors (MOVs)* rather than the more traditional *Gas Discharge Tubes (GDTs)*. Some TVSS manufacturers combine their MOV designs with a *Silicon Avalanche Diode (SAD)* front-end. This is because whilst MOVs can withstand high amperages their response time is not as quick as SADs which react within less than five nanoseconds and provide the initial response.

1.5 Summary

Electricity generation is entering a new era driven by the need to meet ever growing demands and provide energy from more environmentally-friendly resources. Power problems are increasing in their frequency and effect upon an ever more networked world.

Critical and essential loads must be protected. A *Power Continuity Plan* provides a process for analysing the present situation and designing a solution that can cater for future expansion, load demands and an environment where power interruptions are expected to increase. Selecting the right UPS topology, its specification, installation, monitoring and maintenance are fundamental to the overall long-term reliability and resilience of a *Power Continuity Plan*. UPS topologies are discussed next in *chapter 2*.

2. UPS Topologies and Designs

In this chapter:

- Understanding the general components in a UPS and how they work.
- Examining the three Static UPS designs, their strengths and weaknesses.
- An introduction to UPS accessories and their power protection roles.
- A brief comparison between Static On-Line and Rotary UPS.

Introduction

A UPS is installed between a critical load and its source of ac power - typically a mains power supply - to provide two functions: firstly, a secure power source when the mains supply fails and secondly, a clean, stable and regulated supply when mains is present.

The three Static UPS defined in *EN/IEC 62040-3:* differ in their abilities to perform both roles and so provide varying degrees of security and levels of power protection. Line Interactive and Off-Line UPS are limited by their design for small applications including home and small office systems. In comparison, On-Line UPS provide superior electrical performance, reliability and resilience and can be found powering loads ranging from critical servers and telecoms PBXs to entire industrial manufacturing sites and data centres.

This chapter explains the differences between the Static UPS designs, and in particular, discusses their strengths and weaknesses so that the right topology can be selected for the application. During the late 1980s, UPS selection was a far trickier task as both SMPS and UPS designs were far less generic. Some computer manufacturers used PSUs that could not work reliably on any type of waveform other than a sinewave and standardised on a particular UPS topology (typically On-Line) to sell to their customer bases. Nowadays both UPS and SMPS designs are more generic giving users a far wider supplier and topology range to choose from.

A fourth type of UPS known as a *Rotary UPS* is also available. A brief overview of the technology is provided for comparative purposes at the end of this chapter.

2.1 UPS Design

2.1.1 Inverters

All UPS designs incorporate an *inverter*. This digitally creates an *ac* waveform from a *dc* supply to power the connected load.

Diagram 2.1 – A typical inverter symbol

In an On-Line UPS the inverter is designed for continuous operation and its output waveform is a sinewave. This type of UPS is classified under EN/IEC 62040-3: as *Voltage and Frequency Independent (VFI)* because its inverter operation is unaffected by changes in either the voltage or frequency supplied by the mains power supply. Line Interactive and Off-Line UPS use less sophisticated inverters in a standby mode. Here the inverter is only used to support the load when the mains power supply fails or fluctuates outside pre-set input voltage and frequency windows. The typical inverter used in a Line Interactive UPS may supply either a sinewave or modified sinewave (step-wave) output dependent upon its design. The inverter in an Off-Line UPS is the least sophisticated and typically produces a square-wave output.

The mains power supply is generated as a true sinewave. Some loads, like an SMPS, can operate from a step-wave or square-wave shaped supply. However, this should be limited to short durations to prevent component stress and heat build up, which results from the SMPS having to draw more current from these inferior waveforms than when operated from a true sinewave supply.

Using an inverter in standby mode can also introduce *transfer time* problems, leading to millisecond breaks in *ac* supply to the load. Transfer time is the period it takes to power up the inverter and connect it to the load. This is not instantaneous for Line Interactive and Off-Line UPS and breaks of up to 8ms or more can occur depending upon the design of the inverter and UPS itself. The same potential problem occurs but to a lesser degree when the mains power supply is restored. Here the inverter is not normally powered off until the mains power supply has become more stable.

The load capacity of a UPS is limited by the size of its inverter and this is measured in terms of VA (inverter output *Voltage* x *Amps*). An inverter may be rated in Europe for a 230Vac 50Hz single-phase or 400Vac 50Hz three-phase output, and its output voltage may be configurable to between 220-240Vac or 380-415Vac. Output voltage and frequency regulation will be UPS design dependent. Inverter efficiency also varies and can range from around 86 to 96%. This factor has to be taken into account when sizing a UPS battery set and particularly for large UPS when calculating their impact on room ambient temperatures and air-conditioning.

2.1.2 Rectifiers

The constantly running inverter of an On-Line UPS requires a continuous source of *dc* and this is supplied by a *rectifier* connected to the mains power supply.

Diagram 2.2 – A typical rectifier symbol

Rectifiers can generate a high level of harmonics, dependent upon their design, method of operation and the type of UPS they are used within. *Chapters 4* and *9* provide further information on this topic.

In addition to supplying the inverter with a source of *dc* power, in a transformer-based On-Line UPS design, the rectifier also charges the battery set. In a transformerless On-Line design the set-up is slightly different. Here a *booster-converter* sits between the rectifier and inverter. This increases the *dc* voltage from the rectifier (or battery set) to the higher *dc* voltage level required by the inverter. The battery set itself is charged by an independent battery charger powered from the output of the booster-converter.

Both charging regimes are usually temperature compensating. This prevents over charging by reducing the voltage supplied to the battery set when operated in high ambient temperatures and can extend the working life of the battery set by up to 15%. UPS manufactures can employ a number of other techniques to protect their battery sets as discussed in *chapter 6*.

For re-charging a battery set, a reasonable target time is 80% within 12 hours. Where this cannot be achieved, further charging capacity may have to be added in the form of up-rated or additional battery chargers. These must be mains powered rather than connected to the output of the UPS. When plotted on a graph, the recharging process is non-linear and it can take several hours for the remaining 20% capacity to be charged.

Some UPS designs now incorporate a *Cycling Charging Method (CCM)*. For a fully charged battery set, CCM removes the charging current for a pre-defined time period ranging from 24 hours to several days. Without a charging current, a battery set will self-discharge but at a very slow, minimal rate. The UPS monitors its battery set *dc* voltage level and reconnects the charging current at the end of the time period or when the *dc* voltage level reaches a threshold value. CCM improves UPS system efficiency, reduces wear-and-tear on the battery set and helps to extend its life. It does not affect the total runtime capacity of the UPS as the discharge is minimal.

Line Interactive and Off-Line UPS use a relatively simple battery charger connected to their mains power supply.

2.1.3 Battery Sets

The battery set provides a *dc* supply on mains power supply failure to the inverter. The length of time an inverter runs on batteries is known as battery runtime, autonomy or back-up time. The specific period is a factor of the *Ampere-hour (Ah)* rating of the battery set and the load applied. The lower the load the longer the runtime for a specific Ah rating. For example, a 10kVA/8kW three-phase UPS with a 14Ah battery set will typically provide 15 minutes runtime at full load but may provide 30 minutes or more, when powering a reduced load of 5kVA/4kW (50% of its capacity).

Diagram 2.3 – A typical battery set symbol

A battery set is sized in *Watts* using an algorithm that takes into account many factors such as room ambient temperature, UPS system and inverter losses and *dc* busbar voltage.

A battery set may comprise of a single, or multiple battery strings connected in parallel. A battery string consists of one or more battery blocks connected in series and the Ah of the battery blocks used defines the total Ah of the battery set.

On mains power supply failure, the battery set will start to discharge and the UPS will monitor the *dc* voltage supplied to the inverter. When this approaches a set threshold, the battery set is disconnected to prevent *deep discharge* (a state from which a battery set may not recover when a charging current is re-applied). If the mains power supply is restored or an alternative source of *ac* power connected before the threshold is reached, normal UPS operation is resumed and the battery set is automatically recharged.

One of the ways in which a UPS design can protect its battery set is to ensure the rectifier or battery charger presents a low (and preferably <1%) *ac ripple*. This is an *ac* element superimposed onto the *dc* output waveform of a rectifier or battery charger. Manufacturers strive to reduce this to a minimum. For a battery set, a high *ac* ripple can lead to increased battery temperature, speed up corrosion of the positive plate and reduced battery working life. In addition, inverters can also generate ripple currents when operating on battery power. Some UPS have additional protection for this which smooths out the waveform drawn from the battery set during discharge.

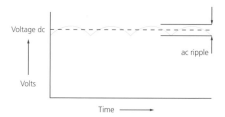

Diagram 2.4 – ac ripple

2.1.4 EMI/RFI Filters

Electro-Magnetic Interference (EMI) and *Radio Frequency Interference (RFI)* filters are commonly used to protect the UPS and load from mains-borne spikes and electrically induced noise.

EMI/RFI filters vary in their complexity and usage within the three Static UPS topologies. Their primary purpose is to protect the UPS from spikes and electrical noise by suppressing or 'clamping' their peak voltages to more acceptable levels. The filters can also help to prevent any pollution, generated by the high-frequency electronics within the UPS itself, from disrupting upstream or downstream equipment.

2.1.5 Bypasses

An On-Line UPS is generally the only type to incorporate an automatic bypass power path. This provides the UPS with a level of resilience in case of system failure. If this occurs, the bypass automatically transfers the load to the alternative bypass power path.

Diagram 2.5 – A typical bypass symbol

This is known as safe failure to mains and can occur for a variety of reasons including an internal fault condition or overload (short-circuit). When the fault condition is cleared, the bypass automatically transfers the load back to inverter output. It can also occur at the end of battery discharge if the mains power supply (or alternative supply of *ac* power) has not been restored.

To transfer the load from inverter to the bypass supply or *vice versa*, requires that the inverter output and bypass supplies are synchronised. The UPS therefore monitors its bypass supply voltage to ensure it is within a pre-set range of typically up to ±25% and that its frequency is within ±5% before transfer can take place. When the bypass supply is not within these parameters its operation is disabled. These parameters can be configured for more sensitive applications.

The capability of an On-Line UPS to function during overload is quoted as a percentage of its rating for a set time period. For example, 1.5In (150% of rated nominal current) for two minutes. Both the inverter and bypass have overload limitations placed upon them but to varying capacities.

Above its overload capability an inverter will start to current-limit (a controlled restriction of output power) to protect itself. If the inverter output waveform begins to collapse, the load is automatically transferred to the bypass supply. If the overload is greater than the bypass can sustain, the UPS switches off and the load is dropped.

An automatic bypass is one of the defining characteristics of an On-Line UPS and makes this type the preferred choice to power critical loads. As discussed, at the end of battery discharge a load can be effectively dropped if a source of *ac* power has not been reconnected. A dual-input supply option can help to overcome this, but it is not a standard option for all On-Line UPS. Where available, it can be configured so that the rectifier and bypasses are fed from two separately derived supplies, even from different substations. This halves the potential impact of losing one substation supply and can prevent the load from being dropped by an inverter when its battery set reaches full discharge.

A further advantage of an automatic bypass is that it allows a UPS to be sized according to the load running current rather than its start-up in-rush. SMPS loads, for example, can have high in-rush currents lasting for several milliseconds. For any UPS design, a high in-rush can present an overload which will force its inverter to current-limit to protect itself. On overload, an On-Line UPS transfers its load to bypass until the overload is removed i.e. the in-rush current reduces to a normal running current within the nominal rating of the UPS.

Generally, an automatic bypass switch will be a *Static* type with a break-free transfer. This is an expensive device and where the UPS has such an internal bypass it is commonly called a *Static Bypass*. UPS below 3kVA typically use a relay-based assembly with a break of around 2-4ms, well within the hold-up time of most SMPS powered loads.

When activated, an automatic bypass typically connects the UPS load to raw mains, creating a direct path for power disturbances to reach the load. Some On-Line UPS are designed to route their automatic bypass supply through their built-in input and output EMI/RFI filters to provide some degree of protection. Where this is not possible, an *Isolation Transformer* may be used (before the UPS or in its bypass supply) to provide a complete separation of the input and output electrical supplies, known as Galvanic isolation.

Additional power paths (shown in *diagram 2.6*) may be provided by:

- **Maintenance Bypasses:** either internal or external to the UPS to allow service work to be undertaken without disruption to the load - discussed in *section 2.3.1*.

- **Centralised Static Switches (CSS):** to provide automatic transfer and maintenance bypass functions within parallel UPS configurations - discussed in *chapter 5*.

Line Interactive and Off-Line UPS generally do not have an internal automatic bypass. Their inverters 'current-limit' on high overload and with no bypass supply to turn to, their loads run the risk of crashing unless the overload is removed.

This weakness can be overcome by installing Line Interactive and Off-Line UPS with an external maintenance bypass with an automatic transfer feature. If the external bypass sees the UPS output start to fail, it will automatically transfer the load to the mains power supply.

Figure 1: Static bypass active

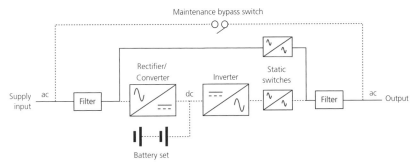

Figure 2: Maintenance bypass active

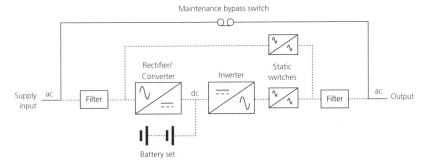

Figure 3: Static bypass active with dual input

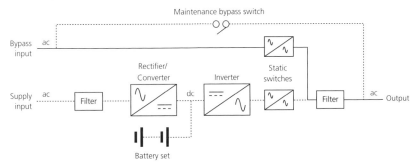

Figure 4: Maintenance bypass active with dual input

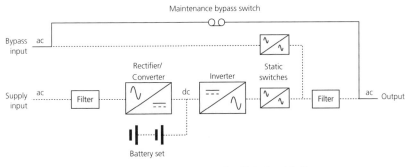

Diagram 2.6 – On-Line UPS power paths with single and dual inputs

2.2 Static UPS Topologies

2.2.1 On-Line UPS - VFI (Voltage and Frequency Independent)

An On-Line UPS is also known as a *Double-Conversion* system because of its two voltage conversion stages: rectifier (*ac* to *dc*) and inverter (*dc* to *ac*).

The inverter is constantly running and produces a digitally-generated sinewave with tightly regulated voltage and frequency levels (±1% and ±0.5% respectively) to power the load.

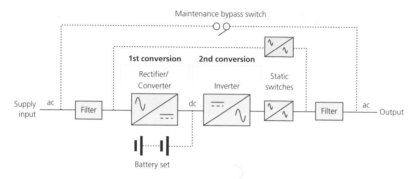

Diagram 2.7 – On-Line double-conversion UPS schematic

The inverter is connected to a *dc rail* (busbar) to which the battery set, booster-converter (transformerless UPS only) and rectifier are also connected. The rectifier is connected to the *ac* supply and typically has wide input voltage and frequency windows of ±20% and ±10% respectively. Within these values, the rectifier will supply the inverter and charge the battery set. Typically, the rectifier input voltage window can be widened for a reduced load.

When the mains power supply fails or fluctuates outside of these ranges, the rectifier turns off and the battery set is used to power the inverter. If mains power, or an alternative standby power source (for example, a standby generator or fuel cell) is not connected to the UPS before the battery set reaches its disconnect threshold, the inverter will switch off.

Some modern On-Line UPS can also be configured to operate in a number of modes (selected manually or automatically) to suit the time of day, load type and mains power supply quality available. These include:

- **Economy mode:** here the UPS is set to power the load as a Line Interactive UPS to achieve a higher operating efficiency (up to 98%). This could be overnight, for example, when critical loads are inactive. The inverter is powered but not active. The load is connected to the mains power supply but through the internal EMI/RFI filters to provide some degree of protection, via the built-in automatic bypass. If the mains power supply fails or fluctuates, the automatic bypass transfers the load to the inverter.

- **Smart Active mode:** here the UPS automatically decides whether to run in On-Line or Economy mode depending upon the state of the mains power supply.

- **Voltage Stabiliser mode:** here the UPS conditions and regulates the mains power supply but does not attempt to provide any battery back-up.

- **Standby-Off mode:** for standby system applications such as emergency lighting. As the mains power supply fails, the UPS is powered up and the inverter supplies the load. This mode allows the UPS to operate in one of the Central Power Supply System (CPSS) modes defined in EN 50171.

On-Line UPS typically range from single 700VA units to 800kVA power modules that can be used in *parallel* configurations to achieve large installations (sized in MVA). In addition, it is common for UPS above 10kVA to be capable of single and three-phase operation. On-Line UPS are also the preferred choice for long runtime applications because their inverters are rated for continuous operation.

2.2.2 Line Interactive UPS - VI (Voltage Independent)

Line Interactive UPS offer the next level of power protection to On-Line UPS.

When mains power is present, UPS output is supplied via a built-in AVS operating within a set input voltage window. An EMI/RFI filter may also be used to protect the AVS and load from spikes and transients by clamping their peak voltages to more acceptable levels. When the mains power supply fails or fluctuates outside the pre-set input voltage (or frequency) window, the inverter is powered up and a relay connects the load to the inverter output with an inevitable transfer time of 4-8ms. The inverters within Line Interactive UPS vary in design and output waveform. They can be designed to supply a sinewave or modified sinewave known as a step-wave. Whichever waveform is supplied, the inverter output will typically be regulated to within ±5% i.e. much wider than the output regulation provided by an On-Line UPS.

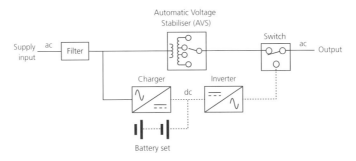

Diagram 2.8 – Line Interactive UPS schematic

Line Interactive UPS have internal battery sets typically sized to provide a five-minute runtime at full load. Longer runtimes require either over-sizing the UPS for the particular load or an inverter rated for longer operation at full load, which may be the case for the larger sized UPS in a particular range. Where this is the case, the UPS will have a rear panel connection for external battery extension packs. However, unless the charging capacity is also increased the recharge time may exceed the nominal target of 80% within 12 hours.

Line Interactive UPS are normally used to protect applications including: PCs and small file servers, keyphone telephone systems, modems, switches and routers. They are compact and available in either a tower or rackmount or dual format. Common sizes range from 500VA to 3kVA.

2.2.3 Off-Line UPS - VFD (Voltage and Frequency Dependent)

Off-Line UPS offer basic power protection.

When mains power is present, UPS output is supplied via a built-in EMI/RFI filter to provide limited protection from spikes and transients by clamping their peak voltages to more acceptable levels. A simple circuit charges the battery set. The inverter is 'off-line' in standby mode. When the mains power supply fails, or fluctuates outside the pre-set input voltage (or frequency) window, the inverter is powered up and a relay connects the load to the inverter.

As the inverter is normally switched off, this type of UPS is known as an Off-Line (Standby) system and there is an inevitable break in supply to the load (typically 4-8ms) as the inverter is initiated. The inverter output is typically a square-wave.

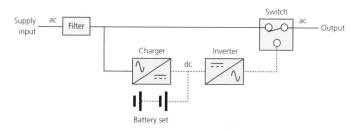

Diagram 2.9 – Off-Line (Standby) UPS schematic

This is a basic, compact UPS used for small essential loads requiring only some form of momentary or short duration battery back-up. The UPS is normally limited to the protection of applications such as work stations, terminals and low power communications devices below 1kVA at 230Vac single-phase, by its design and performance.

The typical internal battery runtime is around five minutes at full load and longer runtimes are only available by over sizing the UPS. There is no external battery extension pack capability. The most basic form of the design may not even provide any remote monitoring capabilities.

2.3 UPS Accessories

Most UPS manufacturers provide a range of UPS accessories designed to provide their systems with additional functionality. The most common are discussed below.

2.3.1 External Maintenance Bypasses

A *Maintenance Bypass* is used to transfer the UPS load to the mains power supply to allow maintenance, service work or removal (external only) without disruption to the load. Service work can therefore be carried out during normal working-hours and the need for load downtime is removed.

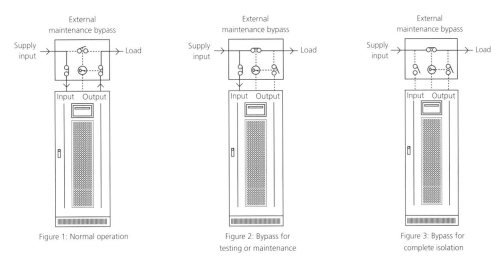

Figure 1: Normal operation   Figure 2: Bypass for testing or maintenance   Figure 3: Bypass for complete isolation

Diagram 2.10 – External maintenance bypass power paths

The bypass will use a manual switching method to transfer the load between UPS output and the mains power supply. This can comprise of a single transfer switch (three or four pole) or an array of isolators. To prevent damage to the UPS or load disruption from incorrect operation, mechanical or electronic interlocks may be used. Typically for load transfer switching one of the following methods is used:

- **Break-Before-Make (BBM):** this is commonly used where the loads can withstand a short break in supply of between 2-4ms and/or the inverter output cannot automatically synchronise with its bypass supply.

- **Make-Before-Break (MBB):** this will connect the UPS input to its inverter output, momentarily and can place a short-circuit on to the inverter which could potentially damage those that have not been designed to accommodate such an event.

Chapter 9 provides further information to consider when installing an external bypass.

An external bypass may be wall or rackmounted. This type of bypass is also known as a *wrap-around bypass* and is generally installed next to the UPS as a separate cabinet or panel. Connections may be 'Plug & Play' or hardwired or a combination of the two dependent upon the ratings involved. Some hardwired bypasses may also include a mains powered socket to supply electrical power for service tools or a PC during maintenance.

An external maintenance bypass can include a key switch where there is concern over unauthorised use. It may also be necessary to use mechanical-interlocks (Castell) to ensure the bypass is operated in the correct sequence, to prevent damage to the UPS or load. This can happen if the bypass panel allows back-feed from the bypass supply to the UPS output terminals. In addition to manual transfer, some external bypasses can also include an automatic transfer function. This will act in the same way as the automatic bypass within an On-Line UPS to provide a further level of resilience.

Some UPS also include an internal isolator-based bypass arrangement. This will only partially isolate a UPS as there will still be live power connections on the input and output sides within it. The isolators typically lie behind internal panels which have to be physically removed or opened. As part of the UPS design, they are electrically interlocked to reduce the potential for damage to the UPS if incorrectly operated.

Bypass installation may therefore be internal or external to the UPS and their operation may be manual, automatic or a combination thereof. It is vital, within a *Power Continuity Plan*, that the position of the devices and the paths used to power the load are monitored. When internal to a UPS the bypass is automatically monitored and alarm signals generated when it is activated. External bypass operation can be monitored if the design incorporates a D-sub communications port providing volt-free contact signals or a means to integrate it directly with the UPS.

2.3.2 Parallel Kits

On-Line UPS from around 10kVA can be used in parallel configurations to achieve higher operating resilience and system capacity levels. *Chapter 5* covers this area in detail. Closed-loop communication parallel kits are the primary choice for most UPS and the chapter discusses the benefits of common and separate battery sets, decentralised and centralised static bypass systems and maintenance bypass issues.

2.3.3 Battery Extension Packs

UPS up to around 30kVA have capacity for internal battery sets. Where this is not the case, or additional runtime is required, external battery extension cabinets or rackmount trays are used. These are normally designed to aesthetically match the UPS as far as is reasonably practical. An alternative is to use cladded or uncladded battery stands. This is more common for large battery sets due to their size and weight and can also provide better access for testing. *Chapter 6* discusses batteries and alternative sources of power such as flywheels, fuel cells and super capacitors. Flywheels and fuel cells are promising, emergent technologies but batteries still remain the most widely used solution for UPS and many other systems.

2.3.4 UPS and Environmental Monitoring

UPS monitoring and control software is widely available for a number of operating systems. It is generally supplied on a CD-ROM or can be downloaded from a UPS manufacturer's website. In addition to the software, most manufacturers supply a range of hardware accessories as plug-in cards or standalone devices to extend functionality and control. Alarm monitoring, and in particular, planned responses are important aspects of a *Power Continuity Plan* and *chapter 8* covers these in more detail.

2.4 Rotary UPS

Rotary UPS are mechanical uninterruptible power supplies that convert Kinetic energy into electrical energy. There are two competing approaches known as:

- **Rotating Transformer:** based on a regulated isolated rotating transformer.

- **Induction Coupling:** comprising of a diesel engine, two-speed concentrically mounted induction coupling and alternator.

Rotary UPS typically start at around 500kVA in size ranging to up to 2MVA or more in parallel combination. Their application is limited to very large installations.

Rotary UPS represent a second school of thought when it comes to the provision of uninterruptible power. Compared to a Static On-Line UPS, Rotary UPS manufacturers argue that their sets generate little in the way of harmonics, can achieve higher *Mean Time Between Failure (MTBF)* values, have better fault clearance capabilities and are more suitable for leading power factor loads (*chapter 3*). As will become evident reading this guide, Static On-Line UPS designs can be installed in configurations that negate many of these arguments. The specific disadvantages of Rotary UPS include:

- **Higher capital, installation and environmental costs:** a Rotary UPS can be up to 40% higher in cost than a comparative Static On-Line UPS. As a motor-generator-based device their installation can be more complex and present ventilation, vibration and exhaust gas removal issues. Rotary UPS can also operate at up to 30dBA higher noise levels, which can lead to significant noise pollution on site.

- **Increased size and weight:** Rotary UPS are larger in comparison and can require up to 20% or more footprint area within a plant room or dedicated UPS area. Their physical size and the fact that they are built-to-order systems can make system expansion an issue unless sufficient provision has been allowed at the project design stage.

- **Increased service costs:** whilst advances have been made in bearing and lubrication technology, traditionally some Rotary UPS are sensitive to high ambient temperatures and can require more frequent maintenance than a Static On-Line UPS. In addition, they have a higher *Mean Time To Repair (MTTR)*, especially when bearings have to be replaced, which can take several days.

The scope of this book covers Static UPS designs rather than Rotary and more information is available in publications from third-party bodies (such as the *Chartered Institution of Building Services Engineers - CIBSE)*, as well as Rotary UPS manufacturers.

2.5 Summary

Table 2.1 provides a summary of the strengths and weaknesses of each Static UPS design. Off-Line UPS should only be considered for very basic applications and should never be used with critical loads. Line Interactive UPS provide additional benefits and some are available with a sinewave output and longer runtime capability. However, they do not provide the levels of performance achieved with an On-Line UPS design, which remains the choice for critical load protection.

UPS Topology	Strengths	Weaknesses
On-line **(Double-Conversion)** *Ultimate* *Power Protection*	Output voltage/frequency regulation UPS inverter rated for continuous operation Long runtime battery extension options Automatic bypass for faults and overloads Parallel operation and expansion options	Higher purchase price
Line Interactive *Intermediate* *Power Protection*	Output voltage stabilisation Spike and electrical noise filtering Lower cost	More sensitive to mains disturbances Inverter transfer time Waveform suitability Runtime limitations
Off-line **(Standby)** *Basic* *Power Protection*	Spike and electrical noise filtering	No voltage stabilisation Inverter transfer time Waveform suitability Runtime limitations Limited power ratings

Table 2.1 – Static UPS comparison

Whichever UPS topology is deployed within a *Power Continuity Plan*, certain fundamental calculations have to be made with respect to the load size and runtime required. *Chapter 3* now discusses UPS sizing and how to select the right UPS from the generic ranges available.

3. UPS Sizing and Selection

In this chapter:

- Understanding the difference between in-rush and running currents.
- Explaining the use of VA, Watts and Power Factor when sizing a UPS.
- Examining the practical issues that can affect the choice of UPS solution.
- An overview of the UPS ranges a typical manufacturer will supply.

Introduction

Having identified the critical, essential and non-essential loads, the next phase in a Power Continuity Plan is to size those that require protection.

Sizing in itself can take some time as there can be differences between the power ratings stated (on rear panel rating labels and in operating manuals) and the true values drawn. This is generally because most hardware manufacturers use power supplies rated for maximum, worst case conditions which are sometimes far in excess of the actual power that can be drawn. Where this is the case, loads can typically be seen running at only 50-60% of this total capacity. In addition, any ratings given may be in Amps or Watts to further complicate matters and there can be quite a difference between actual in-rush (start-up) and running power requirements.

Portable power analysers, RMS (Root Mean Square) volt-meters and current clamps can provide useful information upon which to base sizing calculations. Power analysers, for example, have typically been used by UPS suppliers to provide data from which to generate hardware manufacturer-specific sizing charts. Loads are plugged into the analyser, or a hardwired connection is made, and measurements provided. RMS volt-meters and current clamps are more commonly used within large electrical installations to measure peak and RMS values at a local distribution board within a building.

Apart from determining the actual load types and their sizes, other factors need to be considered if the right products are to be installed. These include areas such as the expected response to overloads, which should only be intermittent, the battery runtime required and potential for future system expansion. Whilst an On-Line UPS has a built-in automatic bypass, running close to its design limits with regular overloads is never considered good practice. The bypass is for emergency situations and if overloads are a frequent and regular occurrence, it is always best to oversize the system.

Other matters to consider include power distribution, the fault tolerance (resilience) levels to be reached and the type of electrical installation in terms of the supply and load voltage and frequency requirements.

3.1 UPS Sizing

3.1.1 Load Types

Here the *Power Continuity Plan* focuses on the type of loads considered critical enough to warrant power protection and their requirements in terms of in-rush and running currents, supply voltage, frequency and stability.

Some critical loads, especially sensitive medical and scientific equipment, require tight voltage and frequency regulation and this is only possible from the continuously running inverter of an On-Line UPS. Essential loads do not need the quality of supply provided by a UPS and can be powered directly from a generator to reduce the overall size of UPS to be installed. Non-essential can be allowed to fail when the mains power supply does so.

In terms of type, loads are referred to as either *linear* or *non-linear*, depending on how they draw their current from the mains power supply waveform and will be one of the following:

- **Inductive:** a load whose current waveform lags the voltage waveform and has a potentially high in-rush current at start-up (which may be tempered by a soft-start facility), for example, an SMPS, transformer or motor.

- **Capacitive:** a load whose current waveform leads the voltage waveform, with potentially a high in-rush current at start-up, for example, a Blade server.

- **Resistive:** a load with no inductance or capacitance, for example, a resistive load test bank heater element, where the device typically has no initial switch-on surge and the current drawn rises immediately to a steady, running-current state.

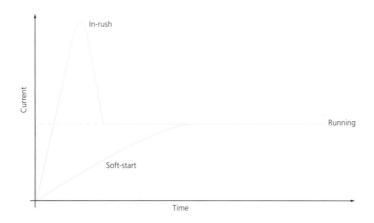

Diagram 3.1 – Types of start-up currents

This classification takes into account the power factor of the load, which is discussed further in the next section, as it can greatly influence the overall size of UPS and generator to be installed.

3.1.2 Apparent Power - Volt-Ampere (VA)

Volt-Ampere (VA) is a unit of measure for the *Apparent Power* drawn by an electrical device. Once known, this figure can be matched to an appropriately-sized UPS. VA is calculated by multiplying the RMS source Voltage (V) by the current drawn in Amps (A).

Apparent Power (VA) = Volts (V) x Amps (A)

For example, if an electrical device is connected to a 230Vac single-phase supply and the current drawn by this device is 10 Amps, the resulting VA value would be:

10 x 230 = 2300VA or 2.3kVA

For a three-phase load, the calculation is slightly different. A 15kVA three-phase UPS will supply a maximum of 5kVA per phase (15÷3) under normal conditions. Therefore, to size a UPS for a three-phase load, the VA per phase must first be calculated. Then, the three values have to be compared to ensure a relatively even load sharing across the phases. If this is the case, the largest VA per phase can be multiplied by three to calculate the size of the UPS. If the loads per phase are not well balanced, this approach can lead to a greatly oversized UPS. For example, for a load drawing 2kVA on phase one (1), 3kVA on phase two (2) and 10kVA on phase three (3), the UPS could be sized at: 3 x 10kVA = 30kVA. However, if the loads were balanced to 5kVA per phase then a 15kVA UPS could be used.

UPS (and generators) are most commonly rated in VA, kVA or MVA. However, this does not always provide a useful basis for comparison as the same VA-rated systems from a selection of manufacturers can supply different Watt ratings.

3.1.3 Real Power - Watts (W)

Watts is a unit of measure for the *Real Power* (also referred to as *Active Power*) dissipated by a load. Once known, this figure can also be matched to an appropriately-sized UPS. It is just as important to calculate the Watts value as it is the VA for any given load. This is particularly true for a UPS, as excess demands of either the Watts or VA can force a UPS into an overload condition. The Watts value is also used to size the required battery set (see *chapter 6*).

The Watts drawn by a linear resistive load can be calculated using the formula:

Real Power (W) = Amps (A) x Volts (V)

For example, if a heater element, is connected to a 230Vac single-phase supply and the current drawn is 10 Amps, then the Watts dissipated will be:

10 x 230 = 2300W or 2.3kW

For a three-phase load, the calculation is slightly different. A 30kW three-phase UPS will supply 10kW maximum per phase (30÷3) under normal conditions.

To size a UPS for a three-phase load in Watts, the Watts per phase must first be calculated. Then, the three values have to be compared to ensure a relatively even load sharing across the phases. If this is the case, the largest Watts per phase can be multiplied by three to arrive at a final UPS size. If the loads per phase are not well balanced, this approach can again lead to a greatly oversized UPS and it is recommended that the loads are redistributed across the three phases. For example, for a load drawing 4kW on phase one (1), 6kW on phase two (2) and 20kW on phase three (3), the UPS could be sized at: 3 x 20kW = 60kW. However, if the loads were balanced to 10kW per phase then a 30kW UPS could be used.

For capacitive and inductive loads a further element has to be taken into consideration in that their voltage and current waveforms are out of phase with one another. This gives rise to a further type of power, known as *Reactive Power* (VAr = Volts x Amps reactive), in proportion to the reactance of the load. Reactive power is power not used by the load and returned to source. When the current waveform is out of phase with the voltage waveform the load is producing less power for the same amount of current drawn and the supplied power is not being effectively delivered (utilised) to the load.

The Watts drawn by an inductive or capacitive load can therefore be calculated using the following formula which takes into account the degree to which the current and voltage waveforms are out of phase with one another, referred to as *Power Factor*:

Real Power (W) = Apparent Power (VA) x Power Factor (pF)

3.1.4 Power Factors

Power factor (for linear loads) is sometimes referred to as *Displacement Power Factor* or *Phase Power Factor*. It is the ratio of real power (W) to apparent power (VA) in an *ac* circuit and corresponds to the phase angle difference between the voltage and current waveforms drawn. Power factor is calculated as a decimal number or percentage i.e. 0.65pF = 65% between 0-1pF and 0-100% respectively.

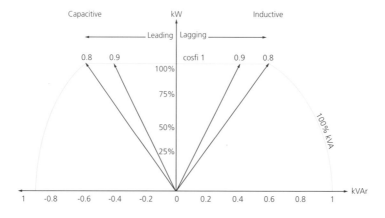

Diagram 3.2 – Typical UPS output power factor performance graph

For example, for an inductive load where the current is lagging the voltage by 40°, the resulting power factor would be equal to CosØ (where Ø is the phase angle between the voltage and current waveform). For example, for 40° the power factor would be 0.766 lag or 76.6% lag.

By convention, an inductive load is defined as a *positive* reactive power and a capacitive load is defined as a *negative* reactive power. However, power factor is never shown as being positive or negative. It is simply shown as either *lagging* or *leading*.

Power factor can be expressed in a power vector triangle as shown in *diagram 3.3*.

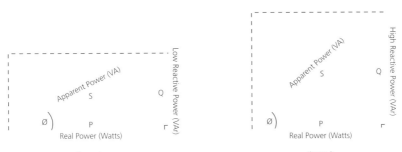

Figure 1:
Low displacement angle = low Reactive Power - high Real Power

Figure 2:
High displacement angle = high Reactive Power - lower Real Power

Diagram 3.3 – Power vector triangles

The power vector triangles show that:

- Power Factor = P÷S = W÷VA = CosØ
- S = $\sqrt{(P^2+Q^2)}$
- VA = $\sqrt{(W^2+VAr^2)}$

The power vector triangles show how changes in the phase angles affect power factor, apparent and real power values, leading to the following formulae:

Power Factor (pF) =
- Real Power (W) ÷ Apparent Power (VA) = CosØ

Real Power (W) =
- Apparent Power (VA) x Power Factor (pF)
- VA x CosØ
- $\sqrt{(\text{Apparent Power}^2 - \text{Reactive Power}^2)}$

Apparent Power (VA) =
- Real Power (W) ÷ Power Factor (pF)
- $\sqrt{(\text{Real Power}^2 + \text{Reactive Power}^2)}$

Reactive Power (VAr) =
- $\sqrt{(\text{Apparent Power}^2 - \text{Real Power}^2)}$

a) Lagging Power Factor

Loads with a *lagging power factor*, have a current waveform that *lags* behind the voltage waveform by a factor equal to the reactance of the load, typically between 0.5 - 0.95. *Diagram 3.4 (*using the example provided earlier) shows that a 2300VA load with a lagging power factor of 0.766 would have a real power value of 1762Watts or 1.76kW.

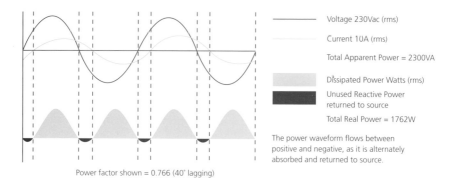

Power factor shown = 0.766 (40° lagging)

Diagram 3.4 – An inductive load with a lagging power factor

b) Unity Power Factor

Loads with a *unity power factor* have current and voltage waveforms in phase with one another. *Diagram 3.5* (using the example provided earlier) shows that a 2300VA load with a unity power factor of one (1) would have a real power value of 2300Watts or 2.3kW.

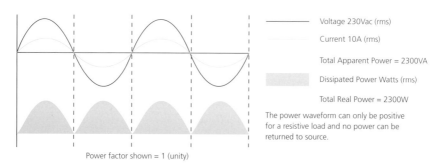

Power factor shown = 1 (unity)

Diagram 3.5 – A resistive load with a unity power factor

UPS have traditionally been designed to support loads with lagging and unity power factors. Provided that their VA and Watts values were not exceeded, normal operation would be maintained. Coping with leading power factors is a relatively new phenomenon for UPS manufacturers and care has to be taken when planning such an installation because leading power factors can place an overload on a UPS, which it may not even recognise or react to.

c) Leading Power Factor

Loads with a *leading power factor*, have a current waveform that *leads* the voltage waveform by a factor equal to the reactance of the load, typically between 0.8 - 0.95. *Diagram 3.6* (using the example provided earlier) shows that a 2300VA load with a leading power factor of 0.766 would have a real power value of 1762Watts or 1.76kW.

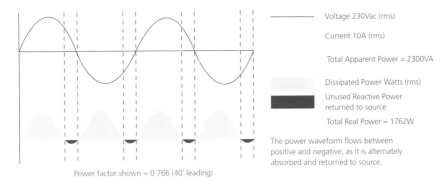

Power factor shown = 0.766 (40° leading)

Voltage 230Vac (rms)

Current 10A (rms)

Total Apparent Power = 2300VA

Dissipated Power Watts (rms)
Unused Reactive Power returned to source
Total Real Power = 1762W

The power waveform flows between positive and negative, as it is alternately absorbed and returned to source.

Diagram 3.6 – A capacitive load with a leading power factor

A typical example of a load with a leading power factor is a Blade server. This is a high-density server with a modular electronic circuit board often dedicated to a single application and housed within a 2U high server chassis. Blade servers allow more processing power within less rack space than traditional file servers, simplifying cabling and reducing power consumption and are being widely adopted within large data centre and telecommunication environments.

Potential methods to reduce the impact of leading power factors on a UPS include:

- ensuring that they represent a smaller percentage of the total UPS load
- installing power factor correction between the UPS and its load
- increasing the UPS size and also that of the standby generator if installed
- specifying a UPS with leading power factor capabilities

The current most common approach for a UPS installation is to use an active harmonic filter with power factor correction on the output of the UPS. This presents the UPS with a more acceptable load but results in higher capital and installation costs, lower efficiency and the use of more floor space. Over sizing the UPS (and associated generator) also results in additional costs. The most ideal and cost-effective solution is to use a UPS designed to power both leading and lagging power factor loads.

Whilst greater care has to be taken when powering loads with leading power factors, it is also important to take the largest power factor into account when supporting a group of loads, provided that this does not lead to an oversized solution.

d) Effects of Harmonics on Power Factor

The displacement power factor discussed so far is only applicable to the fundamental frequency (50Hz in Europe) and therefore it does not take into account the power factor generated by any harmonics induced into a mains power supply by the load itself. This is referred to as *Distortion Power Factor* and is produced by the harmonics generated by non-linear loads. As these harmonics are typically not in phase with the fundamental frequency, they naturally lead to an increase in reactive power (undelivered power) and therefore decrease the overall power factor of the load. The effect of distortion power factor can be seen in the power vector triangle in *diagram 3.7*.

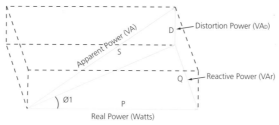

Ø1 - Represents the fundamental component displacement angle

Diagram 3.7 – Three dimensional power vector diagram for non-linear loads

Compared to *diagram 3.3* (page 53) the triangle is now three dimensional and includes an additional distortion vector. This results in an overall power factor, referred to as the *True Power Factor* or *Total Power Factor* and represents a combination of both the displacement power factor and the distortion power factor. When sizing UPS, for any specific load, knowing the true power factor is therefore critical. The triangle shows that:

- Power Factor = P÷S = W÷VA ≠ CosØ
- $S = \sqrt{(P^2+Q^2+D^2)}$
- $VA = \sqrt{(W^2+VAr^2+VA_D^2)}$

From the diagram, in order to calculate the power drawn by a non-linear load the following formulae can be used:

Power Factor (pF) =
- Real Power (W) ÷ Apparent Power (VA)*

* including both displacement and distortion components

Real Power (W) =
- $\sqrt{(\text{Apparent Power}^2 - \text{Reactive Power}^2 - \text{Distortion Power}^2)}$

Apparent Power (VA) =
- $\sqrt{(\text{Real Power}^2 + \text{Reactive Power}^2 + \text{Distortion Power}^2)}$

Reactive Power (VAr) =
- $\sqrt{(\text{Apparent Power}^2 - \text{Real Power}^2 - \text{Distortion Power}^2)}$

For any electrical system, the higher the power factor, the greater the effectiveness of the power being delivered to the load, and the higher the efficiency in terms of the actual work done for the value of voltage and current supplied. The lower the power factor, the more the upstream distribution system must be oversized including supplies, generators and UPS, as more voltage or current is required to perform the same quantity of work.

In terms of the power factors discussed here, it can generally be said that:

• linear loads most commonly produce displaccment power factors
• non-linear loads produce a combination of displacement and distortion power factors

It can also be said that most non-linear loads have a high displacement power factor (probably near to unity). However, their overall power factor is low due to the presence of a low distortion power factor.

3.1.5 Crest Factor

Crest factor is the ratio between the peak current and the RMS current drawn by any load. Most UPS inverters are designed to operate with crest factors of 3:1 (or less) and as long as any connected loads do not exceed the design limits of the UPS, normal operation is maintained.

Most electrical equipment will exhibit a crest factor of between one (1) and two (2), whereas most IT type loads incorporating an SMPS, will tend to exhibit load crest factors of between two (2) and three (3). If a UPS load is in excess of its system design limits (> 3:1) then it is normal practice to oversize the UPS, referred to as '*derating*'. This prevents higher crest factors from potentially damaging the UPS and causing installation problems.

3.1.6 Static and Dynamic Stability

In an On-Line UPS, the inverter provides a continuous, tightly regulated sinewave supply ideal for sensitive loads. The ability of a UPS to maintain this regulated output is referred to as its *static stability*. When powering a linear load, a UPS may maintain a static stability of ±1-2% or ±2-3% when powering non-linear loads.

It is important that a UPS can respond to sudden load changes and still maintain its output regulation. The ability of a UPS to respond to sudden load changes, is referred to as its *dynamic stability*. This is typically rated, for example, at ±5% with a recovery period of up to 10ms. This means - should the load be increased from 0-100% or decreased from 100-0% - its output voltage could vary by as much as ±5% and this variation will be reduced within 10ms to the static stability state. Under these types of load change, output frequency remains unaffected. Where such load changes are common, it is important to factor this into the sizing of a suitable UPS, which in severe cases can mean over sizing it.

3.1.7 Battery Runtimes

UPS selection is affected by the battery runtime required.

Battery runtime is effectively a function of the Ah size of the battery set, Watts drawn by the load, UPS efficiency, battery charge and efficiency, and surrounding ambient temperature. The guideline for optimum battery performance is a room ambient temperature of 20 to 25°C.

Battery discharge performance improves with temperature. However, above the optimum temperature range, their design life reduces. For example, a ten-year design life battery set operated at 30°C will see its life reduced to five years, and at 40°C this will be further reduced to two and a half years. With a five-year design life, such a high ambient can reduce this to less than one year.

Extended runtimes are used where loads must be powered continuously from an alternative power source to the mains power supply. Examples include emergency services, telecoms systems and industrial processes where shutdown could result in life threatening situations or high financial costs. Where extended runtimes are required, two options are available:

- oversize the UPS
- add battery extension packs

Over sizing is common with Line Interactive and Off-Line UPS the inverters of which are not designed for continuous running at full load. On-Line UPS can also be oversized but it is more common for battery extension packs to be installed as their inverters are designed for continuous running, even at full load. Over sizing a UPS does however leave room for additional load expansion at a later date. In the case of an On-Line UPS, it may also provide additional charging capacity as it is generally accepted that the larger the UPS, the larger the charging current they can provide.

Some On-Line UPS designs have up-rated internal charger options for battery extension pack charging. Where this is not the case, the additional battery extension packs must be installed with their own internal chargers and be powered from a separate mains power supply to that feeding the UPS system.

Load shedding can also be used to extend the amount of battery runtime available from a given battery set (on mains power supply failure). Here specific loads are identified and prioritised by the amount of runtime they require on battery. If some loads are shutdown quickly, this reduces the load on the UPS itself and increases the runtime available from the battery set for the remaining loads.

For runtimes of several hours (particularly with larger UPS above 10kVA) a standby generator may be installed together with a short duration battery set (up to 30-minutes) to cover generator start-up and provide contingency in case it fails to start.

3.1.8 System Expansion

UPS selection is affected by the potential for load and runtime expansion.

Once the load has been sized, it is necessary to include a figure for future expansion. The most common approach is to allow for 25% within five years. For On-Line UPS above 10kVA, this can also be achieved using the parallel architectures discussed in *chapter 5*.

3.1.9 Overloads

UPS selection is affected by the quantity, size and frequency of overloads.

Overloads occur when a UPS is faced with power demands in excess of its VA, Watts or crest factor ratings. They may be temporary or continuous. For example, an initial switch-on surge lasting between 50 to 100ms with a high amplitude of up to twenty times normal running current.

Whilst UPS have a built-in overload capacity, this is a safety feature which should not be abused. Constantly running a UPS in overload will reduce its long-term reliability and whilst on bypass the UPS system MTBF reduces to that of the mains power supply itself.

When faced with a severe overload, a UPS will 'current-limit' to protect itself and may even shutdown. Best practice is to size the UPS to meet the current and future running currents of the load (plus any potential intermittent overloads). The automatic bypass of an On-Line UPS is designed to handle a large number of transfers but over the long-term, repetitive transfers can cause wear-and-tear and potentially lead to a system failure.

3.1.10 Power Distribution

UPS selection is affected by the location and number of loads to be powered. The two most common forms of distribution include:

- **Decentralised:** using multiple UPS supporting local loads or load clusters, either standalone or installed within rackmount cabinets.

- **Centralised:** a single UPS, sometimes in a dedicated area, supporting an array of loads or rack cabinets over a wide area and possibly from a dedicated distribution board.

There are many factors that will influence which method of power distribution is chosen. Often one or more will be the most dominant influence on a given site and any total cost of ownership calculations made.

a) Capital Costs

UPS are typically classed as a capital budget spend. It is possible to compare the two approaches on a financial capital basis but this can be misleading if other factors are not taken into account. *Diagram 3.8* demonstrates how the cost per kVA falls as the size of a UPS increases and an installation moves towards a more centralised solution.

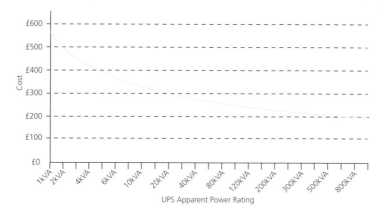

Diagram 3.8 – UPS cost to rating comparison

However, care has to be taken when comparing approaches due to the price range of UPS for the different technologies: Line Interactive UPS are around 40% cheaper than an equivalent On-Line UPS at the same rating. Standby UPS are even cheaper. Therefore, 50 Off-Line UPS at 300VA will generally work out cheaper than a 15kVA UPS, which by default will be an On-Line type, however, the power protection provided by the Off-Line UPS will be poorer. In another example, the cost of 15 On-Line UPS at 1kVA can be more expensive than a single 15kVA UPS.

Aside from the actual capital cost of the hardware, other one-off costs need to be considered relating, for example, to first-time installation. The specific areas covered in *chapter 9* are relevant here.

Even though a centralised system can appear more cost-effective from a hardware comparative viewpoint, initial installation costs will be higher and this is especially true if future expansion is built into the original installation. For example, a 120kVA UPS could be installed with the potential for another 120kVA to be installed in a *parallel-capacity* configuration (to achieve 240kVA) at a later date. A decentralised approach will, therefore, work out cheaper initially but can include hidden costs of increased cable runs, including those for remote monitoring, the required space for multiple installations and potentially extra maintenance visits during their lifetime.

b) Operating and Maintenance Costs

Operating costs are typically included in revenue budgets and unless specially identified can be masked within a final category total e.g. electricity, heat and lighting. UPS running costs can therefore be missed even though they can be significant, especially for older, less efficient systems. Running costs are directly proportional to UPS efficiency and anything less than 100% means that energy is being wasted. UPS efficiency is fast emerging as a topic for discussion amongst UPS manufacturers and the leading organisations are attempting to publish a guideline document. For large power ratings, the savings from a 1% improvement in operating efficiency can, of course, be quite substantial over the working life of a UPS. For example, when comparing two 20kVA UPS (one with a 94% system efficiency and the other 91%) a 30% reduction in heat output within any given period can be achieved, resulting in lower electricity consumption and air-conditioning requirements.

Maintenance is another classic example of a hidden revenue cost. A single maintenance contract for a 200kVA UPS can cost less than that for a site-wide contract for one hundred 2kVA UPS.

c) Power Optimisation

In a centralised approach it is easier to optimise UPS loading and ensure its power is efficiently controlled and distributed. For example, the loading on decentralised UPS may vary and it is not uncommon to find up to 50% of the capacity in a decentralised system under utilised. The problem, however, is that it becomes very difficult to redistribute this within a building unless the UPS or loads can be physically relocated.

d) Remote Management and Control

A UPS must be monitored on a regular basis and its alarms reacted to. Using the previous example, it is more likely that a 200kVA UPS will be remotely monitored on a 24/7 basis by an external UPS service team. In a decentralised approach this may be physically impractical, especially over an entire site if all the UPS cannot be connected to a network or *Building Management System (BMS)*.

e) Access For Maintenance, Battery Testing and Replacement

A large centralised UPS is usually installed within a dedicated and sometimes restricted area. This prevents unauthorised access and removes the potential for accidental switch-off or tampering. It also allows work to be carried out on-site in a health & safety controlled environment. This can include a preventative maintenance visit, battery testing and even full battery replacement. In a decentralised approach, it is sometimes not possible to complete anything other than a general inspection without removing the UPS to a holding area or off-site. Within a rackmount cabinet, access may also be restricted unless the UPS are installed on easy-to-slide-out rails or contained within a dedicated UPS rack cabinet system that can be isolated using a maintenance bypass. A further issue is that it is common to find a centralised UPS installed with a maintenance bypass to allow service work to be performed without disruption to the load. Decentralised UPS are often installed without such a bypass, resulting in maintenance (or even a full system swap-out) leading to system downtime.

f) Future Expansion

Future expansion and scalability is always an under estimated issue. System demands consistently rise over time and so does the amount of uninterruptible power required. It can sometimes be hard to justify extra installation costs and to reserve space in a plant room for a potential UPS expansion. However, this can be a more viable approach for an organisation than trying to find spare room within data centres and rack cabinets at a later date. For either approach, the existing electrical supplies must also have spare capacity designed into them at the start.

3.1.11 Resilience

Resilience can be defined as the capacity of any system exposed to hazards to adapt, by resisting or changing in order to reach and maintain an acceptable level of functioning and structure. It is also known as the *fault tolerance* of a system.

Resilience levels are affected by the UPS topology chosen and its distribution throughout a system. For example, On-Line UPS include an automatic bypass and therefore a safe failure to mains mechanism which is not present in Line Interactive and Off-Line designs.

On-Line UPS above 10kVA are also typically capable of being installed using the parallel architectures described in *chapter 5* to provide additional capacity and/or N+x resilience. For example, two 10kVA UPS operated in a *parallel-capacity* system can power a 20kVA load or in a *parallel-redundant* system, support a 10kVA load with N+1 redundancy. This means that UPS above 10kVA are generally installed in a centralised manner with power distributed to individual loads, often through a dedicated power distribution board.

Parallel architectures offer superior power protection and higher levels of resilience. However, this is not always the case with, for example, plug-in modular systems reliant on a centralised processing set-up. These systems tend to use small 1kVA or larger sized power modules which can be plugged into the framework to achieve power ratings up to several hundred kVA. The weakness is their flexibility and reliance on a single processor. Whilst the modules can be 'hot swapped', there is no way to test one on-site before it is connected into the central framework. A UPS module, for example, damaged during transit, could introduce a fault when connected which could severely disrupt operation of the entire system and force it to shutdown.

UPS below 10kVA are not generally capable of parallel connection and are either installed as standalone units or in conjunction with an *Automatic Transfer Switch*. This can be configured to automatically provide one of two separate *ac* supplies.

3.1.12 Supplies - Phases, Voltages and Frequencies

The mains power supply into an industrial estate, factory or other large building is typically a three-phase (plus neutral) supply at 400Vac 50Hz within Europe *(see appendix B)*. Each phase is colour coded. Historically, in the UK the colours were Red, Yellow and Blue, with a Black neutral.

These were changed (under BS 7671 – *The IEE Wiring Regulations, Sixteenth Edition* introduced on 31 March 2004) to Brown, Black and Grey, with a Blue neutral to bring the UK more closely in line with Europe. The supply available from a typical office wall socket, or hardwired fused spur, is known as single-phase. Within Europe it will have a voltage of around 230Vac and frequency of 50Hz. The maximum current that can be drawn from such a supply in the UK will be determined by the supply rating which is typically, 10, 13, 16 or 20 Amps.

Where the system is installed within a building will therefore influence the UPS range and model to be used. For example, whether to select a UPS with either a three-phase or single-phase input. It should be noted that the output from a single-phase UPS will be single-phase. However, some UPS are available with both a three-phase and single-phase input option (3/1 or 1/1), from which they can provide a single-phase output. This is generally available as an option from 8kVA and above. The load demand will also affect which type of UPS can be used. A three-phase load will require a three-phase output UPS.

For a three-phase installation, during normal operation a UPS will typically ensure that the current drawn (from the mains power supply) per phase is balanced, regardless of its load. However, should the UPS have to switch to bypass, the load is transferred directly to the mains power supply and any load imbalance could lead to overheating of upstream conductors and supply cables. In addition, for a 3/1 UPS configuration, phase one (1) must be capable of powering the entire load if the bypass is activated.

Where the supply voltage or load requirements are different to: 230Vac 50Hz single-phase or 400Vac 50Hz three-phase i.e: 110Vac within industrial environments, separate step-up or step-down transformers may be required on the input and/or output of the UPS.

Load or mains power supply frequency can also be an issue if there is a mismatch between them. Here an On-Line UPS can be used as a frequency converter providing 50/60Hz or 60/50Hz operation. When used in this way, the automatic bypass is disabled to prevent possible damage or disruption to the load.

The size of the incoming supply can also influence the size and type of UPS chosen. This is more generally the rule for larger UPS above 100kVA. Where supplies have to be up rated or additional supplies installed, it can be costly and result in ground works around the site and possibly upstream at local substations.

3.2 UPS Range Selection

Once the load has been sized, the UPS topology, range and particular model can be selected. Manufacturers like Riello UPS group their systems into four specific areas:

* IT
* Network
* Industrial and Enterprise
* Rackmount (Net-Tel)

3.2.1 IT Applications 300VA to 3kVA

For smaller Information and Communications Technology (ICT) applications including home PCs and SoHo (Small Office/Home Office) and data and voice networks.

UPS for IT applications include Off-Line, Line Interactive and On-Line designs up to 3kVA. Off-Line UPS are usually compact devices designed for desktop or wall mount installations. Line Interactive and On-Line UPS use tower or rackmount case formats and are designed to sit next to their respective loads. The cost and relative size of IT UPS allows a decentralised approach to be taken.

On-Line UPS in this range are typically a transformerless design. This helps to achieve a compact, low weight, noise and heat output UPS which is suitable for mass distribution and ease of installation. Some applications such as those within medical environments or electrically noisy sites may require Galvanic isolation. Here a transformer is housed in a separate cabinet positioned on the input or output side of the UPS. The size of UPS for IT applications leaves little provision for standard output sockets and it is normal for these to be of the IEC320 type. A UPS will provide up to eight of these. A UPS designed for the SoHo market in particular may have local domestic type sockets for ease of use. Hard wiring may also be an option for larger systems.

Most IT UPS up to 2kVA can be powered from a normal 13A wall socket, except where the UPS has a large internal charger fitted which increases its current draw above 13A. In such an instance, the supply connection has to be made using a 16A or 32A Industrial (Commando) type connector or hardwired fused spur. This also will apply to UPS rated from 3kVA upwards. UPS for IT applications will generally have an internal battery which may be user-replaceable behind an easy-to-remove cover. Larger Line Interactive and On-Line UPS models will provide a connection for battery extension packs and these may themselves have their own built-in chargers.

An important factor to consider is remote monitoring (*see chapter 8*) and these types of UPS usually provide either a D-sub type or USB port (or both) for connection to a dedicated remote monitoring and control package. UPS monitoring and control software will be provided from a dedicated download website or on a CD-ROM. Network interfaces and Simple Network Management Protocol (SNMP) adapters are also available as slot-in or external accessories.

 ### 3.2.2 Network Applications 3-80kVA

For corporate data and voice networks, including Internet Service Providers (ISPs) and telecommunications.

UPS for Network applications are designed to act as a centralised power source and their design is typically transformerless. The installation tends to be hardwired at both the input and output terminals due to the power required. The UPS may also require connection to a three-phase incomer and the loads themselves are more likely to require three-phase, and potentially some form of dedicated power distribution switchgear.

For three-phase UPS in this range, in the UK, harmonics compliance to G5/4-1 must be considered. The methods to mitigate UPS generated harmonics are discussed in *chapter 4*.

The fixed installation format of a Network UPS means that the design must allow for ease of on-site service. The UPS should therefore have a short MTTR with easy access to PCBs and slide-out assemblies. Larger models can be operated in parallel or N+1 configurations to improve system resilience, MTBF and availability.

UPS from 8kVA in this range will have an internal maintenance bypass. For a Network sized UPS, the installation of an external maintenance bypass becomes more important due to the critical nature of the loads being powered. The load may be operated on a 24/7 basis and the external maintenance bypass allows routine or emergency service work to be carried out during normal working-hours, without disruption to the load.

Batteries will be housed internally or in matching cabinets or racks standing nearby the UPS. Long extended runtimes may be provided by a combination of battery packs and an external standby power source such as a generator. The generator will either be installed within the same plant room or outside the building (ground floor or roof top location) in a protected environment. Fuel cells are also increasingly considered as a suitable alternative to generators within this size range. Extended runtime provision for these larger UPS and the physical space required to house them becomes more important as does the overall placement of the UPS within the building to reduce cable runs, ensure adequate alarm monitoring and provide a suitable environment. For larger installations the UPS may be sited in a dedicated UPS room or within a plant room.

3.2.3 Industrial and Enterprise Applications 10-800kVA

For enterprise-wide data and voice networks, industrial processes, security (emergency lighting, fire and security systems) and large hospital applications.

Industrial UPS differ to Network UPS in that they are traditionally transformer-based with either a 6-pulse or 12-pulse rectifier fitted as standard. The transformer provides a higher degree of robustness but with slightly lower efficiency, and higher heat and noise generation than a transformerless design. The UPS may be used to protect not only industrial processes but large site-wide installations such as data centres.

As the installation increases in size so does the complexity of power distribution and the need for attention to be paid to discrimination within the building electrical supply to prevent nuisance circuit-breaker tripping and disruption to other connected loads.

To prevent harmonics generated by the UPS affecting upstream equipment, transformer-based UPS can be installed with a passive harmonic filter. It is more common for this type of UPS to be installed in a parallel or N+1 configuration and the higher capital cost allows alternative standby power sources to be considered such as flywheels and fuel cells. As the bypass supply is routed outside the output transformer, a separate isolation transformer is available for the bypass supply if Galvanic isolation is required.

3.2.4 Rackmount Applications (Net-Tel) 700VA-30kVA

Rack cabinets have become a common installation format for multiple server projects to reduce footprints and cable runs used within computer rooms. UPS manufacturers have responded by creating rackmount UPS formats from their standard product ranges and a range of accessories. A different UPS case design for installation in either a 600mm or 800mm-deep rack cabinet is commonly used. This is the internal depth (front to back) and most UPS will fall short of either 600 or 800mm to allow for rear panel cable connection which may be plug-in or hardwired. Rack cabinets have a standard internal front panel width of 19 inches (483mm) and in terms of height are measured in 'U' where 1U =1.75" or 44mm. Available rack cabinet sizes are 600, 800, and 1000mm deep with heights ranging from around 6U to 47U or greater. Rack cabinets, therefore, provide a generically sized space into which any corresponding equipment can be housed including UPS and typical network hardware such as file servers, routers and hubs. All rack cabinet measurements are internal rather than external and care has to be taken when planning installations within small areas.

UPS can be installed in standard computer room cabinets where the rack is strong enough to take the overall UPS system weight. A typical rack cabinet has a loading of 150-300kg and may be able to hold the UPS battery packs in self-contained battery trays fitted to telescopic slides (if suitably sized for the weights involved) or secured onto shelves and placed behind removable covers to limit access. Where this is not possible, battery packs may be floor standing to prevent cabinet supports buckling. Alternatively, the entire UPS system can be installed in its own rackmount cabinet which can be installed next to the load cabinets. Here the rack cabinet will require a high loading capacity in terms of the weight it can support and may even be customised further in terms of the addition of top-vented cooling fans, filters and case IP rating (to cater for harsh environments).

In terms of UPS design, most UPS manufacturers have made versions of their popular IT application sized UPS (700VA-3kVA) available in rackmount format including Line Interactive and On-Line (up to 10kVA). Larger rackmount sizes are also available from a small number of manufacturers using On-Line transformerless UPS designs. These UPS come in a variety of input/output phase combinations (1/1, 3/1 or 3/3) with either internal or external battery sets, and can be installed into standard rack cabinets (depth and weight permitting). They can also offer parallel architectures and so provide additional resilience and a scalable solution for fast growing sites with space restrictions.

3.3 Summary

Correctly sizing the UPS load and matching this to the right UPS size and topology is an integral aspect of a *Power Continuity Plan*. There are, however, additional considerations and in today's environment, a key decision has to be made as to the type of On-Line UPS design to deploy. This is considered in *chapter 4*.

Chapter 5 provides an in-depth review of the ways to improve the resilience of an On-Line UPS system to achieve the highest levels of availability. *Appendix C* provides sample product specifications for consideration.

4. On-Line UPS Designs

In this chapter:

- Examining transformer-based and transformerless On-Line UPS designs.
- Exploring ways to achieve low total harmonic distortion levels.
- Discussing static switch operation and possible configurations.
- Comparing the two On-Line UPS designs using a variety of practical means.

Introduction

On-Line is one of the three Static UPS topologies defined within EN/IEC 62040-3. Two approaches are available, referred to as: transformer-based and transformerless.

Both UPS produce a tightly regulated source of uninterruptible power. They primarily differ in the way they generate the *dc* busbar voltage required by their inverters and therefore their output stages. This leads to differences in their physical size, efficiency, noise output and the levels of input harmonic distortion they generate.

Transformer-based On-Line UPS are the more traditional design and are available in sizes from 8kVA to 800kVA. The most common applications for this type of UPS tend to start above 120kVA. This type of UPS has a robust transformer isolated inverter output making it more suited to protect applications on, for example, industrial sites where there is a high degree of electrical noise, spikes, transients and potential high short-circuit currents.

The transformerless design is the more modern of the two and is commonly available from 700VA to 120kVA. The design has become the standard for most IT environments below 120kVA. Most of its advantages derive from the fact that this type of UPS does not have a built-in transformer. It is therefore more compact, with a smaller footprint and generates far less noise and heat, and lower input harmonic distortion levels.

As the two UPS ranges overlap in terms of power rating, selecting the right one for an application is not always easy. The solution is to review both types and their specific advantages in relation to: initial purchase costs, physical footprint, running costs, the actual installation environment, and in particular, the levels of input harmonic distortion they generate.

Both designs can be operated in parallel (as discussed in *chapter 5)* to achieve high levels of availability and resilience.

4.1 General UPS Design

4.1.1 Transformer-Based UPS

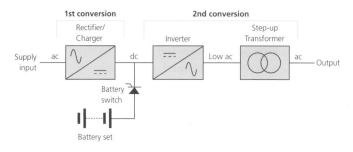

Diagram 4.1 – Transformer-based On-Line UPS

The rectification stage most commonly relies on a phase controlled *rectifier-charger* to convert an *ac* power source (mains power supply or generator) into a unidirectional 'low-ripple' *dc* voltage to charge a battery set and power the inverter. The battery set is coupled to the rectifier output and the *dc* busbar via a switching device.

One of the main benefits of a rectifier-charger is that it can provide a percentage of its output current (load dependent) to charge a battery set. This can be especially useful for large battery sets where a fast recharge time is required.

The inverter generates an *ac* supply from its *dc* power source which is fed into a *step-up transformer*. The primary function of the transformer is to increase the inverter *ac* voltage to that required to power the load. The transformer also protects the inverter from load disruptions, whilst providing Galvanic isolation.

The rectifier in this type of On-Line UPS typically supports a *dc* busbar voltage range of 384-480Vdc. This is an advantage because the lower the *dc* busbar voltage the smaller the overall battery set size, as fewer blocks are required for each battery string. However, at this level, the *dc* busbar voltage is not high enough to power an inverter set to generate a 230Vac phase-to-neutral supply. For this, the *dc* busbar must be higher, at least 650Vdc (2x325Vac peak-to-peak), as shown in *diagram 4.2*.

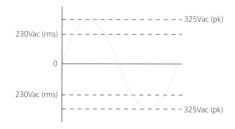

Diagram 4.2 – Sinewave showing 230Vac rms and peak values

The problem is overcome by passing the inverter output through the step-up transformer. In this way, the inverter can be set to generate a lower phase-to-neutral supply of 115Vac which the transformer then increases to the required output level of 230Vac phase-to-neutral (or 400Vac in a three-phase output system).

Some UPS manufacturers include a step-up transformer before the rectifier-charger as an alternative or in addition to the one connected to the inverter. The latter is not very common as it increases the overall cost, size and weight of the UPS and the battery set.

4.1.2 Transformerless UPS

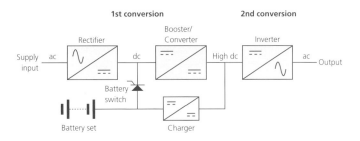

Diagram 4.3 – Transformerless On-Line UPS

The first stage combines a rectifier and *booster-converter* to generate a *dc* supply for the inverter. An *uncontrolled three-phase bridge rectifier* converts the *ac* supply into a *dc* voltage. This is passed through a *mid-point booster circuit* to step the *dc* voltage up to typically between 700-800Vdc from which a battery charger and inverter are powered.

In the second stage, the inverter takes the supply from the booster-converter and inverts this back to an *ac* voltage to supply the load. There are no step-up transformers as the inverter is supplied with the required *dc* voltage level from which to generate the 230Vac phase-neutral supply. An added benefit of this voltage conversion method is that the rectifier can typically operate when supplied from either a three or single-phase input supply. This can usually be configured at installation for systems up to 20kVA.

Transformerless UPS operation relies on a mid-point booster, which during normal operation, uses the mains power supply neutral as a reference point. On mains power supply failure, the booster takes its reference from the mid-point of the battery set. For this reason, in a transformerless UPS, 50% of the battery set is installed on the positive (+ve) side and 50% on the negative (–ve) side, to ensure one half is positive and one half negative with respect to the neutral at all times.

4.2 Rectifiers and Battery Charging

4.2.1 Transformer-Based UPS

a) Rectifier-Chargers

The charging current supplied by the rectifier is load dependent. The UPS can provide additional current for charging where its output power is less than its nominal rating and within the limits of its maximum charging current. However, high recharge currents are known to damage batteries and so the rectifier-charger will:

- limit the maximum current for recharging to 15% of the battery Ah rating
- provide 80% of the recharging power with limited current and increased voltage, and the remaining 20% at a lower constant voltage, known as a '*float voltage*'

Rectifier-chargers are sized in terms of the power they can deliver (kW) and are classed as 6-pulse or 12-pulse. The terms are derived from the number of thyristors (also known as *Silicon Controlled Rectifiers or SCRs*) used by the rectifier to control its *dc* output voltage level. The number of thyristors dictates the number of pulses required for this purpose. A *6-pulse rectifier* uses six sequential pulses per full cycle and a 12-pulse twelve. Most UPS systems up to 60kVA have a 6-pulse rectifier as standard with a 12-pulse option. Larger systems from 250kVA typically have a *12-pulse rectifier* as standard.

b) Phase Controlled Rectifiers

A 6-pulse rectifier is also known as a *full* or *phase controlled rectifier* due to the way it controls the firing-angle of each of its six sequential thyristors to adjust its output *dc* voltage level. This will be between zero and the maximum that can be generated based on the *ac* source. The earlier the firing-angle, the higher the rectifier output voltage. The basic principles of thyristor operation are shown in *diagram 4.4*.

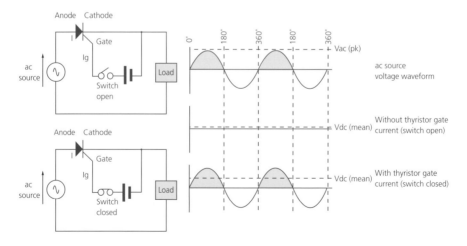

Diagram 4.4 – Half-wave uncontrolled rectifier

The circuit shown is a simple *half-wave rectification circuit,* where only the positive half of the *ac* waveform is conducted by the thyristor. The circuit comprises of an *ac* source, load, gate current source and thyristor. To enable the thyristor to start conducting (on-state) it must be both forward biased (anode positive with respect to the cathode) and a current must be injected into the gate terminal, relative to the cathode. In the diagram, the gate current source is shown as a battery. When the switch is closed and the gate is continually injected with current (Ig), the thyristor is able to conduct, and current flows each time it becomes forward biased. This occurs between 0-180°. As a result, the positive half of the waveform passes through, the mean *dc* voltage increases, and the negative half is blocked. Once the thyristor has been switched on, it will continue to conduct until the commutation point, which occurs naturally at the zero-crossing. Even if the gate current was removed mid cycle (between 0-180°), the thyristor would continue to conduct until the zero-crossing point.

Diagram 4.5 shows the same circuit but with the gate current source switched by a trigger circuit. It is still a half-wave rectification circuit (referred to as a *phase controlled half-wave rectifier*) but the point at which the thyristor switches on is controlled by the trigger.

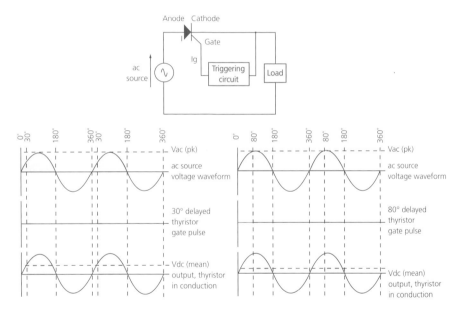

Diagram 4.5 – Half-wave controlled rectifier

If no gate current (Ig) is injected, the thyristor does not conduct and the *dc* voltage produced remains at zero. Using phase control techniques, the trigger circuit controls the point (phase angle) at which the thyristor is fired with respect to the zero-crossing point. The waveform, in *diagram 4.5,* shows that when the trigger point is delayed by 30° from the zero-crossing point, the thyristor begins to conduct and allows current to flow during the period between 30 and 180°. This is referred to as the *phase conduction angle.* As a result, the mean *dc* voltage rises to a level dependent upon the value of the *ac* source voltage. If the trigger point is delayed until 80°, the mean *dc* voltage lowers as the period of conduction is reduced to between 80-180°.

c) 6-Pulse Rectifiers

Diagram 4.6 shows the design of a typical three-phase, 6-pulse rectifier comprising of three sections, one per phase of the incoming supply. Each section has two thyristors, one at the top and one at the bottom. In phase one, the top thyristor (P1+) is used to control the firing angle relative to the positive half of the waveform. The bottom thyristor (P1-) is used to control the firing angle relative to the negative half of the waveform.

This principle also applies to the thyristors connected to phases two (2) and three (3). It is important that the rectifier thyristors are fired in a specific order in relation to the rotation sequence of the incoming supply phases.

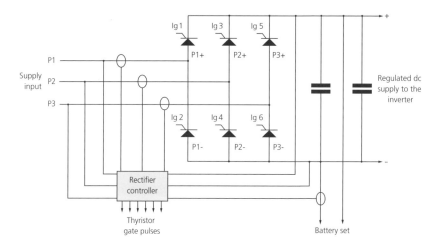

Diagram 4.6 – 6-pulse, three-phase rectifier

For example, if the rectifier is supplied from a source using the connection sequence phase one (1) - Brown, phase two (2) - Black and phase three (3) - Grey, its thyristors must be fired in the sequence P1+, P3-, P2+, P1-, P3+, P2-, P1+, P3- and so on.

As discussed, for a thyristor to conduct it must be forward biased. For a three-phase, phase controlled rectifier, each of the positive and negative halves of the three waveforms (relative to their thyristors) are only forward biased between 30-150° from the zero-crossing point. The firing angle is controlled between these points.

Diagram 4.7 shows how a 6-pulse rectifier controls its *dc* output voltage. In *figure 1*, the thyristors are triggered at 30° (60° from zero-crossing).

If the trigger is delayed still further until 50° (80° from zero-crossing), *figure 2*, then the *dc* output voltage reduces. The rectifier capacitors significantly smooth out its output waveform to achieve a low *ac* ripple component and enable the rectifier to supply power to the inverter and charge the battery set at the same time. A high *ac* ripple could cause long-term battery damage and reduce the resilience of the entire UPS system.

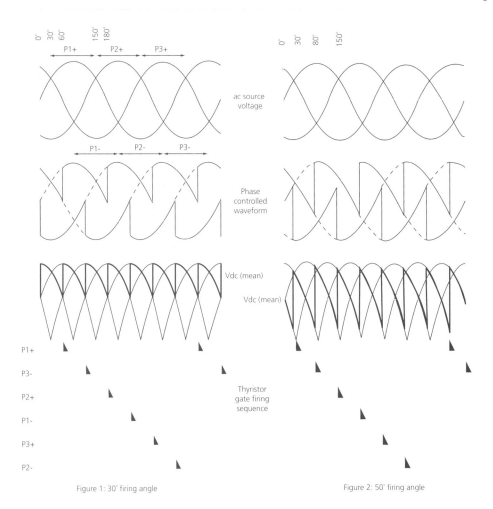

Figure 1: 30˚ firing angle

Figure 2: 50˚ firing angle

Diagram 4.7 – 6-pulse phase control waveforms

By ensuring that the thyristor firing angles are as near to equal as possible, the load is balanced across the three incoming phases. Only slight variations occur when the firing angles change. Most UPS manufactures allow the time it takes for the rectifier to start-up (to reach its maximum output voltage) to be adjusted. This is typically referred to as '*walk-in*' or '*soft-start*' and prevents the UPS system from creating a large in-rush of energy that could cause disruption to upstream hardware.

d) 12-Pulse Rectifiers

Diagram 4.8 shows two typical examples of a 12-pulse rectifier circuit.

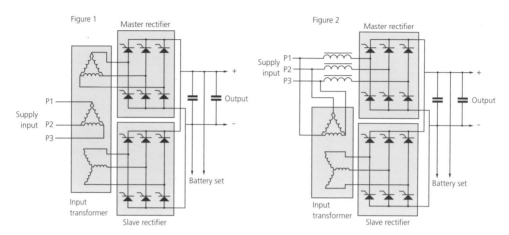

Diagram 4.8 – Two typical 12-pulse rectifiers

These are simply two 6-pulse rectifiers operating in parallel (master-slave) configuration, using the same basic phase control principles.

Their output is connected to a common *dc* busbar. They both share the same basic principle using an input transformer to provide a 30° phase displacement between the two incoming *ac* supplies, which are then fed into each of the 6-pulse rectifiers.

In *figure 1*, the input transformer has two secondary windings which provide the phase displacement and step up the incoming voltage. When this is supplied to both the master and slave rectifiers, the *dc* busbar can be increased for the connection of a higher Vdc rated battery set.

In *figure 2*, the master rectifier is fed directly from the mains power supply and the slave rectifier input is fed via the phase displacement transformer. This is the preferred method for a transformer-based UPS as it achieves a smaller overall solution and lower material costs.

In a 12-pulse rectifier, the three-phase voltages supplying the two individual 6-pulse rectifiers are displaced by a 30° phase angle to generate the symmetrically displaced waveforms required. A 12-pulse rectifier typically generates between 8-11% *Total Harmonic Distortion (THDi)*. This is significantly less than a 6-pulse rectifier (27-35%).

4.2.2 Transformerless UPS

a) Rectifier, Booster-Converters

The rectifier provides one function: to power the booster-converter, which in turn powers the inverter and charges the battery set. A control system ensures a stable, regulated *dc* voltage is supplied to the inverter at all times and that the inverter can operate regardless of UPS output load variations or mains power supply fluctuations or disturbances. The mains power supply input to the rectifier is first passed into a full wave uncontrolled three-phase bridge rectifier circuit. This converts the incoming *ac* voltage into a source of unregulated unidirectional *dc* voltage. The level of this voltage is determined by the voltage level of the incoming *ac* supply. If the incoming supply voltage increases or decreases, the level of unregulated *dc* voltage produced also increases or decreases accordingly. Following the primary rectification stage, the unregulated *dc* voltage is fed into the booster-converter.

The mid-point booster circuit shown in (*diagram 4.9*) is used to increase the rectifier output *dc* voltage level, from either the battery set or rectifier, to between positive (+ve) 365-410Vdc and negative (–ve) 365-410Vdc with respect to neutral, depending on the mode of operation and the load applied to the UPS.

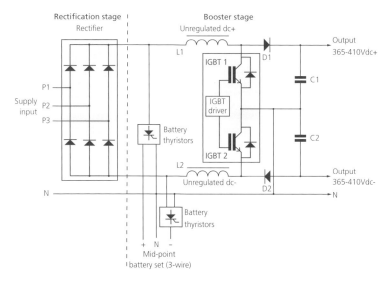

Diagram 4.9 – Mid-point booster circuit

The booster-converter operates using an energy storage and transfer principle between the inductive components of the circuit (L1 and L2) and the capacitive components (C1 and C2). Within the circuit, the unregulated output *dc* voltage from the rectifier is evenly split with respect to the incoming neutral. The positive side is positive and the negative side is negative with respect to neutral. For example, 300Vdc equates to positive (+ve) 150Vdc and negative (–ve) 150Vdc.

The IGBT (as referenced in *diagram 4.9*) is an *Insulated Gate Bipolar Transistor*. It has traditionally been used within inverter designs and is discussed in detail in *section 4.4.1*. IGBTs can now be found within modern rectifier designs such as the mid-point booster-converter circuit discussed here and other rectifier designs.

When IGBTs (1) and (2) are switched off, in theory capacitor C1 will naturally charge up to the level of the unregulated positive *dc* voltage via inductor L1 and diode D1. Capacitor C2 will also charge up to the level of the unregulated negative *dc* voltage via inductor L2 and D2.

When IGBT (1) is switched on it will connect one side of the inductor L1 directly to the neutral point. This increases the current and magnetic energy stored within the inductor L1 via the IGBT.

Once the required level of magnetic energy has been stored (obviously up to the maximum capacity of the inductor), the IGBT is switched off. By doing so, the stored magnetic energy is transferred into capacitor C1 via diode D1. This increases the voltage across the capacitor which in turn increases the voltage available to power the inverter. When the IGBTs are switched on, diodes D1 and D2 block the return current flow and prevent the energy within each capacitor from being discharged through the IGBT.

The switching process is the same for the negative half of the circuit, with only capacitor C2 charging up negative with respect to neutral. This enables the UPS to independently control both the positive and negative halves of its booster-converter output voltage. IGBT switching and therefore the control of the energy transferred is performed using *Pulse Width Modulation (PWM)* and this typically operates around 16kHz.

PWM allows the booster-converter output voltage to be accurately controlled and takes into account the operational state of the UPS, the voltage level of its battery set, the mains power supply voltage and connected load.

When the mains power supply fails, the battery set is connected automatically to the booster-converter via the battery thyristors and the inverter continues to receive a seamless *dc* source.

This type of rectifier, and booster-converter circuit can operate from either a three or single-phase input. However when supplied from a single-phase supply, the rectifier will generate a far lower unregulated *dc* voltage and must be driven harder in order to achieve the required *dc* voltage levels. It also has a high *input power factor, table 4.1,* achieved from the way in which the current waveform is drawn in phase with the voltage waveform.

Typical rectifier, booster-converter input power factor @ 400Vac				
UPS Load	25%	50%	75%	100%
Input pF	0.90	0.965	0.966	0.967

Table 4.1 – Typical rectifier, booster-converter input power factor

4.3 Rectifiers and Harmonics

4.3.1 6-Pulse Rectifiers

6-pulse rectifiers are widely used in a number of applications but have a design weakness. They generate high THDi levels of between 27-35%. The actual figures are dependent upon the UPS design and mains power supply impedance. Two methods can be used to reduce the harmonics generated:

- install a *passive harmonic filter* in series with the UPS
- use a 12-pulse rectifier in place of the 6-pulse set

Diagram 4.10 shows the typical input current waveform for a 6-pulse rectifier. A perfect current waveform would be sinusoidal with no harmonics present. In the diagram, the 6-pulse input current is rich in low order harmonics, principally the 5th, 7th & 11th harmonics.

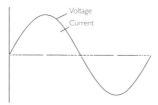

Diagram 4.10 – Typical input current waveform for a 6-pulse rectifier

The following formula is used to calculate the full range of predominate harmonics generated by a particular rectifier:

$$H = (n \times p) \pm 1$$

Note: n = an integer (1,2,3,4,5 and so on) and p = the number of pulses

The harmonics generated by a 6-pulse rectifier include:

- $H = (1 \times 6) \pm 1$ = 5th & 7th harmonic
- $H = (2 \times 6) \pm 1$ = 11th & 13th harmonic
- $H = (3 \times 6) \pm 1$ = 17th & 19th harmonic
- $H = (4 \times 6) \pm 1$ = 23th & 25th harmonic

Table 4.2 (overleaf), shows the actual values measured at the input to a UPS fitted with a 6-pulse rectifier, the calculated predominate harmonics and the effects of the UPS load on the THDi value. The last two columns simply show the harmonic frequencies.

THDi reduces for a 6-pulse rectifier under load and therefore most UPS manufacturers will only state their generated harmonics levels at full load.

Typical 6-pulse rectifier input harmonics percentage (%) @ 400Vac					Harmonic Frequencies	
Harmonic Number	25% Load	50% Load	75% Load	100% Load	Harmonic Order	Frequency (Hz)
1	74	89	94	96	1st	50
3	4	2	1.5	0.5	3rd	150
5	58	43	33	28	5th	250
7	30	10	3	4.5	7th	350
9	1	1	0.5	1	9th	450
11	7	9	7	5.5	11th	550
13	7	1	3	4	13th	650
15	1	1	1	1	15th	750
17	2	4	3	1	17th	850
19	4	1	2	2	19th	950
21	1	1	0	0	21st	1050
23	2.5	2.5	2	2	23rd	1150
25	1	1	1	1	25th	1250
THDi	67	45	34	29		

Table 4.2 – 6-pulse rectifier-generated harmonics

4.3.2 12-Pulse Rectifiers

UPS with a 12-pulse rectifier are more expensive as they use two 6-pulse rectifiers in parallel. The advantages of a 12-pulse rectifier over a 6-pulse set include:

- reduced levels of THDi to around 8-11% as it effectively eliminates the 5th and 7th harmonics to a higher order, where the 11th and 13th become the predominant
- the UPS is more suitable for applications where the load can change significantly during operation as the harmonics generated are not greatly affected by the load

Diagram 4.11 shows a typical input current waveform for a 12-pulse rectifier. The actual current waveform is not quite sinusoidal and some harmonics are present.

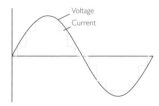

Diagram 4.11 – Typical input current waveform for a 12-pulse rectifier

The waveform is superior to that of the 6-pulse set shown in *diagram 4.10.*

The input current contains higher order harmonics (11th & 13th). To determine the full range of predominate harmonics generated, the same calculation can be used.

The harmonics generated by a 12-pulse rectifier include:

- H = (1 x 12)±1 = 11th & 13th harmonic
- H = (2 x 12)±1 = 23th & 25th harmonic

Table 4.3 shows the actual values measured at the input to a UPS fitted with a 12-pulse rectifier. The data shows how little the THDi changes with respect to load compared to a 6-pulse set.

Typical 12-pulse rectifier input harmonics percentage (%) @ 400Vac				
Harmonic Number	25% Load	50% Load	75% Load	100% Load
1	99.6	99.6	99.7	99.7
3	1.5	1.5	1	1
5	2	2	2	1.5
7	1.5	1	1	1.5
9	0.5	1	0	0
11	2.5	7	6.5	6
13	6.5	2	2	3
15	0	0	0	0
17	1	1	1	1
19	1	1	1	1
21	0	0	0	0
23	2.7	2.5	3.5	2.5
25	0	1	1	1
THDi	8.7	8.4	8.1	7.7

Table 4.3 – 12-pulse rectifier-generated harmonics

4.3.3 Rectifier, Booster-Converters

The THDi generated by a rectifier coupled to a booster-converter will typically be between 24-28% depending on the UPS and load. The waveform is distorted but it is superior to that achieved by a 6-pulse rectifier, as shown in *diagram 4.12*.

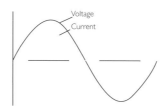

Diagram 4.12 – Typical input current waveform for a rectifier, booster-converter

The input current is rich in low order harmonics: 3rd, 5th, 7th and 11th.

Table 4.4 lists the typical values for the individual harmonics generated.

Typical rectifier, booster-converter input harmonics percentage (%) @ 400Vac		
Harmonic Number	Harmonic Frequency (Hz)	Harmonic Component Value (%)
1	50	100
2	100	0.4
3	150	16.9
4	200	0.4
5	250	14.5
6	300	0.4
7	350	5.7
8	400	0.3
9	450	1.8
10	500	0.2
11	550	4.4
12	600	0.2
13	650	3.7
14	700	0.3
15	750	0.2
16	800	0
17	850	3.2
18	900	0
19	950	3.0
20	1000	0.2

Table 4.4 – Rectifier, booster-converter-generated harmonics

4.3.4 Mitigating Total Harmonic Distortion

Harmonics issues need to be addressed at the design stage of a *Power Continuity Plan* because consumers are responsible for the harmonic levels induced into their three-phase mains power supply. A UPS can sometimes be fitted with a harmonic filter (post installation) but this can be costly as extensive internal wiring changes may be required.

For a transformer-based UPS, using a 12-pulse rectifier in place of a 6-pulse set will reduce the levels of THDi generated. Coupling this with a passive filter will reduce this further to around 4%.

For a transformerless UPS, THDi levels of less than 4% can be achieved by installing an active harmonic filter. However, 3% can now be achieved by some designs whose rectifiers are IGBT-based, removing the need for the additional active harmonic filter. This type of design is expected to become the norm because it also reduces initial costs and system footprints, whilst increasing input power factors to greater than 0.99.

4.3.5 Passive Harmonic Filters

A passive harmonic filter (*diagram 4.13*) is basically a tuned harmonic trap consisting of a smoothing choke (L_L) connected in series with the rectifier and an LC filter (L_R & C_R), connected in parallel.

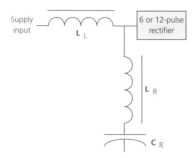

Diagram 4.13 – Passive harmonic filter schematic (1 phase)

a) 6-Pulse Rectifiers

A passive harmonic filter comprises of inductive and capacitive elements connected in circuit to provide a near zero impedance path for the specific tuned harmonic frequency, in this case the 5th harmonic. The filter will also reduce higher order harmonics such as the 7th but not as effectively. This is because the level of impedance for the higher order frequencies naturally increases for a filter tuned to the 5th harmonic. As the frequency of harmonics present increases, the filter naturally becomes less effective.

For a UPS (at 100% load) with a 6-pulse rectifier and 5th harmonic passive filter, a THDi reduction from 29% to 5-8% is possible. The passive harmonic filter will also improve the input power factor of the UPS system due to the way in which the harmonics are reduced.

The passive solution attenuates harmonics most effectively under full load conditions. When the UPS is less than fully loaded the passive solution is far less effective, and in some cases may not be much better than a system with no harmonic filter at all.

b) 12-Pulse Rectifiers

A passive harmonic filter can be used with a 12-pulse rectifier in much same way, with the exception that it is tuned to trap the 11th harmonic. This filter will again reduce higher order harmonics such as the 13th but not as effectively.

A UPS at full load, with a 12-pulse rectifier and 11th harmonic passive filter, will typically see a reduction in THDi from 8% to around 4%. As with a 6-pulse rectifier, the filter will also improve the input power factor of the entire system and is most effective at full load, (*see table 4.5 overleaf*).

Typical 12-pulse rectifier input harmonics percentage (%) @ 400Vac with a passive harmonic filter				
Harmonic Number	25% Load	50% Load	75% Load	100% Load
1	99.7	99.8	99.9	99.9
3	1.5	1.5	1	1
5	2	2	2	1.5
7	3	2	1	1
9	0	1	0	0
11	1	1	1	1
13	4	2	1.5	1
15	0	0	0	0
17	1	1	1	1
19	1	1	1	1
21	0	0	0	0
23	3	3	3	2.5
25	1	1	1	1
THDi	7	5.4	4.6	4

Table 4.5 – 12-pulse rectifier passive filter performance

c) Input Power Factor Correction

The nearer the input power factor of the UPS is to unity (1), the lower the amount of reactive power generated and the more efficient the UPS system. For transformer-based UPS, the typical input power factors are:

- 0.8 for a 6-pulse rectifier
- 0.85 for a 12-pulse rectifier

Installing a passive harmonic filter in series will improve the input power factor to 0.9. However, their performance remains load-related because of the way a phase-controlled rectifier operates. This in turn affects the input power factor generated (*see tables 4.6 and 4.7*).

Typical 6-pulse rectifier input power factor @ 400Vac				
UPS Load	25%	50%	75%	100%
Input pF	0.65	0.72	0.75	0.8

Table 4.6 – 6-pulse rectifier affects on power factor

Typical 12-pulse rectifier input power factor @ 400Vac				
UPS Load	25%	50%	75%	100%
Input pF	0.77	0.8	0.83	0.85

Table 4.7 – 12-pulse rectifier affects on power factor

4.3.6 Active Harmonic Filters

a) Operating Principle

During normal operation of a transformerless UPS the input current is evenly spread across the three incoming phases, *diagram 4.14*. The shape of the current waveforms naturally generate high levels of 3rd, 5th and 7th harmonics and high neutral currents. It is these harmonics that produce the high THDi levels measured at the UPS input.

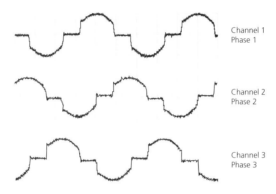

Diagram 4.14 – Input current waveforms with no harmonic filter

In order to reduce the THDi generated, the input current waveforms must become more sinusoidal and this reshaping is performed by an active harmonic filter (*diagram 4.15*) by adding suitably shaped current to the normal input current around the zero-crossing points.

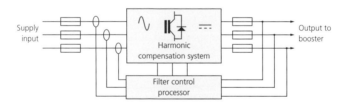

Diagram 4.15 – Active harmonic filter schematic

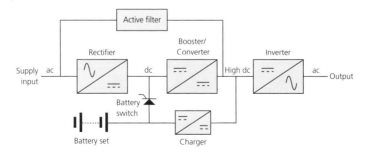

Diagram 4.16 – Transformerless UPS design with an active harmonic filter

The active harmonic filter is installed in parallel with the rectifier, booster-converter circuit between the mains power supply and the *dc* busbar. This filter acts as an *ac-dc* converter and draws current from the supply at specific intervals depending upon the shape of the UPS input current waveform. It is electronically monitored and controlled using a robust and reliable technology known as *Digital Signal Processing (DSP)*.

The filter passes the additional power drawn from the supply through to the *dc* busbar electrolytic capacitors. This helps to maintain a high operating efficiency for the UPS as a whole as no power is wasted.

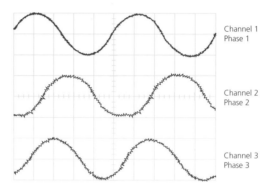

Diagram 4.17 – Input current waveforms with harmonic filter

Diagram 4.17 shows the input current drawn from the three input phases of a transformerless UPS when fitted with an active harmonic filter. The input current drawn by a standard UPS is not sinusoidal and the reshaping of the current waveform has dramatically reduced the THDi generated by the UPS to less than 4% at full load.

Diagram 4.18 shows a breakdown of the individual current components produced and added by an active filter (one phase only).

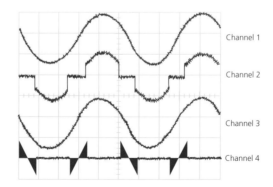

Diagram 4.18 – Current waveform components

- **Channel 1:** shows the overall input to the UPS and active harmonic filter (phase 1).

- **Channel 2:** shows the input current drawn by the UPS without an active harmonic filter (phase 1).

- **Channel 3:** shows the internal inductance current.

- **Channel 4:** shows the current drawn by the active harmonic filter used to reshape the overall input current from around the zero-crossing point (phase 1).

b) Neutral Currents

THDi reduction also significantly improves the input neutral currents to the UPS by up to 4.5 times and helps to simplify electrical installation and reduce overall costs. *Diagram 4.19* shows both the neutral current and the measured total harmonic distortion values for each phase. In *trace 1*, the active harmonic filter is disabled. As expected, each phase now measures approximately 24% THDi and the neutral current is very high relative to the THDi levels.

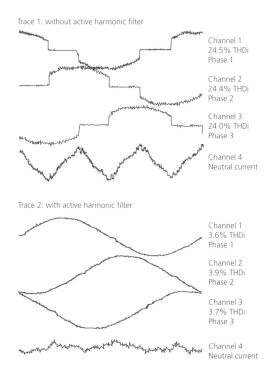

Diagram 4.19 – Current waveforms with and without an active filter

With the filter enabled in *trace 2*, the input current waveform becomes sinusoidal. The THDi for each phase is minimised to less than 4% and the neutral current greatly reduced.

c) Active Harmonic Filter Characteristics and Performance Comparison

Transformerless UPS efficiency is unaffected when an active harmonic filter is installed. THDi and input power factors are, however, load dependent. The following tables compare a 60kVA transformerless UPS with an active harmonic filter and one without. The tables highlight the improvement in harmonics and input power factor values.

UPS Load % (In)	60kVA with Active Harmonic Filter (THDi) %	60kVA Standard Model (THDi) %
25	28	36
50	6.4	25
75	4.4	25
100	4.7	25

Table 4.8 – UPS input current total harmonic distortion (THDi)

UPS Load % (In)	60kVA with Active Harmonic Filter (pF)	60kVA Standard Model (pF)
25%	0.928	0.900
50%	0.991	0.965
75%	0.995	0.967
100%	0.997	0.967

Table 4.9 – UPS input power factor (pF)

Harmonic Number	Harmonic Frequency (Hz)	60kVA with Active Harmonic Filter %	60kVA Standard Model %
1	50	100	100
2	100	0.7	0.4
3	150	1.2	16.9
4	200	0.5	0.4
5	250	0.5	14.5
6	300	0.6	0.4
7	350	1	5.7
8	400	0.2	0.3
9	450	1.4	1.8
10	500	0.5	0.2
11	550	1	4.4
12	600	0	0.2
13	650	0.4	3.7
14	700	0	0.3
15	750	0.3	0.2
16	800	0.2	0
17	850	0.4	3.2
18	900	0.2	0
19	950	0.8	3.0
20	1000	0.3	0.2

Table 4.10 – Full input harmonic analysis (up to 20th harmonic)

4.4 Inverters

4.4.1 Transformer-Based UPS

a) Inverter Design

Modern inverter designs use IGBTs in place of more traditional switching components such as power transistors and thyristors. IGBTs combine the fast acting and high power capability of the *Bipolar Transistor* with the voltage control features of a *MOSFET gate* to form a very versatile, high frequency switching device, which in turn has given rise to more powerful, efficient and reliable inverters. *Diagram 4.20* shows the component symbol and basic requirements that enable an IGBT to operate as a switch within an inverter.

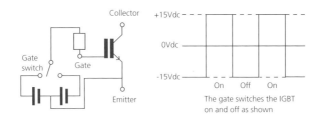

Diagram 4.20 – IGBT symbol and switching method

b) Inverter Operation

Diagram 4.21 shows how a single section of the inverter in a transformer-based UPS, is connected and switched.

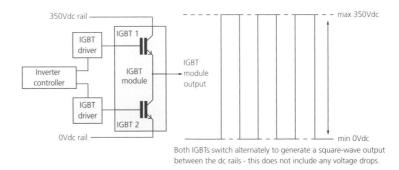

Diagram 4.21 – Transformer-based UPS IGBT operation

The inverter section uses two IGBTs connected in series across a *dc* rail. Each of the IGBTs has a driver circuit to enable independent switching and both circuits are controlled by the inverter control system. When IGBT (1) is switched on, the output voltage will rise to 350Vdc as it is connected to the 350Vdc rail. If IGBT (1) is switched off when IGBT (2) is switched on, the output voltage from IGBT (1) will fall to 0Vdc as its output is connected to the 0Vdc rail.

By alternating the switching (on and off) of the IGBTs, a square-wave is produced with a voltage between zero and 350Vdc. Switching on both IGBTs simultaneously is avoided by the control system as this would connect the *dc* rails together which could damage the assembly.

The output waveform produced is not sinusoidal and requires pulse width modulation to generate a purer sinewave and control both the voltage and power delivered to the load.

c) Pulse Width Modulation (PWM)

PWM functions by varying the on-off switching periods of the IGBTs. This takes place at frequencies far higher than that of the fundamental frequency and typically in the region of 3-16kHz.

Diagram 4.22 shows the relationship between the change in pulse width of the on-off switching periods and its effect on the output sinewave. When the pulse widths are narrowed, the output voltage and power delivered is low. When the pulse widths are increased, the output voltage and power delivered also increases.

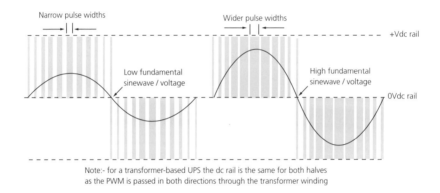

Diagram 4.22 – Pulse width modulation (transformer-based UPS)

PWM allows the inverter to maintain a stable output voltage, regardless of the loads applied and connected *dc* voltage level. This is important as the inverter on mains power supply failure will be powered directly via a battery set (in a transformer-based UPS) and its *dc* voltage could vary considerably during the discharge cycle in this scenario. The peak level of each pulse is limited by the *dc* busbar voltage as the inverter can only switch from the *dc* voltage available.

d) PWM Inverter Process

Diagram 4.23, figures 1 and 2, show how a single-phase inverter is connected to the output transformer and how the switching sequence operates. This type of inverter is commonly referred to as an *H-bridge inverter*.

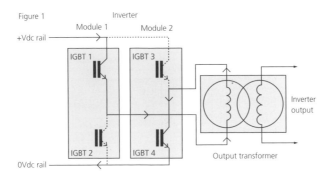

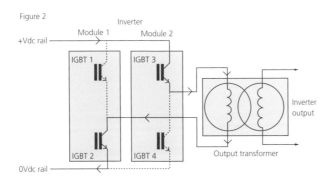

Diagram 4.23 – Inverter switching principles

IGBTs (1) and (4) are pulsed using PWM to force current to flow in one direction through the transformer windings for a specified period, dependent upon the UPS output frequency. These IGBTs are switched off and IGBTs (2) and (3) are pulsed in the same manner to force current through the transformer in the other direction. The resultant PWM generated waveform is then stepped up by the dual-wound transformer and filtered before it is delivered to the load via a static switch. The same process is used for both single and three-phase UPS inverters. In both cases the transformer references their output phases to the neutral. For a three-phase UPS, however, the switching sequence is more complicated. Each of the three generated waveforms (displaced by 120°) are stepped up via a *Delta Star Transformer* to add the neutral reference.

e) Single and Three-Phase Inverter Design

The basic schematic for a single-phase inverter is shown in *diagram 4.24*. The inverter receives power from the rectifier or battery set and then uses PWM to generate a low *ac* voltage. This is stepped up by the output transformer before being filtered and connected to the load via the static switch.

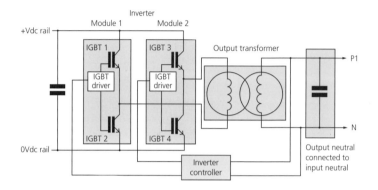

Diagram 4.24 – Single-phase inverter schematic

The basic schematic for a three-phase inverter is shown in *diagram 4.25*.

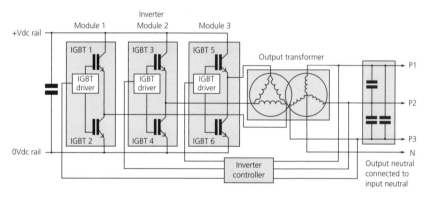

Diagram 4.25 – Three-phase inverter schematic

The most notable difference between the single and the three-phase inverters is that there is an IGBT block per phase which produces three separate voltage waveforms each displaced by 120°.

4.4.2 Transformerless UPS

a) Insulated Gate Bipolar Transistors (IGBTs)

Inverter IGBT components and switching principles are described in *section 4.4.1*.

b) Inverter Operation

In a transformerless UPS system, the inverter is connected across the mid-point *dc* rail generated by the rectifier booster-converter circuit and therefore the *dc* rails are both positive and negative with respect to the neutral.

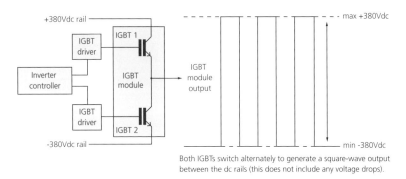

Both IGBTs switch alternately to generate a square-wave output between the dc rails (this does not include any voltage drops).

Diagram 4.26 – Transformerless UPS IGBT operation

Diagram 4.26 shows how a single section of a transformerless UPS inverter is connected and switched. The inverter section comprises of two IGBTs connected in series across a positive 380Vdc and a negative 380Vdc rail. Each of the IGBTs has a driver circuit to enable independent switching, with both driver circuits controlled by a control system.

When IGBT (1) is switched on, the output voltage with respect to neutral will rise to +380Vdc as the output is connected directly to the 380Vdc positive rail. If IGBT (1) is switch off and IGBT (2) is switched on, the output voltage will fall to -380Vdc with respect to the neutral as the output is connected to the negative 380Vdc rail. By alternately switching the IGBTs on and off, a square-wave is produced between -380 to +380Vdc with respect to neutral. Both IGBTs are prevented from switching on simultaneously and connecting across the *dc* rail to prevent damage and possible inverter assembly failure.

The diagram shows the basic switching principle and the next stage is to apply PWM to generate a sinewave supply from the square-wave output.

c) Pulse Width Modulation (PWM)

The PWM process is again used within a transformerless UPS but operates at around 8-16kHz depending upon the UPS design and operating conditions of the UPS.

d) PWM Inverter Process

Diagram 4.27 shows how the PWM controlled IGBTs are used to switch the output between the two *dc* rails from the rectifier booster-converter circuit. IGBT (1) switches the positive half and IGBT (2) the negative half of the output waveform.

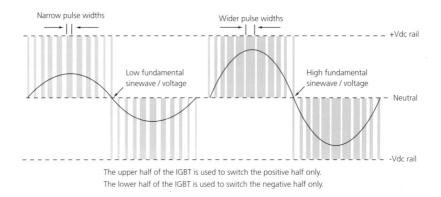

Diagram 4.27 – Pulse width modulation (transformerless UPS)

The levels of *dc* produced by the circuit enable the inverter to directly generate the *ac* voltage level required by the load. *Diagram 4.28* shows a 230Vac RMS voltage waveform. The peak value of a 230Vac waveform is 325Vpk and this type of rectifier booster-converter circuit produces the high *dc* voltage required to power the inverter in a transformerless UPS.

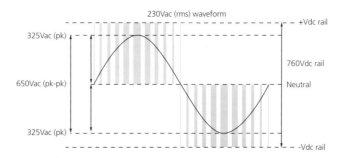

Diagram 4.28 – Inverter output waveform

e) Single and Three-Phase Inverter Design

Diagram 4.29 shows the basic layout of the single-phase transformerless UPS inverter. The inverter receives power from the rectifier booster-converter and generates the required level of *ac* voltage using PWM. This is filtered to remove unwanted PWM switching frequencies and is finally passed via the static switch to the load.

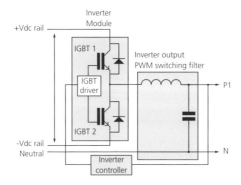

Diagram 4.29 – Single-phase inverter schematic

The single-phase transformerless UPS inverter has one main advantage over the transformer-based system. It uses only two IGBTs to perform the switching as opposed to four, reducing both cost and energy losses within the system. The most notable difference between the single and three-phase inverter (*diagram 4.30*) is that there is an IGBT block per phase, each producing a single 120° displaced voltage waveform.

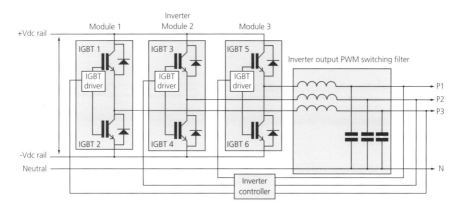

Diagram 4.30 – Three-phase inverter schematic

4.5 Static Switches

4.5.1 General Operation

The connected loads are powered by the inverter through a thyristor-based static switch. In the unfortunate event of a UPS fault or output overload condition, the static switch automatically and instantaneously transfers the load from the inverter to a bypass supply. When the fault condition is cleared, the load is automatically transferred back to the output of the inverter. A static switch therefore provides additional resilience to the UPS by providing a safe failure-to-mains facility. This also increases the overall MTBF with respect to power continuity.

The static switch can only safely operate when the inverter output and bypass supply are in synchronisation. If the UPS system cannot maintain an adequate level of synchronisation the static switch is automatically disabled to prevent unnecessary damage and complications.

One important issue when installing a UPS is to configure the output voltage from the system as close to the bypass supply voltage as possible. Then, if the static switch has to transfer the load from the inverter onto the bypass supply, the load will not be subjected to any sudden changes in supply voltage.

The issue of sudden voltage changes is automatically addressed by the UPS only when transferring the load from the bypass supply back onto the inverter. When doing this, the UPS temporarily adjusts the inverter output voltage to match that of the bypass supply. Once the load is connected, the inverter output voltage is reduced to the specified level.

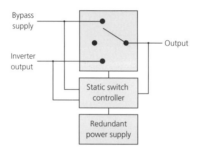

Diagram 4.31 – Static switch schematic

Diagram 4.31 provides a basic arrangement drawing and shows that the system has three operational states:

a) UPS On Line - load connected to the inverter

When the UPS is operating normally, the static switch connects the load to the inverter. Should a disturbance or mains power supply failure occur the load is fully protected.

b) UPS On Bypass - load connected to the bypass supply

A UPS system can be operating in bypass for any of the following reasons:

• A fault within a critical section of the UPS has occurred rendering it unable to continue to supply power to the load.
• The load connected to the UPS has exceeded the maximum rating of the system. To protect the inverter, the static switch has transferred the load to bypass which typically has additional capacity to support an overload condition for a longer period (if not indefinitely).
• A short-circuit has occurred downstream of the UPS and the static switch has transferred the short-circuit fault current to the bypass (mains) supply in an attempt to clear the fault.
• The UPS has been manually transferred to bypass by a maintenance engineer to allow them to work safely within the UPS without disrupting power to the load.

- The UPS has an Economy mode function, whereby the load remains connected to the mains supply until the supply either fails or exceeds a pre-set voltage and frequency tolerance at which point the static switch transfers the load onto the inverter.
- The UPS has been configured to switch to bypass (should the connected load fall below a pre-set value). For example, during a typical working day, the load on the UPS output will be higher due to more equipment being in operation. At night, when the load is reduced, the UPS can automatically switch to bypass to reduce running costs.

c) UPS Output Off - load disconnected

In certain circumstances it may be necessary for the UPS to disconnect all output power:

- The UPS is operating as a Central Power Supply System in an emergency lighting role and therefore must not supply power to the load until the mains power supply fails.
- Power to the load may be disconnected as part of an Emergency Power Off (EPO) process, which shuts down the UPS in the event of an emergency situation.
- A controlled shutdown of the UPS output may be initiated by maintenance engineers to enable them to test sections within the system.

UPS alarm monitoring is discussed in *chapter 8*. Needless-to-say, one of the principle components to monitor is the automatic bypass. When on bypass, due to a fault rather than a pre-selected condition, an alarm signal will be generated to warn that the UPS is not providing any form of power protection or back-up to the load. It should also be noted that a thyristor-based static switch is commonly used for On-Line UPS above 5kVA. Below this, a relay-based automatic bypass is used.

4.5.2 Types of Static Switching Systems

A static switch has no moving parts and is a solid-state device. It is most commonly constructed using a pair of thyristors, connected in inverse parallel. Thyristors are reliable, relatively low in cost, fast and easy to control. Both are triggered simultaneously.

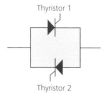

Diagram 4.32 – Single thyristor static switch

Once triggered, thyristor (1) conducts the positive half of the cycle and thyristor (2) the negative. A natural thyristor characteristic is that once it is triggered it will continue to conduct until the voltage across the device reduces to zero, which naturally occurs at the zero-crossing point of the *ac* waveform.

The most commonly used types of static switch systems are shown below:

a) Contactor and Short Burst Thyristor Combination

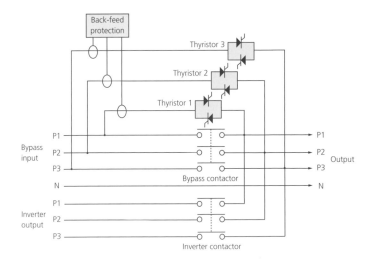

Diagram 4.33 – Contactor and short burst combination

The contactor and short burst thyristor-based static switch system (*diagram 4.33*) uses a combination of contactors and thyristors. This method of switching is still classed as static even though it uses contactors because the actual load transfer is carried out by the thyristors.

During normal operation, the inverter contactor remains closed and the load is powered directly from the inverter. If the UPS is required to transfer the load onto the bypass supply either manually, or due to a fault or overload, the three pairs of thyristors are simultaneously triggered into conduction. This is closely followed by the changeover of the inverter and bypass contactors (bypass contactor closed and inverter contactor open).

Finally, once the system detects the bypass contactor has successfully closed and the inverter contactor successfully opened, the thyristor modules are switched off. This process is seamless and break-free and typically only lasts for a few hundred milliseconds. When reconnecting the load to the inverter output, the process is simply reversed.

This particular system has a small advantage in terms of efficiency as the bypass contactor has fewer losses when compared to a thyristor module during constant operation. As the conduction time of the thyristor is very short, no significant heat is generated. This removes the need for heatsinks which are commonly used to dissipate heat away from such components.

b) Full-Rated Thyristor and Contactor Combination

The full-rated thyristor and contactor-based static switch system (*diagram 4.34*) is still classed as static even though it uses a contactor, as the actual bypass section is constructed from thyristors.

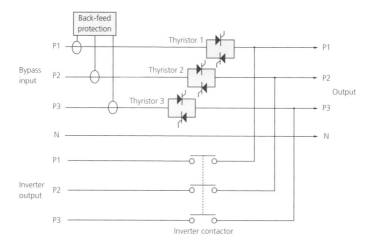

Diagram 4.34 – Full-rated thyristor and contactor combination

During normal operation, the inverter contactor remains closed and therefore the load is powered directly by the inverter. When the UPS is required to transfer the load onto the bypass supply, the three thyristor modules are simultaneously triggered into conduction. This connects the load to the bypass supply at which point the inverter contactor is opened. When the load is reconnected to the inverter, the process is simply reversed.

c) Full-Rated Thyristor System

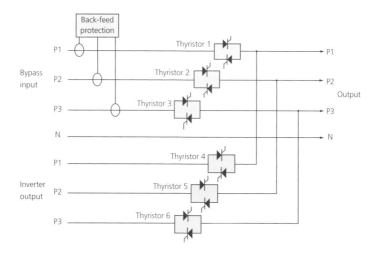

Diagram 4.35 – Full-rated thyristor system

The full-rated thyristor static switch system (*diagram 4.35*) uses two groups of thyristor modules. One group is used to select the bypass supply and the other to select the inverter output. This method of switching is purely static.

During normal operation, the three-phase inverter output thyristor modules all remain simultaneously triggered and therefore the load is powered directly from the inverter. When the UPS needs to transfer the load onto the bypass supply, the three bypass supply thyristor modules are simultaneously triggered into conduction. This connects the load to the bypass supply at which point the inverter thyristor modules are switched off. When the load is reconnected to the inverter output, the process is simply reversed.

4.6 Back-Feed Protection

When the mains power supply fails, the back-feed protection device prevents current from being passed back to the input terminals of the UPS from the inverter output. For example, if a bypass supply thyristor short-circuits, the output from the inverter could be potentially passed through to the input terminals via the faulty component.

A back-feed protection device must be installed to enable a service engineer to work on the incoming supply side of a UPS (even when the input supply has been switched off via an isolator) and prevent the risk of electric shock from any current back-feed from the UPS output. The type of back-feed device employed is determined by the size of the UPS.

4.6.1 Plug-In UPS

For single-phase UPS with an input rating of up to 16A, the back-feed protection device must provide complete disconnection of both the live and neutral input conductors using a specified air gap. Generally, this air gap is provided by means of a relay which opens when the mains power supply fails.

For plug-in UPS, this means that if a fault occurs within the UPS when the user disconnects it from the mains power supply (by removing the supply plug from the wall socket), the back-feed relay should prevent the exposed pins from becoming live and remove any possibility of the user receiving an electric shock. UPS systems over 16A (classed as hardwired) utilise one of two different approaches: mechanical or electronic.

4.6.2 Hardwired UPS

a) Mechanical Back-Feed Device

Some hardwired UPS are supplied with the relay or contactor-based solution as used in a 16A plug-in UPS. This, again, provides a specified safety air gap which opens when the mains power supply is disconnected or fails. Only the phase conductors are disconnected and the neutral always remains connected.

b) Electronic Back-Feed Device

Many hardwired UPS systems utilise a back-feed current detection system. This continually monitors the current flow through the bypass supply. Should a fault occur within the bypass thyristors, it is detected by the UPS which immediately shuts down its inverter.

4.7 EMI/RFI Filters

Transformerless UPS designs incorporate EMI/RFI filters to provide protection to both the UPS system and the connected loads from any mains-borne disturbances. These filters protect the system by clamping or eliminating high-frequency disturbances that could cause disruption or even damage to both the UPS and/or connected loads. The filters typically use a combination of capacitive and magnetic elements sized in co-ordination with the operation of the UPS system.

In addition to providing protection for the UPS and connected loads, the filters also prevent any disturbances generated from within the UPS system affecting the operation of equipment connected to the same supply source. The filters are normally positioned in such a way as to provide a filtered supply to the load when the UPS is in bypass. Filters may also form part of a transformer-based UPS circuit.

4.8 Comparing Transformer-Based and Transformerless UPS

Transformerless UPS were developed in the early 1990s and provided a number of immediate benefits over the traditional transformer-based technology in terms of:

- Physical: size and weight.
- Operating: higher efficiency, lower audible noise and heat output.
- Costs: purchase, installation and running.

Over the last decade the gap between the two approaches has reduced, as UPS manufacturers have been able to apply common technologies and research & development efforts to both designs. This has been driven by cost and size issues as well as demands to improve operating efficiency and reduce harmonic generation. In terms of On-Line performance, both UPS designs provide the same level of performance and are classified as VFI systems according to EN/IEC 62040-3. The principle differences result from their effect on upstream supplies and the operating environment.

4.8.1 Upstream Supplies

a) Input Power Factor

The higher the input power factor, the lower the reactive power (wasted energy returned to the *ac* supply from the UPS) generated by the UPS and the currents drawn from its *ac* supply. The lower the reactive power, the lower UPS running costs. Lower current draws also mean that smaller cable, switchgear and upstream protection can be installed.

	Transformerless	Transformer-based
Input Power Factor	0.96	0.8/0.9^

Table 4.11 – Typical input power factor values for a 60kVA three-phase UPS (^ with a passive harmonic filter)

The rectifier booster-converter used within a transformerless UPS has a higher power factor than an equivalent transformer-based design. Therefore, its current draw from an *ac* supply is less and its operating costs will be lower.

b) Harmonics

A UPS rectifier generates harmonics. This can range from 30% to less than 4% dependent on the type of UPS design, load connected and harmonic filter used.

	Transformerless	Transformer-based
Harmonic Distortion	$\leq 27\%$	$\leq 30\%$
With Harmonic Filter	$\leq 4\%$	$\leq 5\%$
IGBT-based Rectifier	$\leq 3\%$	$\leq 3\%$

Table 4.12 – Total harmonic distortion for a 60kVA three-phase UPS

4.8.2 Operating Environment

a) Efficiency

Efficiency is a ratio of the output to the input power of a system. For UPS, high efficiency represents low losses of electrical energy in terms of heat output which will affect surrounding ambient temperatures. When fully loaded there is some difference in the efficiency ratings between the latest transformerless UPS and transformer-based designs. When compared to older transformer-based UPS designs, the difference in operating efficiency can be even greater and sometimes up to 5-6%.

It should be noted that most efficiency figures are normally quoted at full load. For all UPS, this figure is load dependent and will reduce to around 85% when 25% loaded. Inverter efficiency considers the efficiency of the inverter system only and is often quoted separately.

System efficiency is important where parallel systems are considered. For under loaded parallel-redundant configurations, any reduction in the efficiency of the individual UPS will be magnified by the number used within the parallel-redundant architecture.

The efficiency figures are quoted for on-line operation with a constantly running inverter. When operated in Economy or Standby-Off modes, efficiency up to 99% can be achieved by some UPS designs.

	Transformerless	Transformer-based
System Efficiency	up to 96%	up to 93%

Table 4.13 – Efficiency for a 60kVA three-phase UPS

b) Noise Output

A transformerless UPS uses high-frequency switching (typically up to 20kHz) and is therefore inaudible to the human ear. For such a UPS design the only audible noise is that of the cooling fans and the noise output is unnoticeable in a typical computer room environment.

Transformer-based UPS have a large magnetic (transformer) whose noise output or 'hum' will vary with load. The more the transformer is loaded the higher the noise level generated. This type of UPS may be installed within a computer room environment but more typically the larger systems are installed in dedicated plant rooms. At 800kVA a transformer-based UPS will typically generate 80dBA of noise at 1m.

	Transformerless	Transformer-based
Noise Level @ 1m	50-56dBA	53-62dBA

Table 4.14 – Noise level for a 60kVA three-phase UPS

c) Size and Weight

Removing the transformer has a fundamental affect on the overall size and weight of the UPS. As shown in *table 4.15*, for a 60kVA UPS a 50% reduction in footprint and a 70% decrease in weight can be seen. These represent major advantages over transformer-based UPS within a computer room environment and can remove the need for floor or point strengthening (where false floors are used). The reductions also simplify the logistics involved.

	Transformerless	Transformer-based
WxDxHmm	500x740x1400	1070x740x1400
Footprint	0.37m²	0.79m²
Nett Kg	180	450

Table 4.15 – Footprint for comparable 60kVA three-phase UPS

The transformer-based UPS in *table 4.16* is installed with a 12-pulse rectifier. The reductions are magnified further where an additional harmonic filter is added to either system. For the transformerless design at 60kVA, this can be installed inside the UPS cabinet itself. For the transformer-based UPS a bolt-on cabinet is required.

	Transformerless	Transformer-based
WxDxHmm	500x740x1400	1340x740x1400
Footprint	0.37m²	0.99m²
Nett Kg	190	595

Table 4.16 – Footprint for comparable 60kVA three-phase UPS with harmonic filter

Now the transformerless UPS represents a 62% reduction in footprint and a 68% reduction in weight. These advantages increase further where a modular transformerless UPS is used within a rackmount cabinet system.

4.8.3 Purchase and Running Costs

There are two aspects to cost. Firstly, purchase whereby it is possible to make an immediate assessment between two UPS supplier quotations for comparable ratings. The second one, in terms of running costs, is harder to distinguish between modern transformerless and transformer-based UPS, which can have comparable levels of system efficiency at full load.

a) Purchase

The cost of a transformerless UPS will be around 25-30% lower than for an equivalent transformer-based system. The principle reasons for this are the cost of the transformer itself. In addition, there may be other capital cost savings depending on how an approach to harmonic reduction is applied.

b) Running

As discussed, the higher the UPS input power factor, the lower the currents drawn by the system from its *ac* supply. This can be significant for transformerless UPS powering loads with poor power factors. For example, a transformerless UPS with a 0.96 power factor supplying a load with a 0.6 power factor will draw less current than a transformer-based UPS with a 0.80 power factor supplying the same load. In terms of current measurement the UPS input could be seen to be drawing less current than the actual load (due to its fundamental design characteristics). Any assessment of running costs should be taken over a five or ten year period (the typical writedown periods used by finance for life expectancy and use) and should include additional costs such as air-conditioning provision if required.

4.9 Summary

Selecting which On-Line UPS design to install may be a relatively straightforward choice where only one type of design exists. This is fairly common for UPS below 10kVA where the transformerless UPS design virtually dominates the On-Line market. However, above 10kVA most manufacturers offer a choice between the two technologies and this allows the user to receive unbiased advice and select the most appropriate for their installation. The final decision should be dependent upon a number of factors relating to the load and installation environment. Transformerless UPS have become the standard within data centre environments as they tend to offer, for example, a more compact foot print, higher operating efficiency and lower noise output. However, the strengths of a transformer-based design come into play within an industrial environment. Above all, it must be remembered that the UPS is part of a wider *Power Continuity Plan*, installed to achieve a certain level of resilience and fault tolerance. These aspects are now discussed further in *chapter 5*.

5. UPS Reliability and Levels of Resilience

In this chapter:

- Explaining reliability and availability in terms of the 'high-nines' concept.
- Understanding how parallel operation achieves higher levels of resilience.
- Describing redundancy, capacity and series system architectures.
- Sample reliability calculations.

Introduction

The sophistication and complexity of a Power Continuity Plan will depend upon the level of resilience required, the size of the loads to protect, future expansion and budget available. These are similar constraints to those employed in the design of computer and telecoms systems within large data centres and are equally applicable to small critical file servers and PBXs.

In terms of resilience, a *Power Continuity Plan* is concerned with the use of multiple power paths to ensure *ac* supply continuity (even during maintenance), the ability of the power protection systems to clear fault conditions and achievement of the lowest possible number of single-points-of-failure.

A UPS is always considered the primary building block around which the plan is designed. Dual input supplies and static transfer switches can never be considered viable options for this role but can provide useful support functions to improve overall system design, as this chapter will show.

Various UPS configurations are available including single, parallel and series-redundant systems. Each will result in a different level of resilience, MTBF and availability. However, published figures can be misleading and UPS suppliers can differ in the approach they favour most - especially if they can only offer limited options.

Within a *Power Continuity Plan*, other aspects to consider include: bypass arrangements, the selection of a shared or common battery set and distribution of power to the loads themselves. These are discussed towards the end of this chapter together with some sample availability calculations.

5.1 UPS Reliability Measures

5.1.1 Mean Time Between Failure (MTBF)

MTBF is a useful indicator of the reliability of a UPS system. It is the average operational time between powering up and system shutdown due to failure. The figure is usually measured in hours.

Another indication of reliability is average failure rate. This is the number of failures for a given time period. Over the lifetime of any system, the failure rate is inversely proportionate to its MTBF:

Failure rate $\lambda = 1 \div MTBF$

Failure rates are not constants and UPS failures, like other sensitive electronic devices, follow a Bath Tub curve *(diagram 5.1)* with three distinct periods: A, B and C.

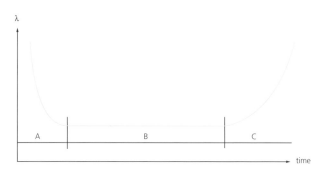

Diagram 5.1 – Bath tub curve

- **Period A - Infant Mortality failures:** corresponds to early failures due to a component, manufacturing defect or transportation problem. UPS manufacturers obviously strive to ensure these are minimised through stringent quality checks throughout manufacturing and test processes. UPS from 10kVA may be run for short burn-in periods (up to 48 hours) at high ambient temperatures to reduce the potential for such failures. Mass manufactured IT sized UPS can suffer what is termed 'dead on arrival' failure. Though subject to stringent test procedures throughout their manufacture, a sudden shock in transit can weaken a soldered joint, for example.

- **Period B - Random failures:** during the normal working life of a UPS the rate of these failures is normally low and fairly constant.

- **Period C - Wear Out failures:** at the end of working life, system failure rates increase. Battery problems are common and can account for over 98% of UPS failures at this stage. Where a UPS has been subjected to high ambient temperatures over long periods, internal cabling insulation can become brittle and breakdown. Other consumable items to monitor include fans and capacitors which eventually wear out with use.

When comparing MTBF figures from various UPS manufacturers it is important to ascertain their basis for calculation. There are two approaches:

* record the number of failures for a particular UPS size over a given time period
* calculate a system value from the known MTBF values of components and assemblies

The first method provides a valid approach if the field population is large and the time period long enough - more than the typical life expectancy of a UPS, which is between five and ten years.

The second approach is more complex and relies on following calculation formats as defined by a standard such as *MIL-HDBK-217D*. The first method is one commonly adopted by UPS manufacturers due to the time and costs involved. If the second method is used, the first can provide a quick check to identify potential calculation errors.

5.1.2 Mean Time to Repair (MTTR)

On-Line UPS are designed to fail safely to mains. Therefore, the MTBF of the mains power supply is also an important consideration along with the MTTR, or average repair time. This is also known as the *Mean Time To Restore* and is the time taken to return a UPS to normal operation from shutdown.

As it is highly unlikely for a UPS service engineer to be on-site at the moment a UPS fails, MTTR should include a travel time element. This also assumes the service engineer has the required parts with them and can repair the fault in a single visit. For comparative purposes, UPS manufacturers may only provide a figure based on the actual repair time.

5.1.3 Availability

Availability is a different measure to reliability and measures both system running and down time. The formula for availability combines MTBF and MTTR values to determine a result measured in 'nines' of availability using the formula:

Availability = (1 - (MTTR÷MTBF)) x 100%

The greater the number of 'nines' the higher the availability of the system, *table 5.1.*

Availability	Level	Downtime Per Year
99.9999%	Six nines	32 seconds
99.999%	Five nines	5 minutes, 35 seconds
99.99%	Four nines	52 minutes, 33 seconds
99.9%	Three nines	8 hours, 46 minutes
99%	Two nines	87 hours, 36 minutes
90%	One nine	36 days, 12 hours

Table 5.1 – Availability in terms of 'Nines'

5.2 Single UPS Installation

This is the most common form of UPS installation below 10kVA. The UPS is connected to the mains power supply and supports the load. The UPS has one power path - a single *ac* supply. This is normally a mains power supply which can be supplemented by a standby generator, if installed. The single power path represents a single-point-of-failure which can also be removed using a dual input supply.

The field population calculated MTBF of a typical On-Line UPS is 250,000 hours, though this will vary between UPS manufacturers. However, when the UPS is bypassed and the load is connected directly to the mains power supply, the MTBF of the entire system reduces to that of the mains power supply. In this instance, if this has an MTBF of 50 hours, the overall UPS resilience reduces to 50 hours.

Such a configuration therefore provides no redundancy. Future expansion is limited if the UPS cannot be operated within a parallel configuration. Where possible the UPS should be installed with a parallel card already fitted and its firmware level may need to be checked and raised when it is brought into a parallel configuration at a later date.

5.3 Parallel UPS Configurations

Parallel operation describes a configuration when the outputs of two or more UPS modules (capable of parallel operation) are connected to supply the load via a common *ac* busbar. A group of parallel UPS modules is referred to as a UPS system and there are two basic configurations known as *parallel-redundancy* and *parallel-capacity*.

5.3.1 Parallel-Redundant Systems (N+x)

Parallel-redundancy occurs where one or more (N+x) additional UPS modules are installed so that the system can continue to support the load should one or more modules fail or be taken out of service. This is probably the most commonly used parallel configuration and is typically installed to protect mission critical applications within data centres, industrial sites and large service operators as they require the highest possible levels of resilience and availability. Compared to a single UPS, a pair of UPS modules in parallel-redundant operation can achieve higher MTBF and availability values.

UPS manufacturers vary in the number of UPS modules they can operate in a parallel configuration with eight appearing as a common standard. For a transformer-based UPS system this means a maximum power rating of 6.4MVA can be achieved using the largest 800kVA module available. Transformerless UPS systems, with a maximum module power rating of 120kVA, can achieve a total power rating of 960kVA (just under 1MVA). Some manufacturers can even allow different power ratings to be used within the same parallel configuration.

Diagram 5.2 shows a parallel-redundant 30kVA N+1 system using three 15kVA UPS modules, equally sharing the load (10kVA per UPS module).

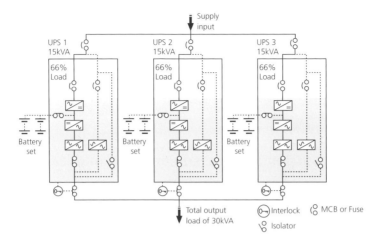

Diagram 5.2 – Parallel-redundant N+1 30kVA UPS system

The primary benefit of parallel-redundancy is improved system resilience and a higher system MTBF than can be achieved with a single UPS. In some cases this can be by a factor of ten. A key factor here is sizing the system to prevent operation of the static switch bypass due to overloads. When this occurs it reduces the overall system MTBF to that of the mains power supply. For a UPS system to be truly parallel-redundant it must be able to remain in this state even when a module is powered down for maintenance and service. *Diagram 5.2* would represent N+2 for a total load of 15kVA.

5.3.2 Parallel-Capacity Systems (N)

A *parallel-capacity* system is created by connecting multiple UPS systems in parallel but without redundancy. Capacity solutions do not therefore increase system resilience. The total capacity of the UPS system is derived from the total number (N) of UPS modules used. This configuration is also known as a *Total Power System*. *Diagram 5.3* shows a parallel-capacity 45kVA system comprising three 15kVA UPS modules, each at 100% load.

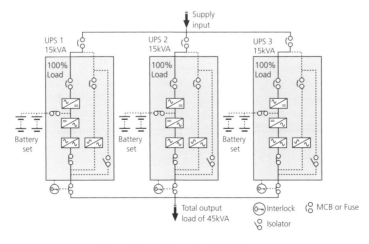

Diagram 5.3 – Parallel-capacity 45kVA UPS system

Comparing the two approaches, the advantages become more evident when considering how to maintain the systems. As a minimum, UPS powering critical loads should have at least one preventative maintenance visit, per annum, during which it may be necessary to isolate a single UPS module. Emergency service visits in response to alarm conditions may also require a UPS module to be taken out of service. Parallel-redundancy allows maintenance work to take place without interruption to the load, even during working-hours. However, in a parallel-capacity configuration, the entire UPS system must be bypassed to allow one or more UPS modules to be powered down for service.

5.3.3 Parallel Conversion and Closed-Loop Communications

Parallel operation is normally achieved by adding a single parallel card to each UPS module within the system. The cards are then inter-linked via opto-isolated cables to form a closed-loop data communications system which allows data to be exchanged between the control sections of each of the UPS modules. This method of communication ensures the control systems for the individual UPS modules remain electrically isolated. It guarantees control system stability and prevents disruption which could potentially jeopardise the supply of power to the load. If one of the interconnecting communication cables is disconnected or accidentally damaged, the entire UPS system will continue to operate using data exchanged between the remaining cables.

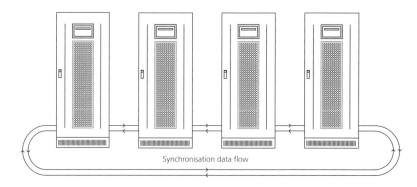

Synchronisation data flow

Diagram 5.4 – Closed-loop communications data flow

Parallel cards can be installed regardless of the age of the UPS and are manufacturer dependent. The only requirement is that all the cards within the UPS system have the same level of firmware. The cards are typically Flash EPROM programmable via a serial port and service engineer laptop. Where this cannot be achieved, on-board memory chips can be upgraded manually. A single UPS module can be fitted with a parallel card, and operated as a standalone system if required. The card simply allows future conversion to parallel operation.

5.3.4 Decentralised and Centralised Control

In a parallel architecture, *centralised control*, relies on one UPS module providing a central processing function which the other modules use as a reference point. This introduces a single-point-of-failure because if the control module fails this will disrupt operation of the entire UPS system.

With *decentralised control*, this weakness is removed. This is the preferred control system for a truly resilient parallel architecture. Each of the UPS modules operates in a *master-slave* configuration, meaning that the first module that initialises within the UPS system assumes the role of *master* and takes control of the *slave* modules. If a fault develops within the master, one of the slave modules automatically takes control and assumes this role. This aspect of its operation also helps to provide the UPS system with unique modes of operation.

Decentralised control allows any suitable UPS module to be connected (or disconnected) and brought into service, individually, without disruption to the load or existing modules. Once connection to the communications loop has been established, the new module is updated with operating status information before it begins to automatically supply its share of the load. The same operating principle is used in reverse to allow a UPS module to be taken out of service. When removed, the remaining UPS modules automatically adjust their load sharing and provided they are not overloaded, the load continues to receive uninterruptible power from the synchronised modules.

5.4 Parallel UPS Operation

5.4.1 Parallel-Redundant Systems

Diagram 5.5 shows an N+1 redundant system using three UPS modules, each sharing 66% of the load, and an isolation/bypass switchgear panel.

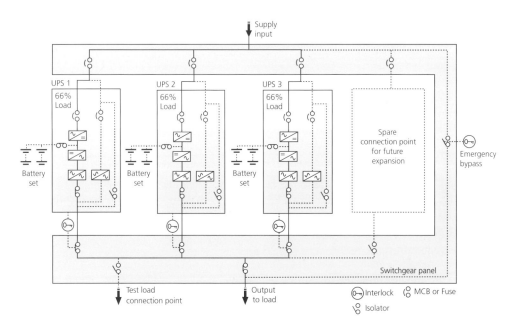

Diagram 5.5 – N+1 parallel-redundant UPS system, with each UPS module equally sharing the total load

The rectifier and static switch bypass supply inputs are taken from a common *ac* supply point (building incomer) and each of the UPS modules is fitted with isolators or circuit-breakers to allow individual disconnection. Each UPS module has its own battery set.

The optional test-load-connection-point enables connection of dummy loads that can be used to discharge or operationally test if required. The output from each UPS module is taken to a common *ac* busbar where it is distributed to critical loads; this system is also fitted with an emergency bypass switch (switchgear panel). For future expansion, a spare connection point has been built into the switchgear panel.

a) Normal Operation (supply present)

During normal operation, when the incoming mains power supply or generator is present, each of the UPS modules will equally share the load.

b) Battery Operation (supply failure)

During battery operation, when the incoming mains power supply or standby generator is no longer available, each of the UPS modules will continue, equally, to share the load. Each module has its own battery set rather than a shared common battery and each should have the same runtime duration and *dc* voltage cut-off thresholds. In addition, each battery set will discharge at slightly different rates. During a long mains power supply failure, where there is no standby generator, the battery sets will discharge until they reach their *dc* disconnect thresholds.

c) Supply Restoration

The UPS modules can be set to automatically restart when mains power is restored. The start-up sequence includes a rectifier soft-start action to reduce the effects of a high in-rush current on the mains power supply, which could otherwise trip upstream breakers. The load is powered from the inverters and the battery sets are recharged.

d) UPS Module Fault Condition

If any of the UPS modules detect an internal fault they will automatically disconnect from the common output *ac* busbar. The remaining UPS modules will equally share the load without disruption in supply. *Diagram 5.6* shows the operation of three 100kVA modules supplying a total load of 200kVA. When a fault condition occurs, the remaining active units continue to share the load equally.

If a second UPS module fails, the remaining operational module will be forced into an overload condition and the load transferred to its bypass supply via the static switch. The bypassing of this operational module will also simultaneously force the two faulty modules into bypass. This method of operation ensures the load receives an adequate source of power automatically and without disruption.

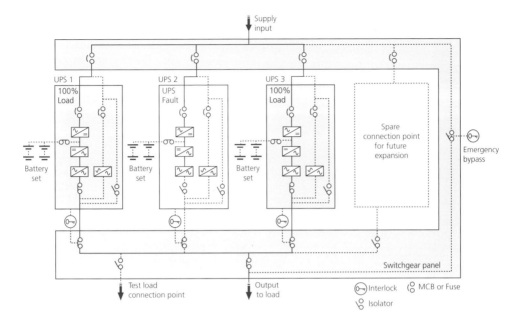

Diagram 5.6 – N+1 parallel-redundant UPS system, with a single UPS module fault condition

e) Overload

When faced with an overload condition (*diagram 5.7 overleaf*), the entire UPS system will react in one of two ways dependent upon the magnitude and duration of the overload. If a small overload occurs, the UPS system will continue to power the load from the inverters, relying on their overload capabilities. For this, the overload must typically be within 100-150% of the nominal rating of each UPS system and their inverters.

However, if the overload exceeds the capability of the entire parallel UPS system, for example, when a downstream short-circuit occurs or a sudden load is switched onto the output of the UPS system, all of the UPS modules will automatically switch to bypass in an attempt to clear the fault. They will remain in this condition until the short-circuit or overload condition is removed whereupon they will return to normal operation. If the overload or short-circuit remains, the UPS system will eventually shutdown.

When in bypass, system resilience is reduced and the load will be connected to the raw mains supply or alternative source of *ac* power. On bypass, each UPS will generate alarm notifications which can be captured at local, network and remote levels. The seriousness of this situation is the reason why alarm monitoring and responses are considered important aspects within a *Power Continuity Plan*.

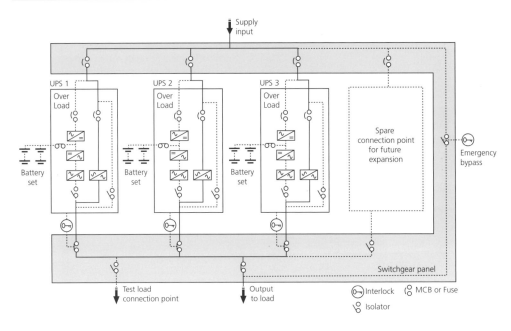

Diagram 5.7 – N+1 parallel-redundant UPS system, in overload condition

f) Emergency Bypass

All of the diagrams show that a manual or automatic *wrap-around emergency bypass* can also be installed for the entire UPS system. This can be a health & safety requirement for a particular site as it allows all the UPS modules to be electrically isolated and powered down. If installed, the bypass must be rated to the mains power supply and be capable of sustaining the in-rush current generated by the load.

g) Dual Input Supplies

The resilience of the configuration can be further enhanced (as shown in *diagram 5.8*) using *dual input supplies*. Here the same UPS system is supplied from separate rectifier and static switch supplies. Most UPS installations rely on common mains power supplies feeding both the UPS and static bypass. This creates a single-point-of-failure within the design: if an upstream circuit-breaker trips (opens) due to a fault, the rectifier and bypass no longer have a source of *ac* power. Using dual input supplies from separately derived sources (even separate substations) removes this problem.

Typically, transformer-based UPS have a dual input facility as standard but in a transformerless UPS this is a factory option as the rectifier and static bypass supplies rely on a common neutral. For more information see '*Electrical Installation*' in *chapter 9, section 9.4*.

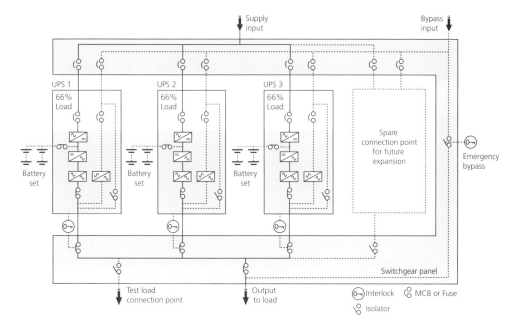

Diagram 5.8 – N+1 parallel-redundant UPS system, with separate rectifier and bypass supplies

5.4.2 Parallel-Capacity Systems

Diagram 5.9 shows a capacity system using, for example, three 100kVA UPS modules supplying a total load of 300kVA (each module sharing the load).

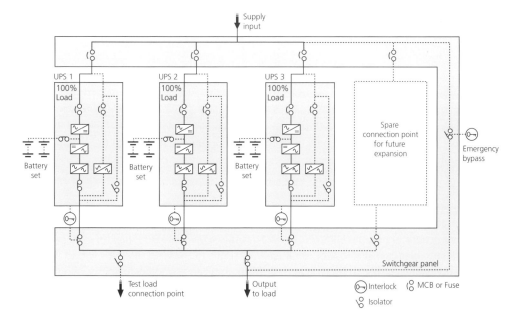

Diagram 5.9 – Parallel-capacity UPS system

The rectifier and static switch bypass supply inputs are taken from a common supply point, with each of the UPS modules fitted with circuit-breakers/isolators to allow individual disconnection. Each UPS module has its own battery set rather than a shared one. The output from each UPS module is taken to a common *ac* busbar from where it is distributed to the load. The UPS system is also installed with an external wrap-around emergency bypass switch. As with a parallel-redundant configuration, the UPS modules can be supplied from separated rectifier and static switch bypass supplies. Operation of the system is the same as a parallel-redundant configuration except for UPS module failure. If a UPS module fails, the remaining operational modules will be forced into an overload condition and the load transferred to bypass. The bypassing of these operational modules also simultaneously forces the faulty module into bypass, thus ensuring the load receives an adequate source of power automatically and without disruption.

The action taken by a parallel-capacity system during overload will depend upon the magnitude and duration of the overload. If it exceeds the rating of the system, all of the UPS modules will automatically switch to bypass in an attempt to clear the fault. If the overload or short-circuit is removed, the system will return to normal operation. If the overload or short-circuit remains, the entire UPS system will eventually shutdown.

5.4.3 Parallel Operation Accessories

Two further methods for increasing the resilience of parallel UPS systems revolve around the use of specific accessories:

a) UPS Group Synchroniser (UGS)

A UGS synchronises the outputs from two separate groups of parallel UPS (*diagram 5.10*), which may be supplied from separate *ac* sources. It enables the outputs from the groups to be configured into a *dual bus* format.

The UGS maintains synchronisation between the outputs of the parallel groups, regardless of input supply variations. For example, one group may be on battery or standby power and the other powered by the mains power supply. The device can generally be used with up to eight UPS modules between two separate groups. The addition of a *Static Transfer Switch (STS)* on the output enables the protected load to be supplied from either of the parallel groups. In this configuration, if one of the UPS groups fails the STS can transfer the load to the second group - providing there is spare capacity.

b) Parallel Systems Joiner (PSJ)

A PSJ operates in a similar manner to a UGS but enables the connection of the outputs from two separate groups of parallel UPS (*diagram 5.11*) into a *dynamic dual bus* for system expansion, fault tolerance and ease of maintenance. If one of the UPS modules within the two parallel systems fails, or has to be switched off for maintenance or emergency service work, the two outputs of the parallel UPS systems are merged by the PSJ (which acts as an output coupling switch) to allow power sharing.

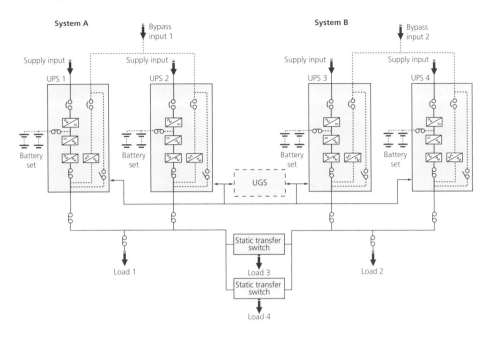

Diagram 5.10 – UPS Group Synchroniser schematic

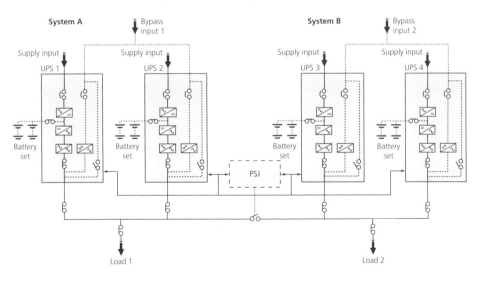

Diagram 5.11 – Parallel Systems Joiner schematic

5.5 Parallel UPS Installation Options

5.5.1 Common and Separate Battery Sets

A common battery set shared by the UPS modules within a parallel configuration can be a single-point-of-failure. This could be justified where there is adequate, regular, on-site battery testing as part of a maintenance plan (to ensure the battery set is always at its optimum levels of charge and capabilities). Cost and physical space considerations within the environment may also lead to such a choice.

If a common battery is to be installed, ideally multiple battery strings should be used to match the number of UPS modules. This removes any potential for a single-point-of-failure to disrupt the entire UPS system.

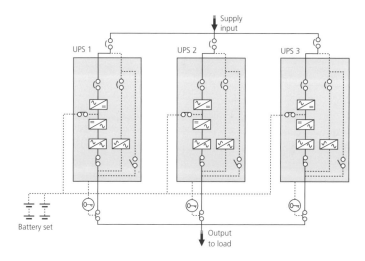

Diagram 5.12 – Parallel UPS system with a common battery set

The advantage of a common battery is that the entire battery set capacity is available to all of the UPS modules regardless of their operational condition. For example, for two UPS modules, each with their own ten-minute runtime, the entire capacity of 20 minutes becomes available to either module should one fail or be taken out of circuit.

Within a parallel configuration, separate battery sets are the preferred choice and where battery charging capabilities allow, multiple (dual) battery sets for each UPS module could be considered, each with a minimum design life of ten years or greater (as discussed in *chapter 6*). However, the total capacity of the connected battery sets cannot be utilised should one UPS module fail as its associated battery set will also be disconnected.

5.5.2 Decentralised and Centralised Static Bypass Systems

A *decentralised bypass* system refers to the situation where UPS module bypassing is reliant upon the static bypasses within each module. Their operation is precisely controlled to ensure synchronised switching to prevent load imbalance, disruption or damage. A *centralised bypass* system *(diagram 5.13)* refers to a single wrap-around static bypass switch, normally housed in a separate cabinet to the entire UPS system.

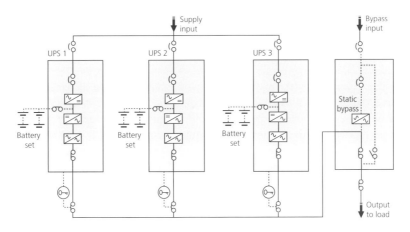

Diagram 5.13 – Parallel-redundant UPS system with a centralised bypass

Where there is concern that this introduces a single-point-of-failure, an additional external static bypass switch can be installed. This approach starts to mimic a decentralised system.

Both approaches offer similar levels of resilience. However, the centralised bypass does lead to a more complex and costly installation and future expansion needs to be built into this device at the time of installation. This is not the case with the decentralised approach.

Both can be used within a parallel system and selection sometimes is influenced by the design of the UPS. A key point, however, is to ensure that installation guidelines are followed in terms of matching cable lengths to prevent loading imbalances during short-circuit or overload conditions.

For large UPS systems (800kVA or higher) and for enhanced resilience, both approaches are recommended in tandem. This offers increased power paths where budget allows.

Some UPS manufacturers can only offer higher rated UPS by paralleling two smaller rated systems within a single cabinet. These systems are sold as a fully rated *single* module and require an external centralised static bypass as a minimum.

5.5.3 Maintenance Bypasses

Within a parallel-redundant UPS configuration, each UPS module will have an internal maintenance bypass. However, to carry out maintenance on any one of the modules in the system will require that module to be isolated. Within a parallel-capacity UPS configuration, each UPS still has its own internal maintenance bypass. However, as all the UPS modules are equally sharing the load, all must be bypassed at the same time for maintenance work to be performed safely. The entire UPS system can be instructed to switch to bypass as and when required in a co-ordinated manner. For complete UPS module isolation, and physical disconnection from both its supply and load, the installation of input and output circuit-breakers/isolators is recommended.

It is also possible to install (for the entire UPS system) an external maintenance bypass panel also known as a 'wrap-around' bypass. This device provides a manually activated, emergency power path around the entire UPS system. It should contain all the necessary switchgear with mechanical interlocks (Castell) and provision for future expansion of the entire system.

5.5.4 Power Distribution and Redundant Power Supplies

Most modern file servers have the facility for dual input supplies. A UPS system can take advantage of this to provide further levels of resilience through the use of parallel *Power Distribution Units (PDUs)* and where necessary static transfer switches.

5.6 Series-Redundant UPS Systems

Series-redundancy typically consists of two UPS modules connected so that either (a) one directly feeds the other (typically low-power applications) or (b) the output of one UPS module is used to supply the bypass of another. If one UPS fails the other automatically powers the load. *Diagram 5.14* shows two of the most common configurations for series-redundancy.

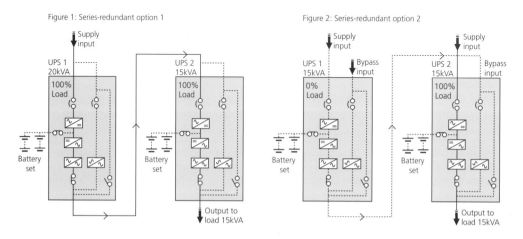

Diagram 5.14 – Series-redundant UPS systems

Option 2 is also known as a *'cold-standby'* arrangement and is the preferred option if series-redundancy is to be adopted. However, there are significant reasons for not adopting this type of redundancy including:

- **Efficiency and costs:** the configuration is less efficient than a parallel-redundant or parallel-capacity system due to the need for UPS module over sizing (*option 1*).

- **Single-point-of-failure:** the configuration has a single-point-of-failure - the first UPS module in the series (*options 1 and 2*).

5.7 Automatic Transfer Switches (ATS)

Automatic Transfer Switches can provide a resilient solution for UPS below 10kVA that cannot be operated in parallel.

An ATS has two *ac* input power sources (A) and (B) which can offer the following combinations:

- (A) supplied from the output of a UPS and (B) from a mains power supply.
- Both (A) and (B) supplied from two separate UPS outputs.
- Both (A) and (B) supplied from two separate mains power supplies.

When one of the power supplies fails, the loads are automatically transferred to the second. The transfer is instantaneous when the two supplies are in phase with one another.

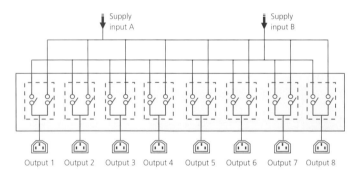

Diagram 5.15 – Automatic transfer switch with two input supplies and eight outputs

In addition, a typical ATS can provide protection against load short-circuits, the ability to switch its output power connections on/off remotely (over a network) and load measurement locally via an LCD or built-in sub-D type communications port. Hardwired versions for higher operating power are also typically available.

5.8 Sample Reliability and Availability Calculations

Chapter 5 has provided several architectures with which it is possible to increase the overall MTBF and resilience of a UPS installation. This section examines four potential configurations and shows their system MTBF and availability values. The MTBF of the mains power supply is site-dependent. For the purpose of these examples, the MTBF is taken to be 50 hours. The module used is a three-phase transformerless UPS, with active harmonic filter and ten-year design life batteries. The MTTR assumed is three hours (to allow for travel and on-site time).

5.8.1 Single UPS Module

This is the simplest installation and relies on a single On-Line UPS fed directly from the mains power supply. In this example, the UPS has a field population calculated MTBF of 250,000 hours. The load is powered from the mains power supply when the UPS fails or is isolated for maintenance. When isolated, the system MTBF then drops to that of the mains power supply (50 hours). This configuration is the least expensive (as only one UPS module is used) and can achieve a projected 99.99% (four-nines) availability.

5.8.2 Synchronised UPS

The solution, in *diagram 5.16*, can achieve a projected MTBF of 450,000 hours and 99.999% (five-nines) availability. It uses two individual UPS (synchronised through a UPS Group Synchroniser) the outputs of which are distributed via two static transfer switches. In this configuration, UPS redundancy is lost if one UPS fails or is shutdown for maintenance, as only the mains power supply provides a secondary power source.

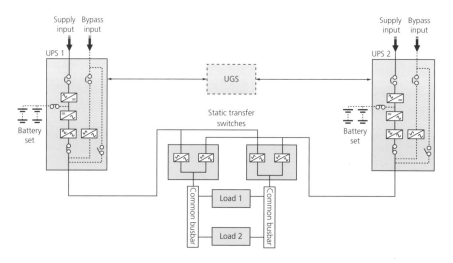

Diagram 5.16 – Synchronised UPS

The overall MTBF of the solution is inhibited by the use of the static transfer switches which present single-points-of-failure. Compared to the first example, the system is relatively expensive for the improvement in reliability and availability.

5.8.3 Parallel-Redundant UPS

The solution in *diagram 5.17* has a projected MTBF of 950,000 hours and 99.999% (five-nines) availability. It uses a pair of parallel-redundant (N+1) UPS with the load split equally between them. If one UPS is removed from circuit, the other powers the load. The MTBF is higher because all functions are redundant and the UPS system can better handle high overload currents. For parallel-redundancy during maintenance an N+2 configuration is required.

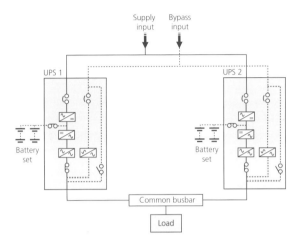

Diagram 5.17 – Parallel-redundant UPS

5.8.4 Synchronised Parallel-Redundant UPS Groups

The solution in *diagram 5.18* has a projected MTBF of 2,500,000 hours and 99.9999% (six-nines availability). It uses a Parallel Systems Joiner to connect the outputs from two separate parallel-redundant (N+1) UPS systems to the loads. All system functions are redundant, even during maintenance and the system can handle high overload currents.

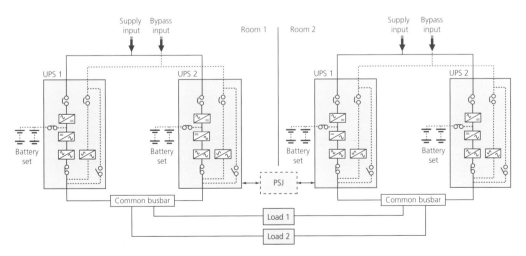

Diagram 5.18 – Synchronised parallel-redundant UPS groups

Table 5.2 provides a summary of the calculated MTBF values.

Solution	Configuration			MTBF UPS	MTBF Maintenance	Redundancy During Maintenance	Availability
	UPS	UGS/PSJ	STS	Hours	Hours		
1	1	-	-	250,000	50	No	99.998%
2	2	UGS	2	450,000	200,000	No	99.9993%
3	2	-	-	950,000	250,000	No (N+1)*	99.9997%
4	4	PSJ	-	2,500,000	750,000	Yes	99.9999%

Table 5.2 – Parallel-redundant architecture system availability (* N+2 would provide redundancy during maintenance)

5.9 Summary

An MTBF of 250,000 hours equates to 28 years operation without failure and is already far in excess of the lifetime of even the most well maintained systems and (one would expect) connected loads. The higher the MTBF, the more available the UPS system - even to the point of achieving five and six-nines availability where effective comparison can be made with Rotary UPS.

Chapter 6 now provides information on the key component for a UPS when the mains power supply is unavailable - its battery set and other alternative power sources.

6. Batteries and Alternative Back-Up Solutions

In this chapter:

- Understanding battery types and technologies.
- Sealed Lead-Acid battery installations.
- Battery sizing, design life and testing.
- Alternative technologies: flywheels, fuel cells and super capacitors.

Introduction

Batteries can be found within two of the primary components of a Power Continuity Plan: the UPS and generator. Their careful sizing and selection is therefore a key consideration, if overall system reliability levels are to be maintained.

Within a UPS, the battery set provides a *dc* supply to the inverter when the mains power supply fails. In a generator, the battery forms part of the automatic starter circuit. When a battery set fails within a UPS, the load can be dropped if there is no mains power supply or an alternative source of *ac* power present. When the automatic starter circuit fails in a generator, its start-up relies on manual intervention.

A *battery block* is a self-contained, electro-chemical device that can store electrical energy for later use. The outer case is generally made of polypropylene PVC (which may be flame retardant to UL94V-0) and has two protruding terminals (positive and negative). Inside the case, positive and negative plates, alternately placed, are immersed in an electrolyte (typically Sulphuric Acid) to form individual cells with an electrical potential. Within this closed circuit, a voltage is created and then stored when a charging current is applied.

The charging process creates a spongy form of Lead Sulphate at the negative electrode and Lead Dioxide at the positive one. The plate with the more positive potential is called the positive plate and the value of this potential is dependent upon the materials used which can include: Lead-Acid, Nickel-Cadmium, Lithium Ion and Silver Alkaline. The charge and discharge rate is dependent upon the internal resistance of the battery. The plates are kept apart by a micro-porous separator providing good insulation and with a low electrical resistance. This allows the free flow of ions and diffusion of the electrolyte. The efficiency of the reaction is normally around 85%. As a battery approaches full charge it will increasingly produce Hydrogen and Oxygen and there may be a loss of electrolyte if some form of recombination system is not employed.

Batteries are sized in ampere-hours (Ah), referring to the amps they can supply per hour.

6.1 UPS Battery Sets

A UPS battery set is made up of a number of battery blocks connected in series into a battery string (or number of battery strings).

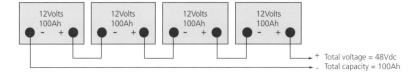

Diagram 6.1 – A single 48Vdc 100Ah battery string or battery set

There are two specific types of battery capable of meeting the performance required by a UPS: Nickel-Cadmium and Lead-Acid.

6.1.1 Nickel-Cadmium (Ni-Cads) Batteries

These were once a popular choice for large telecoms installations and are still specified for some UPS applications, especially in areas with high ambient temperatures, most notably, the Middle East.

Above 10kVA, it is still possible to find UPS capable of providing the charging regime required by Ni-Cads but this may be a factory fit rather than a field selectable option.

The advantages of Ni-Cads are that they are virtually maintenance free, with long design lives of 20 years or more. They are also more suited to a wide ambient temperature range (typically -20 to +40°C).

The disadvantages they present, however, revolve around their high initial cost and (more importantly) impact on the environment due to their Cadmium content. The batteries therefore, have high end of life disposal costs, especially in countries operating stringent environmental policies and regulations.

6.1.2 Lead-Acid Batteries

This is the most popular sort. It is available in three generic types including: industrial, automotive and traction with typically five, 10 and 15 year design lives.

For a UPS, the industrial type is the most appropriate due to its plate design, electrolyte, and charge/discharge performance. This type of battery is also found in a number of similar applications including telecoms, security and fire alarm panels, emergency lighting and standby power systems.

Industrial Lead-Acid batteries themselves are available in a number of designs, sizes and formats, to meet the range of high and low-rate discharge performances that their applications demand. These general types include: open-vented and valve-regulated.

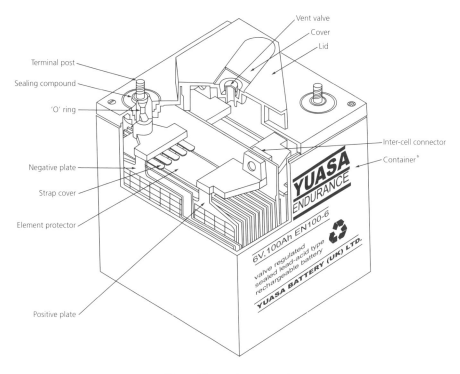

Diagram 6.2 – VRLA battery internal view

a) Open-Vented (Wet Flooded) Batteries

Open-vented batteries are typically used for large installations requiring a high Ah rating. They are not suitable for office or data centre environments. When full charging rates are applied, they can gas at levels which may present health & safety issues. Their installation, therefore, requires an isolated battery room, with wash-down facilities and bunding in case of acid leaks or spills. Open-vented batteries are top vented. They must, therefore, be positioned in a vertical plane which limits the number of potential installation formats available for them. For example, they are not suitable for use in battery and rack cabinets. For these reasons they are typically installed on stands which may be cladded (panel covered) or uncladded.

b) Valve-Regulated Lead-Acid (VRLA) Batteries - AGM and Gel

VRLA batteries (traditionally called *Sealed Lead-Acid* or *SLA* maintenance-free batteries) are more suitable for office and domestic environments and UPS installations.

Within a UPS installation, their sealed, compact size and low gas emissions make them ideal for use within battery compartments, external cabinets or rackmount trays. They can be mounted either vertically or horizontally as they are sealed, with pressure valves that only open in extreme circumstances.

VRLA batteries can typically be 'boost-charged' to around 80% capacity, followed by a 'float-charge', and will tend to gas at around 100ml per Ah, per cell, per annum. This is well within acceptable safety levels and is less than the 4% maximum specified for aircraft and enclosed spaces.

As an example, a 160Ah battery set comprising four battery strings will generate less than one cubic metre per month or 0.04 cubic meters per day. Accepted guidelines advise less than 1% (v/v) Hydrogen gas concentration within any given room with air changes at no less than 1.2 per hour. The calculated emission is therefore negligible, even for such a large battery set.

VRLA batteries are categorised as sealed and maintenance free. The fact is they are more sealed and maintenance free than open-vented or Ni-Cad batteries. They still, however, require regular inspection and testing.

To prolong their working life, VRLA batteries are designed to minimise electrolyte evaporation and gas emissions whilst on charge. Their plates are fitted into a plastic PVC case using a tight fit approach. The lid is sealed into position and the electrolyte sprayed into the case under vacuum. The normal working pressure of the battery is three pounds per square inch (PSI). Rather than the vent caps used in open-vented designs, VRLA batteries use pressure valves that only open to vent gas under extreme conditions. A blown vent valve is a certain sign that a battery block has failed.

VRLA batteries often contain a recombination system to reduce gassing. This feature impedes the release of the Hydrogen and Oxygen gasses generated by the galvanic action of the battery during charging. The most common form is a catalyst that causes the Hydrogen and Oxygen to recombine back into water whilst the battery is charged and the system can achieve 99% efficiency.

Absorbed Glass Mat (AGM) technology has become a standard for VRLA batteries. The AGM design promotes recombination and absorbs the electrolyte but in a liquid form to make it more readily available to the plates where it can help to achieve higher charge/discharge rates. The plate separator within such batteries is a Boron Silicate fibreglass. This is a micro-porous matrix that absorbs free electrolyte and acts like a sponge and reservoir. As all the electrolyte is contained within the absorbent matrix, it cannot spill, even if the plastic case ruptures. This type of battery set is also known as a *starved electrolyte* or *dry* type because the fibreglass mat is 95% saturated by the electrolyte with no excess liquid acid.

The *Gel* filled VRLA design uses an alternative recombant technology consisting of a special Acidic Thyrotrophic Silica gel in place of the liquid electrolyte. A certain amount of water is lost from the gel during the first year of operation but thereafter water loss is minimal. The battery works in the same manner under gas pressure and the Oxygen evolved migrates to the negative plate through fissures in the virtually dry gel.

The positive plate is tubular in shape and has small amounts of Tin and Calcium, whilst the negative plate contains some Selenium Calcium and Aluminium.

The Gel filled VRLA battery is not as suited to UPS applications. It has higher internal resistance making it less suited to high-rate discharging. It does, however, have some advantages in terms of a wider operating ambient temperature range (-40°C to +55°C) and extended design life of up to 18 years.

6.2 UPS Battery Pack Installation

Within a battery block, its cells will typically have an internal voltage variance between 1.75-2.275Vdc depending on whether the cell is charging or discharging. 2Vdc is generally taken for calculation purposes. Each battery block will be made up of a number of these cells and the most common type is a 12Vdc block comprising of six 2Vdc cells. 6Vdc battery blocks are also available and these are made up of three 2Vdc cells.

A UPS has a *dc* busbar which can typically range from 12-576Vdc. This means that a number of battery blocks must be connected in series to reach the specific busbar voltage. For example, a 576Vdc busbar will require 48 x 12Vdc batteries connected in series. This is known as a battery string, the ends of which are connected to the positive and negative terminals of the *dc* busbar respectively (and possibly a mid-point connection if the UPS is a transformerless design). Within a battery string, it is only the individual battery block voltages that are added together. The batteries must also be of the same Ah rating. For example, a 100Ah string at 48Vdc for a 1.5kVA On-Line UPS would comprise of 4 x 12Vdc, 100Ah blocks.

Two or more battery strings can also be connected in parallel to achieve higher Ah rated battery set capacities. Within this configuration the Ah increases but the Vdc remains the same. For example, two 48Vdc, 100Ah battery strings would create a combined battery set of 2 x 100Ah = 200Ah at 48Vdc. The discharge rate of this battery is 200 Amps per hour at 48Vdc or in terms of *real power* 200 x 48 = 9.6kW (400 Watts per Cell). Again, each string must contain the same number of batteries. Some battery manufacturers allow different Ah-rated battery strings to be used within a combined battery set. For example, for a 1.5kVA 48Vdc system, the battery set could comprise for a one-hour runtime of: 4 x 12Vdc, 38Ah plus 4 x 12Vdc, 12Ah i.e. two 48Vdc strings of 38 + 12Ah totalling 50Ah.

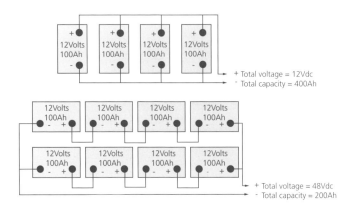

Diagram 6.3 – Parallel battery strings

6.2.1 Internal Battery Sets

Battery sets may be internally housed, for UPS typically 30kVA and below, or supplied in external cabinets, on stands (cladded or uncladded) or as part of a rackmount system.

Care has to be taken when deciding how to house battery sets. When discharging, batteries are *endothermic* and absorb heat but on charging they are *exothermic* and dissipate heat. On discharge, the heat is negligible but on charge the heat generated can be around 0.02 Watts per Ah per 12Vdc. Battery blocks should not, therefore, be too tightly packed together into a space and sufficient room should be left for case expansion and heat dissipation. This is especially important if a block goes open-circuit, to avoid thermal runaway. Ease of access to battery terminals is also a major consideration within confined spaces for testing and potentially, disconnection and replacement.

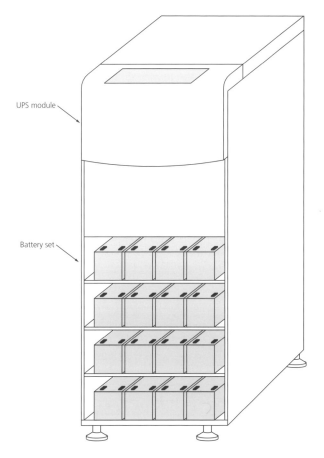

UPS module

Battery set

Diagram 6.4 – A 30kVA UPS with internal battery compartment

Within the UPS cabinet in *diagram 6.4*, the top half is populated with a UPS module and the lower half with battery trays. This type of UPS would also have connections for an additional external battery cabinet.

6.2.2 External Battery Cabinets

Diagram 6.5 shows a typical 200kVA UPS with a matching battery cabinet. Here the UPS cabinet has no room for an internal battery and an external battery extension cabinet is used. The batteries are secured onto battery trays which are then slotted into position and the battery set is connected to the UPS using *dc* cable links.

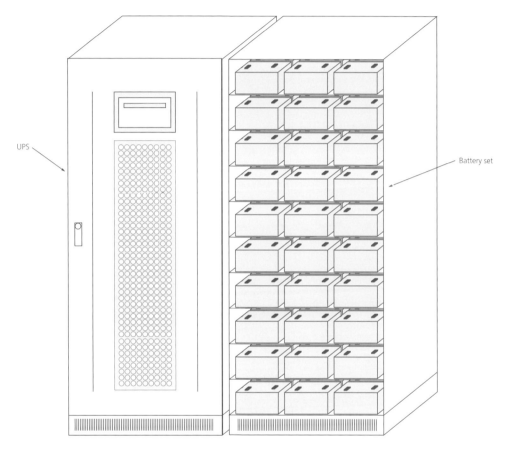

UPS

Battery set

Diagram 6.5 – A 200kVA with an external battery extension cabinet

For UPS below 10kVA, external battery cabinets will be matched, even to the point of having similar plastic front panels to the UPS. This is not the case for longer runtimes and UPS where the battery cabinet size has to be larger. Here, the battery cabinets may be colour matched to the UPS with removable panels for access and trays onto which the battery strings can be installed, sometimes pre-assembled.

Any cabinet should provide good access for maintenance, battery testing and replacement, as well as heat and gas dissipation. A clear area near the cabinet is always recommended for safe working.

6.2.3 Battery Stands

Battery stands (or racks) are specified in terms of the number of tiers and rows they have. For example, *diagram 6.6* shows a five-tier, one-row open (uncladded) battery stand.

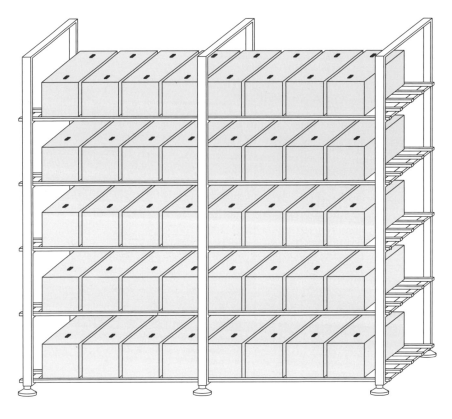

Diagram 6.6 – An open battery stand, five-tier, one-row

Battery stands are most commonly used for very large battery sets, especially those using open-vented batteries.

Open battery stands are generally installed within secure rooms (for health & safety reasons) and to prevent general access. The two main concerns are: accidental contact with a battery set which can contain potentially lethal currents; and the control of gas emissions, where relevant. When installed into a stand, battery terminals are exposed and this problem can be overcome by using rubber terminal shrouds. Stands may also be cladded with bolt-on panels to restrict access.

Whilst most cabinets will be populated with their battery sets off-site (providing that project logistics accommodates this) battery stands tend to be populated on-site. In addition, it is not uncommon for the battery stands themselves to be supplied in a kit form rather than pre-assembled. Both aspects need to be factored into the project management side of a *Power Continuity Plan*.

6.2.4 Rackmount Systems

The typical rackmount cabinet in a data centre has a maximum loading of between 150-300kg. Even if the entire UPS system and loads total less than this, health & safety issues have to be considered. For example, the centre of gravity of the cabinet and manual handling arrangements. For long runtimes up to 12 hours at 2kW, UPS manufacturers can sometimes supply specially manufactured rack cabinets into which an entire UPS system can be installed, including the battery packs, automatic bypass and power distribution.

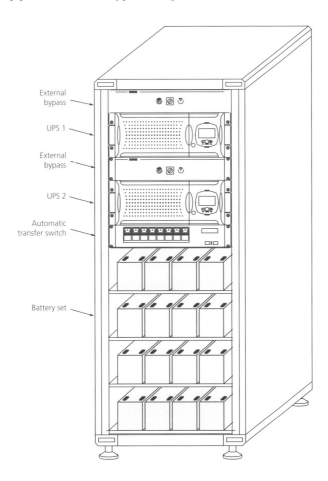

External bypass

UPS 1

External bypass

UPS 2

Automatic transfer switch

Battery set

Diagram 6.7 – A complete rackmount UPS system

These can provide a cost-effective solution where small footprints and high density runtimes are required. Within a rack, consideration should be given to access of the entire UPS and battery set. Here, the installation may use either telescopic slides or fixed shelves. Again, health & safety risks should be assessed as the weight of the batteries (or UPS module) may be sufficient to cause the rack to topple over during removal (if installed near the top). On-site lifting gear may also be required for siting of the complete cabinet.

6.3 Battery Set Sizing

The battery within a UPS must be sized to provide a specified runtime in minutes or hours at a specific Watts or kW or MW load. These load-specific factors are incorporated into a general battery sizing algorithm that will also take into account a number of other issues relating to ambient temperature and the inverter and system efficiencies of the UPS being considered.

Whilst battery manufacturers provide discharge curves and tables to assist selection, UPS manufacturers generally have bespoke battery sizing programs designed around their own UPS characteristics. Their battery packs also tend to be somewhat uniform, based around battery ranges and their source of battery cabinets or stands.

The UPS and battery set combination proposed in a solution will be the nearest matching to the calculated load. For example, for a total load (including UPS losses) of 20kW the nearest UPS is a 30kVA/24kW system. For a runtime of 30 minutes, the nearest battery option may be a 38Ah battery set, which will provide 25 minutes at 24kW or 33 minutes at 20kW.

For any given load, the runtime period must be sufficient to keep the loads running, allow the start-up of standby generators (both automatic and manual if necessary) and sufficient time for the completion of automatic server shutdown routines. When sizing a battery set for a UPS the primary factors to consider include:

- site power history, and in particular, the duration of previous mains power supply failures
- critical load sizes
- if there is a maintained standby generator on site
- the length of time required for load shedding and an orderly shutdown
- the available environment, for example, space, temperature and humidity
- overall cost for a long runtime versus an individual standby generator or fuel cell

Comparing battery runtime performance between UPS suppliers can be difficult unless a common basis for comparison is adopted. The best solution is to ensure all runtimes are quoted using the same load Watt ratings and load power factors. For example, for a 10kVA UPS supporting an 8kW load at 0.8pF, the runtime from a 12Ah internal battery set would be 14 minutes. However, at a 75% load (6kW) and 0.6pF the same UPS would provide almost 20 minutes. If the load and power factor values are not clearly defined comparisons can therefore be misleading.

6.4 Battery Life, Performance Optimisation and Testing

6.4.1 Battery Design Life

Batteries are the major consumable within a UPS system. They have a design life and will age through use whether cycled (charged/discharged) or not. The standard design life is five years at 20-25°C for 250 charge/discharge cycles. Ten, 15 and 20 year design life options are also available.

Whether a design life is met or not will depend on a number of factors including the number of charge/discharge cycles, ambient temperature, maintenance and overall quality of the battery itself. It is always recommended that full battery replacement costs are considered at the start of a *Power Continuity Plan* and that they are apportioned into yearly maintenance budgets. For a five-year design life battery, replacement should be considered around year four, and for a ten-year within year eight. Within any battery string, a block that fails (open circuit) effectively reduces the performance of the entire string and possibly to the point where there is no runtime available. Battery testing and maintenance are ways of potentially avoiding this.

If a generator is used within a *Power Continuity Plan*, attention should also be given to the battery used within its auto-start circuit. This battery will generally be a Lead-Acid automotive-type and can be inspected and tested in a similar manner to the batteries used in a UPS.

One of the most important factors of battery aging and performance is ambient temperature. The optimum temperature range for a VRLA battery is 20-25°C. Higher ambient temperatures do actually improve performance but rapidly age a battery, as shown in *diagram 6.8*.

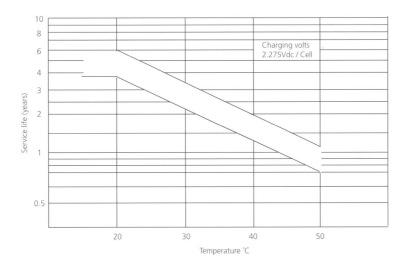

Diagram 6.8 – Lead-acid battery design life falling with increased temperature

Table 6.1 shows the effect in a tabular format. 20°C is the optimum battery temperature. At 30°C, the battery design life halves. This table further highlights the need to control the ambient temperature around a battery set if a premature and potentially costly replacement is to be avoided. This will invariably lead to system downtime and if not caught early enough, a complete system failure which only becomes evident when the battery set is placed under load during a mains power supply failure.

Temperature °C	20	25	30	35	40	45	50
% Service Life	100	71	50	35	25	18	13

Table 6.1 – Lead-acid battery life expectancy versus temperature range

6.4.2 External Battery Testing

There are various methods for electrically testing batteries:

- automatic battery set testing by the UPS
- load bank discharge testing
- battery set, string and individual cell testing

Most UPS will test their batteries on a regular basis (normally every 24 hours) and will alarm if there is a battery fault condition. The test places a load onto the battery set and the discharge performance is monitored. However, this provides only a general indication of the overall state of the set rather than an individual report on the health of each block. Simply measuring the float voltage across the battery set does not provide a true indication either. Whilst the batteries in a set will generally age in a uniform manner, individual blocks can fail earlier than others and become unable to sustain a reasonable level of charge. Under such circumstances, when placed under load, the battery set discharge voltage almost inevitably collapses.

The most appropriate method of testing a battery is to use a load bank. This places a load on the battery set and measurements can be taken intermittently to assess its discharge performance. As discussed in *chapter 10*, there are disadvantages to load bank testing including reduced resilience whilst the system is tested. For large battery sets, individual block testing can be more reliable. This can form part of an annual preventative maintenance visit or be provided as a standalone testing service. Either should include a visual inspection, because as a battery ages and approaches the end of its working life, its plastic case can buckle and electrolyte discharge can sometimes be seen around the terminals and valves. Worse still, the case can rupture leading to electrolyte leakage.

a) Impedance Testing

As a battery ages, its internal resistance (restriction to the flow of ions between the positive and negative plates) will increase. Impedance testing consists of applying an *ac* voltage, suitable for the Ah size of battery, through probes attached to the battery block terminals. The impedance (in milliohms) is then measured and recorded. This can be compared to published data from the battery manufacturer and previous recordings if available.

Impedance testing will help to identify battery blocks with high internal impedances (i.e. those about to fail). By measuring the recorded results every six-to-12 months, the testing can identify general deterioration. This is important because battery problems evolve over time (months and years) and can result from a loss of electrolyte, plate or weld cracks or high levels of Sulphating. This is the formation of Lead Sulphate crystals within the electrolyte and at the plate terminals, which reduce charging performance and prevent normal operation. Batteries can be recovered from this situation, if the degree of sulphation is not great, by charging at a higher current for around 12 hours. Care must be taken as the charging current will be higher than normal and heat generated. If the battery does not recover it must be removed and replaced.

b) Electro-Chemical Testing

This is a further non-invasive testing method that uses the principle of *Frequency Response Analysis (FRA)* to compare measured data to algorithms for known battery conditions, specifically Sulphation and electrolyte dry-out. The technique has traditionally been used within laboratories and was designed to identify and predict battery failure within space exploration vehicles and satellites. The latest testers are now portable, hand-held units.

Electro-chemical testing relies on measuring the frequency response to voltage and current signals passed into the battery using probes on the positive and negative terminals. The results can be compared to the battery performance data for 'healthy' batteries, either generated on site or by the battery manufacturer.

The primary difference to impedance testing is that Sulphation and electrolyte dry-out are principle causes of battery failure and poor performance. By measuring these aspects, rather than impedance, a clearer picture of the overall condition affecting the battery will be obtained. Failing battery blocks can be identified earlier and either recharged at a higher rate to reduce sulphation or replaced.

6.4.3 Performance Optimisation

A goal for UPS designers is to achieve a level of intelligent battery management that optimises battery set performance over the longest possible working life. The techniques available to achieve this vary between UPS manufacturers and can be grouped into three areas:

- reducing the number of full or partial charge/discharge cycles
- improving how the UPS charges and protects its battery set
- predictive testing with the aim of identifying potential failures

Most UPS manufacturers will use a selection of the following techniques:

a) Reduced Usage

Here, the objective is to reduce the duration and frequency when the UPS is reliant on its battery set. This can be achieved in a number of ways:

- using a rectifier with a wide input voltage window, typically ±20% at full load, which can be extended to ±60% at a reduced load
- providing the UPS with sufficient internal capacitance to ride through short duration interruptions (up to 40ms) without the inverter having to draw on its battery set
- enabling the UPS inverter to support large load step-changes without having to engage its battery set
- providing configurable self-diagnostics and battery testing in terms of its availability, duration and frequency

b) Improved UPS Battery Management

Here, the objective is for the UPS to provide optimum battery management using:

- temperature-compensating charging to reduce the voltage supplied to the battery set in high ambient temperatures and prevent a high current charge being applied
- a cycling charging method that will disconnect the charge for set periods and so inhibit the chemical reaction within the battery set
- techniques to reduced the *ac* ripple generated within the UPS to < 1%
- provide deep discharge protection to prevent the UPS discharging the battery set to a level from which it cannot recover
- configurable charging and discharging set points for specific battery sets
- dual level charging whereby the battery set receives an initial boost charge to 80% of capacity followed by a slower float charge to full capacity

Some of these methods are discussed in *chapter 4*. One of the primary methods is to have a charger that temperature compensates, especially for high ambient environments, as high temperatures are the primary factor in battery aging. For VRLA battery sets, a charger also has to avoid high-rate charging towards the end of the cycle (at around 80%). This reduces the potential for gassing, positive plate terminal corrosion, heat and thermal runaway. Constant high rate charging can also rapidly age the battery.

Above 80% most charging methods are designed to deploy float charging to enable the battery set to reach a final state of 100% charge. High *ac* ripple also has to be avoided as this can adversely affect performance by overheating and effectively 'cooking' the batteries.

c) Predictive Testing

Most UPS have built-in battery testing but its sophistication varies and the results are 'retrospective'. The preferred method of testing is '*predictive*'. This uses algorithms to compare capacity and voltage measurements taken by the UPS during a partial discharge against pre-recorded data. Any observed deterioration will lead to either further testing or battery replacement. The more traditional method simply provides indication of failure or an imminent failure. Both tests can be automatically and manually initiated.

Whilst UPS self-diagnostic routines have improved, the true state of a large battery set is best assessed using external battery testing. For large sets individual block testing is more appropriate. This can form part of an annual preventative maintenance visit or standalone testing service. Either should include a visual inspection.

Open-vented batteries tend to have glass or clear plastic containers through which electrolyte levels can be seen. They also incorporate valves through which measurements can be taken, and if necessary, top-ups made. For VRLA batteries, the only external indication of aging may be a buckled case and any invasion of the battery itself for testing purposes will effectively destroy it as its valves only open in extreme circumstances. Testing VRLA batteries, therefore, has to rely on non-invasive means.

Whilst load bank testing is considered the only true test, impedance testing can provide a good indication as to the overall health of a battery set, string and even a single battery block.

6.5 Battery Monitoring

Permanently fixed battery monitoring systems are available but their cost can be prohibitive except for large UPS installations. The system consists of a monitoring device connected to each battery block and string. Through an RS-232 communications cable, performance can be monitored continuously (every 30 seconds to five minutes) by a central monitoring device. This can provide data on battery set, string and block charge, float and discharge states, and their temperature and impedance.

6.6 Storage

A battery will age and discharge even when not in use. The typical storage life of a battery is approximately six to twelve months, dependent upon ambient temperature and their internal discharge rate. Without charge over longer periods, battery performance will reduce.

For UPS held within distribution channels, care has to be taken to monitor the actual time the UPS (and batteries) are left without charge to prevent deep discharge, and potentially, a full battery set replacement. Another reason why AGM type VRLA batteries are suitable for use within UPS is that they have a very low self-discharge, from 1-3% per month. In addition, they are more suited to lower storage temperatures as there is no liquid electrolyte to expand during freezing.

6.7 Disposal

Batteries are classed as hazardous waste due to their toxic components and must be disposed of in line with specific national guidelines. In the UK, the *Environmental Protection Act 1990* and *Hazardous Waste Regulations 2005* apply. Applicable European directives include:

*   Waste Electrical and Electronic Equipment (WEEE) Directive 2002/96/EC
*   EU End-of-Life (ELV's) Directive (September 2000)
*   EU Batteries Directive (May 2006)

Essentially, batteries have to be disposed of in a manner that is protective of the environment and this should be carried out by companies licensed to perform such tasks on behalf of the manufacturer (who bears ultimate responsibility).

Working with a UPS supplier (with ISO 14001) provides some peace of mind here, especially if they are also licensed to carry waste. They will, in turn, work with a licensed disposal company.

6.8 Future Developments

6.8.1 Flywheel Energy Storage Devices

Flywheels provide a source of short duration *dc* power and can be used with large applications such as UPS from around 60kVA upwards. They can be used in place of a battery set to provide the 10-45 second ride-through time required for the automatic starting of a standby generator, or simply to reduce the initial discharge of a battery set.

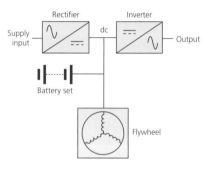

Diagram 6.9 – dc flywheel and UPS schematic

Flywheels can be used in single or parallel operation and are based on the principle of Kinetic energy. A motor-generator is used to rotate a mass at high RPM in a vacuum on frictionless bearings inside a floor mounted cabinet. On demand, electrical energy is discharged to the load in the case of a UPS by connection to the *dc* busbar. The speed of rotation is dependent upon the size of the mass and can vary from 7000 RPM for a steel mass to much higher RPMs around 50,000 for composite materials.

Flywheels provide some advantages over high Ah-rated battery sets and in particular, a potentially longer operating life time of up to 20 years. This is important because flywheels tend to have a higher capital cost which can be off-set against associated battery replacement and maintenance costs. They also do not present the gassing issues associated with large open-vented battery sets.

As a new technology, there is no standard design yet. Manufacturers are competing primarily on the weight and technology of the mass, speed of rotation and bearing materials. Mass construction varies between composites and aerospace grade materials. Bearings and maintenance are also important because some flywheels require periodic bearing changes which are costly and introduce downtime. Other technologies use active magnetic bearings which are said to last the lifetime of the product.

Though efficiencies match those of a battery on float charge, another advantage of a flywheel is its compact size. For example, a 200kW flywheel providing 12 seconds of *dc* power sits inside a 1m² foot print. Recovery time following a mains power supply failure is typically three to five minutes compared to the much slower recharge time of a battery set. Their operation is also less affected by high ambient temperatures.

	Flywheels	VRLA Battery Sets
Space	Compact	Larger
Running Costs	Low power consumption	Low power consumption
Cycling Performance	2000 cycles	250 cycles
Back-up Time	10 - 40 seconds	5 minutes to several hours
Recharge Time	3 to 5 minutes	5 to 6 hours
Maintenance	Annual - pump/bearings change every 3-6 years	Annual - total planned replacement at year 8
Design Life	20 years	10 years
Installation Costs	High	Low
Operating Temperature	0-40°C	20-25°C

Table 6.2 – Comparing flywheel and VRLA battery sets

6.8.2 Fuel Cells

Fuel cells are increasing in popularity across a number of applications due to their high efficiency and low environmental impact in terms of zero exhaust fumes. A fuel cell depends on the chemical reaction which occurs when Hydrogen and Oxygen combine to produce water. A fuel cell harnesses this reaction and will generate electrical energy, in addition to water and heat, as long as a fuel (Hydrogen gas) is present.

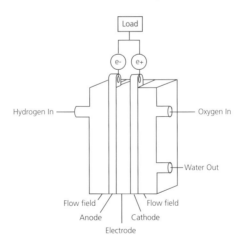

Diagram 6.10 – Fuel cell operation

The design consists of two electrodes (-ve anode and +ve cathode) with an electrolyte sandwiched between them. Hydrogen is supplied to the anode (and ionised by a catalyst which is typically Platinum) and Oxygen to the cathode. Activated by the catalyst, the Hydrogen atoms separate into protons and electrons, which take different paths to the cathode.

The protons and electrons are separated by a thin membrane (made from a specially fabricated PTFE compound) which allows the proton to move through whereupon it combines with Oxygen to produce water and heat. The electrons are then used to produce a *dc* electrical current through an external circuit before proceeding to the cathode. The system produces about 0.7Vdc per cell and uses a number of these cells to generate a high potential voltage.

There are various types of fuel cell designs and some are listed below in ascending order of operational temperature and efficiency:

- **Phosphoric Acid Fuel Cell (PAFC):** this is the most commercially developed fuel cell to date, suitable for use in hotels, hospitals and office buildings. It can also be used in transportation as part of the power system in a large vehicle. The fuel cell consists of an anode and cathode made of finely dispersed Platinum catalyst on carbon paper and a Silicon Carbide matrix that holds the Phosphoric Acid electrolyte.

- **Molten Carbonate Fuel Cell (MCFC):** uses a molten Carbonate Salt as the electrolyte. It has the potential to be fuelled with coal-derived gases or natural gas.

- **Solid Oxide Fuel Cell (SOFC):** uses a thin layer of Zirconium Oxide as a solid ceramic electrolyte, and a Lanthanum Manganate cathode and Nickel-Zirconia anode. This type of fuel cell is more suitable for large industrial applications and electricity generating stations.

Other types of fuel cell include:

- **Proton-Exchange Membrane (PEM) Fuel Cells:** uses a Fluorocarbon ion exchange with a Polymeric membrane as the electrolyte. This type of fuel cell operates at relatively low temperatures and can vary its output to meet changing power demands. Its best application is therefore small, including light-duty vehicles.

- **Direct-Methanol Fuel Cells (DMFC):** similar to the PEM with a Polymer membrane as an electrolyte, this design draws Hydrogen from Liquid Methanol at the anode and eliminates the need for a fuel reformer.

- **Alkaline Fuel Cells:** uses an Alkaline electrolyte, for example, Potassium Hydroxide. Originally developed by NASA for use on space missions, it is most commonly found now in Hydrogen-powered vehicles.

- **Regenerative or Reversible Fuel Cells:** this special type of fuel cell produces electricity from Hydrogen and Oxygen, and can be reversed and powered with electricity to produce Hydrogen and Oxygen.

Fuel cells have two potential UPS applications which include:

- **An alternative source of ac power to mains:** this configuration still requires a battery set. The fuel cell will be powered by natural gas or Hydrogen and the mains power supply is only used if the system fails. Fuel cells can therefore provide advantages where the normal mains power supply is unreliable and there is a suitable supply of natural gas. Such systems provide high-energy conversion, virtually no Nitrogen Oxide or Sulphur Oxide particulates, and when fuelled from natural gas, low Carbon Dioxide emissions. Hydrogen as a fuel source provides zero Carbon Dioxide emissions.

- **Support to an existing battery set:** here the UPS functions as a normal UPS with the fuel cell providing an additional source of *dc* energy. In this instance the cell is brought up to speed on mains power supply failure and it can take up to 15 minutes for operational temperatures to be reached. The advantages are that the fuel cell is more efficient and allows for a much smaller battery set to be installed.

Fuel cells vary in their audible noise output and start-up time. A small 10kW PAFC type, for example, could produce around 50dBA and a 100kW around 75dBA. Unlike a diesel generator there is, of course, no vibration. The start-up time for a fuel cell is dependent upon topology and design and can range from ten minutes to 18 hours. This is the time period taken to achieve an optimum conversion temperature and full power delivery.

6.8.3 Super Capacitors

Super Capacitors, like any other type of capacitor, store electrical energy which can be released on discharge. For small UPS this energy can be used in place of a battery set or to reduce the potential for battery discharge during momentary mains power supply failures. The amount of energy that can be stored depends on the active material used and a capacitor design of this type can achieve up to 30kW of stored energy. A super capacitor consists of two electrodes constructed from a highly activated carbon material, which may also be woven. The carbon activated electrodes provide a large reticulated area upon which an active material such as Ruthenium Oxide is deposited. The material provides an enormous area, for example, 1000 square metres per gramme of material used. Cellulose paper is typically used as the separator between the electrodes with polymeric fibres to provide reinforcement. The electrolyte is usually dilute Sulphuric Acid. In the chemical reaction, the Ruthenium Oxide is converted to Ruthenium Hydroxide and energy is stored.

The energy within a super capacitor is quickly available and the primary advantage they have is that, coupled to an existing battery set, they can inhibit battery cycling for momentary interruptions and help to extend the working life of the set. Their typical working life is ten years and they can operate over a wide temperature range of -30 to 45°C. Their disadvantage is price compared to that of a standard VRLA battery set, which can be a fraction of the cost.

6.9 Summary

Within a *Power Continuity Plan* deploying UPS protection for critical loads, battery set sizing, selection and installation can affect overall resilience. It is also important to remember that any on-site standby generator will also have a battery that will require routine inspection and testing.

Whilst batteries are the predominant *dc* source, for larger UPS systems flywheels are becoming more viable as alternative energy sources. Fuel cells are also emerging as a technology and one that can reduce the environmental impact of batteries, especially at the end of their working life. Generators remain the traditional source of power for a UPS for long duration runtimes and these are now considered in *chapter 7*.

7. Generators

In this chapter:

- Understanding the role of a standby power generator.
- Examining how a generator operates and delivers power.
- How to size a generator to provide alternative power to a UPS.
- Generator installation, testing and maintenance.

Introduction

A generator is a mechanical device capable of providing a source of ac electrical power on demand or as an alternative source to the mains power supply.

Within a *Power Continuity Plan*, a generator is used to provide a standby source of three or single-phase *ac* power to supplement the runtime provided by a UPS battery set or alternative source of *dc* power. The same generator may also be used to power essential loads such as alarms, air-conditioning and emergency lighting.

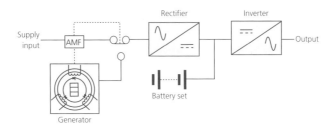

Diagram 7.1 – UPS and generator schematic with AMF panel

An *Automatic Mains Failure (AMF)* panel is an integral part of the installation. It monitors the mains power supply and instructs the generator to start-up on failure and shut down when power is restored. On start-up, a generator can take from five to 60-seconds before it can deliver a suitable supply. This is why a UPS must also be installed with its own runtime support, typically a battery set, sized to run from ten to 30-minutes. This allows sufficient time for either an automatic generator start-up or manual intervention. The amount of time a generator can run for is defined by its power rating and fuel tank capacity.

When running, generators are highly reliable and their resilience can be increased by operating two or more sets in parallel.

7.1 Generator Components and Configuration

Generators can be defined by the type of fuel they burn within their engines. Diesel is the most commonly installed type. This is also the most cost-effective solution but with down sides in terms of emissions: heat, noise and exhaust gases, for example. Alternative fuels include: *Liquid Petroleum Gas (LPG)* and natural gas, which is especially viable in remote areas where it may be easily available.

Modern generators are typically turbo-charged rather than naturally aspirated. The use of a turbo-charger means the overall design is smaller, less expensive and typically as responsive to 100% load changes as a naturally aspirated engine. This is important for UPS installations, especially as the set is only powered up when the mains power supply fails. Following start-up, the generator must be able to accept up to a 100% load, within a relatively short timeframe (three to five seconds) whilst still maintaining a controlled and stable output waveform.

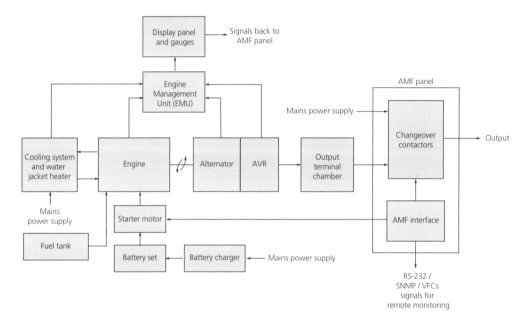

Diagram 7.2 – Typical generator schematic

7.1.1 Engine

Diesel engines have rapidly evolved over the last ten years to meet emerging transportation and environmental needs. Great improvements in performance have been made thanks to advances in metallurgy, lubrication, noise and vibration control.

Diesel engines will typically operate at speeds including: 750, 1000, 1200, 1500, 1800 and 3000 *Revolutions Per Minute (RPM)*. Most 50Hz generators run at 1500 RPM and 60Hz systems at 1800 RPM. Engine speeds (and frequency) are controlled by a governor.

Most engine designs include a lubricating oil priming system. This ensures the internal engine surfaces are wet before the crankshaft is turned at start-up. Large sets of 500kVA, or more, have a continuous priming cycle of a few minutes every hour to maintain lubrication. At start-up, as soon as the engine is up to speed, the main oil pump takes over and the priming system is shut down.

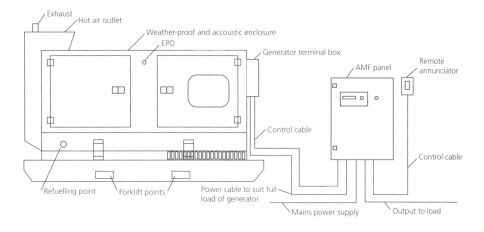

Diagram 7.3 – Typical generator layout

7.1.2 Fuel Tank

A *day tank* (eight hours) is the most commonly installed size and is part of the generator chassis structure. Larger *bulk tanks* can also be installed and on-site fuel storage can be used to ensure continuous operation if required.

For on-site fuel storage, local health & safety and environmental regulations must be observed. A common requirement is for a fuel tank to be *double-bunded* within another tank to capture any fuel spillage.

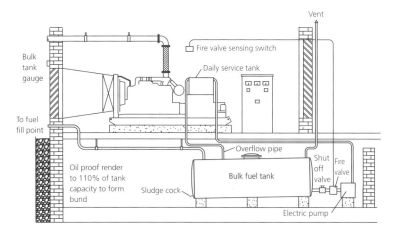

Diagram 7.4 – Generator fuel storage system

Bulk tanks are typically installed within a brick lined housing which may itself have to be lined with an oil-proof rendering to protect both the building and environment. The location of the bulk tanks in relation to the generator also has to be considered. For example, local fire service regulations may require that in emergencies, the fuel from a day tank can be pumped into a bulk tank within 30 seconds. If this is a requirement, the final generator design must include a valve actuator to assist in this process. In addition, particular emphasis should be placed on heating connection pipes during cold periods, fume venting and the siphoning of sludge or water which may accumulate within the tanks.

7.1.3 Governor

The governor controls the speed of the engine (RPM) by regulating its fuel supply. Traditionally, a mechanical governor has been used which relies on measuring a centrifugal force between two rotating weights. This type of governor is far less common today because it responds slowly to load changes and therefore can affect output stability.

Modern turbo-charged generators use electronic governors. This controls fuel flow to the engine by monitoring a signal picked up magnetically from the teeth of the starter-ring flywheel (which varies with engine speed) and comparing this to a pre-set parameter within its speed control unit. The governor then adjusts the fuel flow rate to compensate for any differences.

7.1.4 Alternator and Automatic Voltage Regulator

The alternator converts mechanical energy into electrical energy via an *Automatic Voltage Regulator (AVR)*. This is typically coupled to the engine via a single bearing mounted on the engine crankcase. The AVR regulates alternator output to within prescribed limits.

In larger sets, a two-bearing alternator may be used with both the engine and alternator mounted onto a common base frame with flexible coupling. Both single and three-phase alternators are available. Within larger three-phase generator sets, the alternator may include a transformer in its output stage for direct connection to the final load.

7.1.5 Exhaust and Air Cooling Systems

A generator will produce heat and exhaust gasses as part of its mechanical and combustion process. Generators are typically air cooled and provision may have to be made to prevent too high an ambient temperature where the generator is housed. It may be necessary to force cool air into its environment, and adjacent walls may also, for example, require louvres which open automatically when the generator is in use.

For a diesel generator engine, 30% of the heat produced is represented by exhaust gases which must be vented. As with any diesel burning engine, the fumes will consist of Carbon Monoxide, Carbon Dioxide, water vapour, various Sulphur derivatives namely Sulphur Oxide, Nitrogen Oxide, aldehydes and particulates.

Diesel generators can have *catalytic converters* installed within silencers to help reduce the environmental impact of their exhaust fumes. These will convert the Carbon Monoxide to Carbon Dioxide, burn off the aldehydes and convert the Nitrogen Oxide fumes to Nitrogen and Oxygen. Whilst these assemblies operate at 200 to 300°C they are themselves thermally insulated. For larger sets, two silencers may be used: one to attenuate low frequency and the other high frequency noise.

Where the generator is housed will influence the routing, fitting and final venting point of the generator exhaust system (the connections of which must be checked as part of routine maintenance inspections). Within a basement, plant room, or roof-top enclosure, for example, exhaust piping is typically suspended from hangers mounted on the wall or ceiling. The exhaust pipes may also require lagging to reduce noise and heat emission.

Best practice includes reducing the exhaust run to the smallest possible distance (ideally less than ten metres) to avoid gas flow, volume and pressure problems, especially when ducting has to go around corners and routing the exhaust fumes away from other ventilation systems and windows. Long exhaust runs can reduce generator efficiency.

7.1.6 Starter Battery and Charger

Chapter 6 covered the battery types used within UPS installations. For a generator starter circuit, the battery is normally a Lead-Acid automotive-type as opposed to a VRLA battery. An automotive battery is more suited to the characteristics of the application (short runtime and high discharge rate) and the wide temperature range from 0 to 40°C that a generator can find itself operating within. The battery will typically be trickle charged and this can lead to eventual loss of electrolyte, which should be checked as part of a regular maintenance inspection. The charger will preferably be mains and generator powered.

7.1.7 Automatic Mains Failure (AMF) Panel

Within a UPS installation the principle connecting component is the AMF panel. This is a sophisticated device, mounted adjacent to the generator or within a switchgear room. The AMF panel is essentially part of the generator control circuit and switchgear. It senses the state of the mains power supply and provides the appropriate commands for the generator to start-up or power down. Most AMF panels are configured to instruct the generator to start after a pre-set time on mains failure. This prevents the generator from starting unnecessarily, and during this period, the UPS battery set supports the load. On mains return a suitable delay period is allowed to ensure the returned supply is stable. Only then will the AMF panel instruct the generator to power down.

The AMF panel incorporates electrically and mechanically interlocked contacts, for both the mains and generator supplies to the UPS (and any other loads). This prevents both contactors being closed at the same time which would result in the generator back-feeding onto the grid. The AMF panel can also incorporate an interlocked bypass supply to prevent disruption to the loads during maintenance.

The AMF panel will be microprocessor-based and should provide an array of information and alarms through front panel LEDs, an LCD and communications port. Typically available data should include:

- generator and assembly status: at rest, pre-heating, availability
- alarms: shutdown on low oil pressure, for example
- engine: speed, oil pressure, hours run, battery charge
- generator output: voltage, current, frequency, kW, kVA, power factor
- mains power supply measurements: voltage and frequency
- access to event alarm and history logs

A generator is a complex device and as such it should be remotely monitored in line with the recommendations for alarm monitoring as described in *chapter 8*. Typical alarms will include:

- failure to start after the automatic cranking sequence has been exhausted
- engine over-speed trip
- operation of fire detection systems within the engine room or set enclosure
- loss of signal from the magnetic pick-up for the governor speed control
- low lubrication oil pressure
- coolant and high cylinder over temperature

Remote monitoring is generally made available via a D9 port, which may provide signal contacts (normally volt-free) and RS-232 communications. Volt-free contacts will be used to connect to a BMS panel. Manufacturer specific remote monitoring and control software may also be available to run on local PCs or network management stations.

Other components and considerations will include:

- electric heater jacket
- acoustic noise hood: to reduce noise levels emitted by the generator
- weather-proof enclosure: suitable for outdoor use

7.1.8 Electric Heater Jacket

An electric heater (mains powered) is normally installed to keep operating components at a pre-defined temperature on standby. This prevents freezing temperatures affecting operation and reduces the time it takes for thermal operating efficiency to be reached and exhaust 'soot' emissions on start-up.

7.1.9 Acoustic Noise Hood

The purpose of an acoustic noise hood (or canopy) is to attenuate audible noise levels on-site and within the surrounding neighbourhood. A typical canopy can achieve on average a 10% reduction in noise levels. For example, for a 60kVA three-phase diesel set, a reduction from 90dBA to less than 80dBA at 1m can typically be achieved.

Within a confined space, such as a plant room, the noise can reverberate around the area and depending upon its construction, sound pressure levels within the room could reach 110dBA. This can be reduced through the use of acoustic cladding materials. On-site health & safety requirements may also specify ear-defenders when working close to a running set.

Additionally, air flow into the room and exhaust gassing will increase noise levels. Attenuators are typically installed to reduce this problem. These are metal ducts lined with a porous absorptive material (similar to rock wool) held in place by expanded metal. They reflect and dissipate the noise level but can be quite bulky. Their efficiency depends on the length of ducting, thickness of the absorbent lining, cross-sectional area of the channels and the wavelength of the original sound.

It is always recommended that the specific local authorities are consulted for a new generator installation, especially to check if planning permission is required. In terms of noise pollution, in Europe *2000/14/EC* provides a guide to acceptable levels. For example, where a 10dBA rise above existing noise levels is experienced, complaints can be made, which could lead to expensive enforcement notices and actions.

7.1.10 Weather-Proof Enclosure

A weather-proof enclosure can also act as an acoustic hood. Its primary purpose, however, is to protect the generator from the elements when placed outside a building, either on a ground floor concrete plinth or suitable rooftop location. Various IP ratings are available.

7.2 Generator Sizing and UPS Compatibility

Generator sizing is a fundamental consideration within a *Power Continuity Plan*. The generator has to be sized to power the UPS (taking into account the harmonics that its rectifier will generate) and any other essential loads it may supply. Generators can typically be rated in two ways:

- **Prime Power Rating (PPR):** where the generator supplies power as an alternative to the mains power supply, but on an unlimited basis.

- **Standby Power Rating (SPR):** where the generator supplies power as an alternative to the mains power supply but for short duration, typically one hour in 12.

A generator rated under SPR can be 10% larger than one sized using PPR. This provides an overload capability for a short duration, for example, to meet sudden load demand changes.

For a UPS installation, PPR is the most suitable method and it is extremely important for resilience within a *Power Continuity Plan* that a generator and its UPS are suitably matched. A generator must be able to accept the load of the UPS, and the UPS rectifier and static bypass supplies must be able to operate with and synchronise to the output of the generator.

Generator set manufacturers also have four recognised categories of load acceptance:

Category	Acceptance
One	100%
Two	80%
Three	60%
Four	24%

Table 7.1 – Load acceptance

Categories two, three and four are used in practice for PPR-rated generators. Load acceptance is closely related to the turbo charging system used and also the *Break Mean Effective Pressure (BMEP)* of the engine. This is a function of engine speed, the number of cylinders and the swept volume of each cylinder.

For a turbo-charged generator, load acceptance is within 60 to 70% of its rated output at any one time. Its engine air input is controlled by the speed of the turbo-charger and until this reaches the correct speed, air supply (turbo) lag could disrupt the combustion cycle. This in turn could affect the output voltage waveform of the set.

For load acceptance to occur, a UPS must be able to synchronise to the voltage waveform supplied by the generator. UPS tend to have fairly wide input voltage windows and a generator output is generally well within this. Its frequency however can vary. This problem is overcome by widening the UPS operating parameters to accept a wider frequency range. This may not always be sufficient though, especially for poorly maintained or undersized generators, the output frequency of which can drift too far for the UPS to synchronise to.

A generator can never be matched on a 1:1 aspect ratio with a UPS. This is because a UPS is not a 100% efficient device. Energy is lost in the double-conversion process and the UPS will at times be drawing additional current to charge its battery set. The generator sizing may also have to take into account the powering of essential loads, for example, air-conditioning and emergency lighting. Sizing can also be affected by the harmonics generated by a UPS rectifier. *Chapter 4* discussed potential ways to reduce this problem for transformer-based and transformerless UPS. Whichever method is chosen will result in the UPS drawing higher currents from its supply and this in turn will affect generator sizing.

A final factor to take into account is the ambient temperature around the generator. It is usual to allow a 10°C rise in plant or engine room temperature when a generator is in operation. If the outside ambient air is 20°C the room temperature could reach 30°C. Generator performance degrades in high ambient temperatures; damage can be done to the turbo-charger and exhaust systems. Therefore, in such instances, it is normal to de-rate and increase the overall size of the generator installation.

Recommended practice is therefore to oversize a generator by a factor of one-and-a-quarter to two-times the size of the UPS and to increase this to three-times or more when additional essential loads are to be powered.

7.3 Generator Operation (single and parallel)

The AMF panel is normally installed next to the generator or within a dedicated switchgear area. It will monitor the upstream mains power supply and control the generator as required.

Upstream overloads and short-circuits are also indirectly monitored by the AMF panel but these will only lead to generator start-up following a break in the mains power supply. On mains power supply failure, a typical start-up procedure will firstly wait two-to-ten seconds to ensure the mains interruption is not momentary before proceeding. Start-up occurs when the battery-powered starter motor is engaged with the starter ring on the rim of the engine flywheel. The engine fires up and accelerates to operating speed.

For large generator sets, parallel starter motors or compressors may be used, particularly for sets of 1MVA or greater. When the mains power supply is restored, a typical run-on time of five-to-30 minutes is allowed, dependent on site characteristics, which will include off-load running. There are two reasons why this is necessary:

• the engine will require time to cool down otherwise hot spots can occur, particularly around cylinder blocks, heads and pistons; removing the coolant flow from around these areas will cause the coolant to boil
• the returned mains power supply may not be sufficiently stable for normal UPS operation to resume

In *diagram 7.5* on mains power supply failure, the two normally closed (NC) contactors are opened and the generator started. When up to full speed, the two contactors (NO) are closed. When the generator has accepted the load and steady-state conditions are reached (normally within five-to-ten seconds), the contactor between the loads is closed.

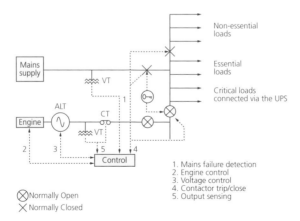

Diagram 7.5 – Single generator schematic

Careful consideration should also be given to contactor operation delays in relation to:

- **Transformers:** their magnetism takes time to decay. If, for example, a secondary supply is connected to the transformer under such rapid switching conditions it can cause circuit protection devices to trip out. The recommended delay is half a second.

- **Induction motors:** the rotor flux may be out of its synchronised position and this will induce high currents that can cause circuit protection devices to trip out. The recommended delay is ten-to-15 seconds.

Diesel generators are highly reliable with an MTBF of several hundred thousands hours once started. Failure to start is one aspect that must be incorporated into a *Power Continuity Plan*. Failure normally results from a flat starter battery, electrical or mechanical fault, or lack of fuel and is the reason why a UPS should be installed with a sufficiently large battery set. Where this is not practical, generators may be operated in parallel with the appropriate switchgear. This can also provide advantages in terms of:

- increased reliability and availability from an N+1 configuration so that the loss of a set will not disrupt operation of the UPS system or any connected essential loads
- as a temporary arrangement to overcome problems with intermittent load characteristics, which can disrupt the output waveform of a single set
- future load expansion

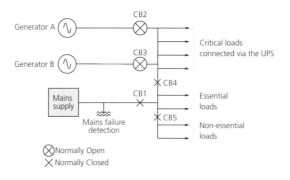

Diagram 7.6 – Parallel generator schematic

The most common parallel configuration is shown in *diagram 7.6*. In this configuration, two alternative methods of system function are available:

- the first set to reach full power assumes the load
- both sets are allowed to run up, achieve output synchronisation with each other and then equally share the load

The first solution has a quicker response (ten-to-15 seconds). However, if the load size is close to the output power rating of the generator, and start-up overload occurs, the generator could be tripped out of circuit and the load dropped. Allowing both sets to synchronise prior to accepting the load can take longer (between 20 and 25 seconds) but helps to overcome the issue of overload.

7.4 Generator Installation

7.4.1 Earthing

Chapter 9, section 9.4.10, discusses earthing in relation to UPS installations and fault clearance. For a generator, the following guidelines apply:

- **TN-C-S and TN-C systems:** if a generator is connected, it must be installed with a triple changeover device to select one supply or the other.

- **TN-S systems:** if a generator is connected, it must be installed with a four-pole changeover device to select one supply or the other. The fourth pole is required to avoid earthing the neutral at a second point.

- **TT systems:** if a generator is connected, it must be installed with a four-pole changeover device to select one supply or the other.

The installation will become more complex if a parallel set configuration is adopted.

7.4.2 Neutral Connections

Care has to be taken with the method employed to switch the neutral conductor as improper operation can disrupt the working of some older style UPS and cause nuisance tripping of downstream earth leakage detection devices (RCDs). Most UPS, and generator installations, rely on breaking the neutral when switching to and from the generator supply. This low-cost solution relies on the UPS being able to withstand a break in supply neutral during changeover.

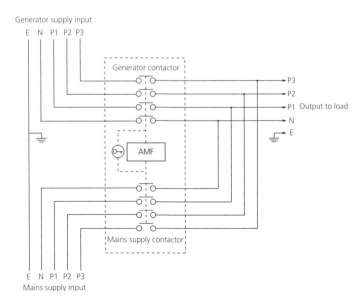

Diagram 7.7 – Generator neutral path: broken neutral changeover

Diagram 7.7 shows the most common form of switching mechanism employed in generator installations. It uses two individual contactors (electrically interlocked) to select between either the incoming mains power supply or the generator output under the control of the AMF panel. It is not a fast acting method and the changeover could take several cycles, but for this period the UPS will be using its battery set to maintain output power.

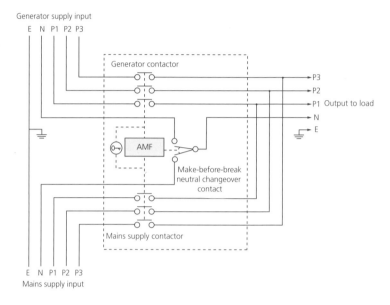

Diagram 7.8 – Generator neutral path: make-before-break neutral changeover

Diagram 7.8 shows the same schematic but this time the neutral changeover is performed by a make-before-break contact. This ensures the neutral remains fixed during changeover between the mains power supply and generator output, which may be required by those UPS that rely on an unbroken neutral, or if there are downstream earth leakage protective devices installed.

An additional means of maintaining a fixed neutral point is to install an isolation transformer. When a *Delta Star Transformer* is used, it can overcome problems associated with the harmonics generated by a UPS but there are more cost-effective means to achieve this (as already discussed in *chapter 4*).

7.4.3 Planning Authorities, Landlords, Fire Services and Insurance

For many reasons the installation of a generator is different to that of a UPS. The fact that the generator produces higher noise levels, may be housed externally, and uses combustible fuels, means that the appropriate approvals must be obtained and relevant organisations informed of the installation before it takes place. In the UK, there are various guidelines to comply with and in particular the *Clean Air Acts of 1956 and 1993*. These are concerned with the rapid dispersal of exhaust fumes and specify the minimum height of the exhaust outlet and its effect on adjacent buildings.

7.4.4 Logistics and Siting

Similar issues exist here as to those for large UPS. Of particular concern is generator size and weight which will require attention in terms of logistics and the physical siting, utilising specialised lifting gear and (possibly) cranes. In addition, as a mechanically active device, like a rotating flywheel, generators are normally fix-bolted to concrete plinths. They will vibrate and the fixing helps to dampen this and prevent movement; as do anti-vibration dampers (rubber or coiled springs) fixed to the base frame.

7.5 Generator Testing and Maintenance

Regular remote monitoring should provide early indication of problems. Mechanical devices like diesel engines should not be left idle for long periods due to weights on bearings and fuel deposits. Best practice guidelines recommend a monthly generator test for up to one hour under load conditions i.e. with the load powered or substituted by a load bank. Shorter test periods are not recommended as they can lead to carbon deposits on the engine cylinders. Inspection should be made of fuel and oil levels, connections (for leaks and spills) and attention should be paid to the starter battery. Annually, the generator should receive a full service with consumable items, such as filters being replaced.

Where both UPS and generators are installed, it is common for them to be covered by a maintenance plan from the UPS supplier. They will work in collaboration with the generator supplier and co-ordinate remote monitoring and on-site work.

This service can be enhanced (where the AMF panel is capable of being monitored remotely) by a centralised service centre or over a local network.

7.6 Future Developments

7.6.1 Gas Turbines

A gas turbine is a further source of alternative *ac* power, which can be used to provide a UPS with a source of standby power. Like generators, gas turbines are combustion devices with similar installation and operational issues. A jet engine is a classic example of a gas turbine. Advances in the technology have lead to commercially viable energy-saving applications and the devices are finding useful roles within power protection projects. There are two specific gas turbine designs:

- **Single shaft:** the design has both the turbine and compressor on the same shaft. An alternator is fed through a gearing system to produce around 1500 to 3000 RPM, from the initial speed which can range from 17,000 to 42,000. Its output is speed controlled via the fuel supply.

- **Two shaft:** the design is not often used in standby configurations. Although it has a higher operating efficiency, its response performance to load changes is poor.

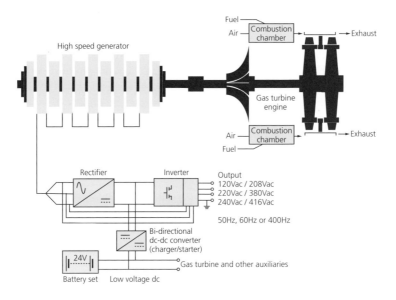

Diagram 7.9 – Micro gas turbine schematic

Micro Turbines (also known as *Micro Gas Turbines*), work at even higher speeds. This design requires no additional gearing as the alternator is run at the same speed as the turbine itself. Its windings are stationary with specially developed permanent magnets rotating between them. These magnets are constructed from rare materials such as Neodymium-Iron-Boron and Samarium Cobalt. Their rotor consists of two or more discs, containing the permanent magnets, on the same shaft. The stator consists of discs which contain the windings.

Each micro turbine will typically generate 10kW of power, which can be increased using a higher number of stator and rotor discs. Micro turbines can generate up to 60kW of power and be operated in parallel.

Micro turbines offer several advantages including a compact design, lighter weight construction and the ability to run on a variety of fuels (natural gas, Bio-gas, Kerosene and Diesel). However, their big advantage is 'greener credentials' when compared to diesel fuelled generators.

7.7 Summary

Within a *Power Continuity Plan*, a generator provides an extended source of alterative standby power. Its selection, however, complicates the installation and introduces a number of factors that have to be considered in relation to noise, exhaust fumes and fuel storage. The UPS battery set should be sized for sufficient time to allow an orderly shutdown of any attached loads if the generator fails to start. Generator start-up is typically the most common-point-of-failure and regular test and maintenance programs will help to prevent such an eventuality.

8. Alarm Monitoring and Remote Control

In this chapter:

- Understanding UPS alarm signals and how to monitor them.
- Reviewing remote communication and control protocols.
- The different UPS software packages and how to use them.
- How to monitor other hardware and the UPS environment.

Introduction

A UPS is a sophisticated microprocessor-controlled system, capable of providing a range of alarm notifications and real-time monitoring information at local, network and remote site levels.

This information needs to be monitored within a *Power Continuity Plan*. Provision must be made for how alarm signals will be monitored and responded to. Failure to act appropriately can result in reduced system resilience. Classic examples include failing to notice that a UPS is operating in bypass or that it failed a battery test the week before a mains power supply failure. Either scenario could lead to a system crash, the loss of data, file corruption and possible hardware damage.

Remote communication provides the ability to receive complex operating measurements concerning the UPS, its performance and environment and initiate server-side shutdown scripts. Remote control provides the additional facility of being able to shutdown a UPS in an emergency, perform test routines and configure the system to adapt its performance to site conditions.

The majority of UPS provide status and alarm information via front panel displays, audible signals and built-in (D-sub D9, D15 or D25 or USB) ports providing RS-232 communications and signal contacts. In addition to these, UPS manufacturers will generally provide a range of slot-in or external connection accessories to enable the UPS to communicate with a variety of devices and systems. Many will be developed in-house or via external third-party organisations, with the potential for customisation.

In addition, generators and many of the other power protection solutions discussed in this guide can be remotely monitored and controlled to provide system-wide visibility of the entire *Power Continuity Plan*.

8.1 UPS Alarm Signals

As discussed, careful consideration has to be given as to how alarm signals will be monitored within a *Power Continuity Plan*. A complex multi-site installation is shown in *diagram 8.1*. This particular set-up shows each UPS with local, network and remote monitoring and control facilities in place.

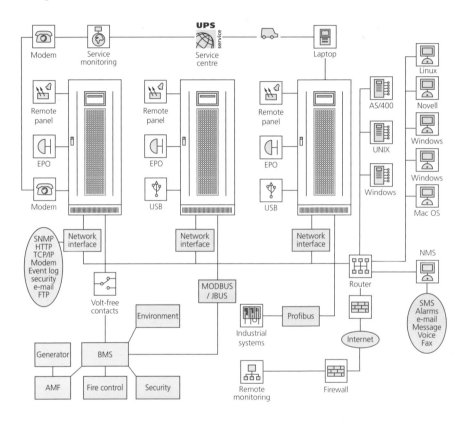

Diagram 8.1 – Complex alarm monitoring set-up within a Power Continuity Plan

This is achieved using a combination of the built-in communication ports within the UPS in addition to compatible hardware and software accessories. Each of the protected loads runs UPS monitoring software for a controlled sequential and priority-based shutdown. All the systems are monitored remotely via a dedicated service centre with four-clock-hour rapid response service engineers on standby. The set-up relies on monitoring the alarm signals from each of the UPS and dedicated alarm response scripts. UPS alarm signals can be grouped into those resulting from:

- a change in operating environment such as a mains power supply failure or overload
- reaching defined UPS operating parameters (set points), for example, a battery set *dc* disconnect threshold or battery runtime limit
- failure of an automatic test routine such as a battery test or the emergence of an internal fault requiring a service visit

The alarm signals are captured from the communications ports on each of the UPS. Typical pin assignments for D15 and D9 ports are shown in *diagram 8.2*. These are representative and the actual pin assignments will vary between UPS manufacturers, as will their use of male and female connectors. It is common for these ports to be on the rear of the unit but in larger three-phase UPS they are typically found behind a front panel for ease of access.

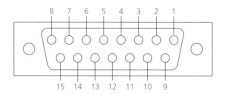
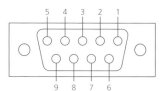

1 - 12V
2 - N/A
3 - Bypass/Fault volt-free contact common
4 - Mains failure volt-free contact normally open (NO)
5 - Mains failure volt-free contact normally closed (NC)
6 - Low battery volt-free contact common
7 - System off activation (EPO)
8 - Inverter off activation (Remote Bypass)
9 - N/A
10 - Bypass/Fault volt-free contact normally open (NO)
11 - Bypass/Fault volt-free contact normally closed (NC)
12 - Mains failure volt-free contact common
13 - Low battery volt-free contact normally open (NO
14 - Low battery volt-free contact normally closed (NC)
15 - Ground - GND

Data Communications Equipment (DCE)
1 - Data Carrier Detect - DCD (out)
2 - Receive Data - RD (out)
3 - Transmit Data - TD (in)
4 - Data Terminal Ready - DTR (out)
5 - Ground - GND
6 - Data Set Ready - DSR (out)
7 - Request To Send - RTS (in)
8 - Clear To Send - CTS (out)
9 - Ring Indicator - RI (out)

Data Terminal Equipment (DTE)
1 - Data Carrier Detect - DCD (in)
2 - Receive Data - RD (in)
3 - Transmit Data - TD (in)
4 - Data Terminal Ready - DTR (out)
5 - Ground - GND
6 - Data Set Ready - DSR (in)
7- Request To Send - RTS (out)
8 - Clear To Send - CTS (in)
9 - Ring Indicator - RI (in)

Diagram 8.2 – Typical D15 and D9 port pin assignments

8.1.1 Audible Alarms

Audible signals are generated from within the UPS or a connected remote status panel and may be coded, using varying lengths to indicate specific alarm conditions. Audible alarm signals will remain 'on' until the alarm condition is removed or acknowledged and silenced.

8.1.2 Visual Alarms

Light Emitting Diodes (LEDs) provide a basic form of alarm notification. LEDs may be single or multi-coloured and indicate the status of the UPS using one of three modes: on, flashing or off. LEDs can be incorporated into a mimic diagram or be used to illuminate specific alarm graphics to provide a quick visual overview of the status of the UPS.

The next level of display is a coloured *Liquid Crystal Display (LCD)* based system with push-button controls. This provides the additional benefits of being able to scroll through key measurements and logs and is, therefore, more informative.

The most sophisticated level of display is a full front-panel graphical type. These typically consist of multiple character back-lit lines that display information in alpha, numeric and symbol formats either as text, alarm codes, representative graphics or a combination of the three. Visual alarm signals remain displayed until the alarm condition is removed.

8.1.3 Basic Remote Alarms

Remote alarm signals from a UPS can be monitored either locally or over a network or remote site connection via the communications ports built into the UPS.

Basic remote alarms such as mains failure or low battery can be used to initiate specific actions within connected applications, such as the proprietary UPS monitoring and control software residing on systems such as the IBM AS/400 and i-Series. This software will monitor the pins of a pre-defined port and respond appropriately when it detects a signal i.e. warning network users that the UPS is running on battery power or instigating an orderly shutdown. There are two ways a UPS can provide basic alarm signals:

a) Opto-Isolators

Opto-isolators are electronic devices that electrically isolate two parts of a circuit but allow a signal (for example +30Vdc/10mA) to pass. They are typically used within UPS below 5kVA and can provide basic 'true/not true' information through specific (D9, D15, D25) port pins including:

• on battery due to a mains power supply failure
• low battery threshold reached
• UPS failure/bypass

b) Volt-Free Contacts

It is more common for larger UPS to provide *Volt-Free Contact (VFC)* signals - also referred to as *dry-contacts*. These provide a similar function to opto-isolators but with a changeover contact and can be rated up to 250Vac/4A. They are typically used to provide information to a remote status or BMS panel or any other compatible proprietary centralised monitoring system. VFCs will provide basic alarm signals through specific (D9, D15, D25) port pins or a terminal strip including:

• on battery due to a mains power supply failure
• low battery threshold reached
• UPS failure/bypass

Some UPS manufacturers provide either a slot-in or external accessory to convert opto-isolator into VFC signals.

A further useful accessory can be a set of user programmable VFCs. This could be an external device that connects to a UPS communications port with up to eight programmable (analog or digital) inputs and eight relay outputs. The device can also be customised to suit the site and UPS monitoring requirements, and monitor general access, humidity and ambient temperature, in addition to various UPS operating modes.

8.2 Remote Communication and Control

8.2.1 Remote Communication

Remote communication can utilise one of several protocols to provide data-exchange between an application and its UPS:

- serial connections including RS-232
- Simple Network Management Protocol (SNMP)
- MODBUS/JBUS
- Profibus

a) Serial Communication

RS-232 and USB ports use specific pins (normally two, three, five or seven on a D-sub connector or two, three and four on a USB). In this type of communication the UPS provides data at a transmission speed (baud-rate) to another serial connection when it is polled to do so. For example, from a connected laptop, file server or remote application. For long distances, the baud-rate is normally reduced to allow for cable impedance and voltage drop: 9600 baud 50m; 4800 baud 100m; 2400 baud 200m and 1200 baud 300m.

As there is no generic standard for UPS serial communications, each UPS manufacturer will provide their own bespoke string of data. Their UPS monitoring and control software package will reside on a connected computer system and process the data for display in graphs, mimic diagrams and measurements. Typical information provided will include:

- mains power supply voltage, frequency and current
- UPS output voltage, frequency, current,
- load kVA and kW
- automatic bypass voltage and frequency
- battery set voltage, charge capacity and runtime
- alarm and system status

Some data may be stored for historical analysis or exported to software packages such as Microsoft Excel for further extrapolation.

Most UPS tend to have at least one D-sub or USB port through which to provide serial communication. Further D-sub and USB ports can be provided through additional slot-in cards or external accessories and duplexers. The USB ports should be compatible with USB 1 or 2.

b) Simple Network Management Protocol (SNMP)

SNMP is a standardised communication system used on Local and Wide Area Networks (LANs/WANs) to monitor and control hardware systems connected to it via *Transmission Control Protocol/Internet Protocol (TCP/IP)* connections.

SNMP uses hardware specific *Management Information Bases (MIBs)* to collect information from polled IP connections. These can be viewed on a *Network Management Station (NMS)* running specific monitoring and control software. This is typically a high-performance work station with a fast CPU and extensive hard disk capacity running HP OpenView, Novell Managewise or IBM NetView. For UPS, the defined MIB is RFC 1628.

A UPS will not provide SNMP communication as standard. In order to turn the UPS into a network-ready peripheral, the connection of a network adapter (hardware agent) is required. This may be in the form of a slot-in card or external accessory. External accessories will require connection to one of the D-sub or USB ports of the UPS, and a source of uninterruptible power (as they are also *ac* powered). Connection can then be made to a network port through a TCP/IP address.

SNMP adapters are configured using a communications method, for example, TELNET or a serial terminal. Care should be taken when selecting the IP address for the UPS to avoid potential conflict with other network peripherals and compliance to both the current and new IP standard (IPv6).

SNMP accessories are also available to simply monitor signal contacts. These can be used to capture general operating status and alarm notifications from several different manufacturers whose kit cannot provide serial SNMP data to the required MIB standard.

c) MODBUS/JBUS

MODBUS and JBUS are communications protocols that create a hierarchical structure (one master and several slaves) from a single RS-232 or RS-485 communication link. MODBUS is an openly published protocol used specifically within industrial environments. JBUS is a variation of MODBUS.

In a UPS installation, the protocols are used to monitor the status of the UPS, report alarm signals and allow integration into, for example, a BMS panel.

A UPS manufacturer should be able to provide a MODBUS/JBUS converter as an accessory. As an external attachment, the converter will require connection to one of the D-sub ports of the UPS.

d) Profibus

Profibus is the most popular type of field bus and is typically used within control and automation. To integrate a UPS into a Profibus Dp network requires a gateway accessory. A UPS manufacturer should be able to provide this and as an external attachment the accessory will require connection to one of the D-sub ports of the UPS.

As discussed above, most external monitoring accessories will require a source of uninterruptible power to ensure operation during a mains power supply failure. The provision of easy to access, plug-in sockets, should therefore be considered as part of the overall installation at the design and planning stage.

8.2.2 Remote Control

Once communication is established using serial RS-232 or SNMP it becomes possible to not just receive information from the UPS but also customise UPS set points, interrogate alarm and history logs and initiate self-diagnostic routines. These activities take place within UPS monitoring and control software packages.

Set points allow the UPS to be customised for site operating conditions and are generally arranged at pre-set security levels: factory, service engineer and user. They can only be changed using the relevant software package from the UPS manufacturer. Typical set points include:

- operating mode
- output voltage and frequency
- battery capacity and low alarm threshold
- automatic restart on mains return
- bypass voltage threshold

8.3 UPS Software Packages

Most UPS manufacturers will provide a range of UPS monitoring and control packages. These will range from simple programs to be used for installation and service, to full network packages that are capable of cross-platform communication and external management over the internet or other gateway. Some leading manufacturers also offer service monitoring packages to supplement processes for emergency call-outs on a 24/7 basis together with remote site monitoring.

8.3.1 UPS Installation Software

Most UPS have set points for on-site customisation. These can be accessed through basic UPS installation software, which is supplied with the UPS and designed to run on laptops, PCs and PDAs. In addition, this software may provide local communication and the ability to interrogate alarm and history logs, display information (bar graphs and measurements) and initiate test routines. The software is generally supplied on a CD-ROM or from a UPS manufacturer's website.

8.3.2 UPS Monitoring and Control Software

UPS monitoring and control software is a more sophisticated package that can provide:

- display of UPS operating information, alarm and history logs and set points
- graphical display of UPS operating conditions
- sequential and priority-based computer and file server shutdown
- event scheduling for timed system boot up and power down
- alarm message management including email, faxes and SMS
- monitoring via a WAP server on a hand-held terminal or internet browser

All UPS manufacturers provide UPS monitoring and control software on a CD-ROM or via a website download. It can be used to monitor a single or multiple UPS on a number of (mixed) platforms:

- Windows 95-OSR2, 98, ME, NT 4.0, 2000, XP, 2003
- Linux
- Novell Netware 3.x, 4.x, 5.x, 6
- Mac OS X, 9.x
- IBM OS/2 Warp and Server
- HP OPEN VMS
- The most widely used UNIX operating systems such as: IBM AIX, HP UNIX, SUN Solaris INTEL and SPARC, SCO Unix and UnixWare, Silicon Graphic IRIX, Compaq TRU64 UNIX and DEC UNIX, BSD UNIX and FreeBSD UNIX, and NCR UNIX

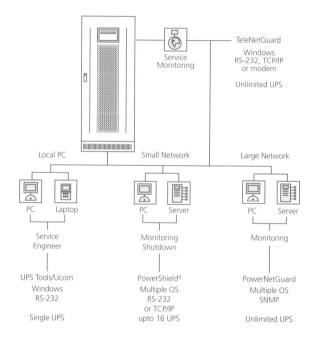

Diagram 8.3 – Typical UPS monitoring software packages

Some network versions such as those for UNIX may require additional licenses from the UPS manufacturer for the software to run. Whilst such software packages run on LANs, and across different platforms, more sophisticated versions are available for data centres and in particular wide area networks. These provide the added advantage that the software can display UPS over geographic areas, building plans and maps, and use SNMP for monitoring and control.

a) Architecture

UPS manufacturers vary in their approach to monitoring and control across a network environment. There are two common approaches:

- **Centralised:** where a specified server is used to control the orderly shutdown of the mixed platform network.

- **Decentralised:** where each individual server or PC runs its own copy of the monitoring software, and controls its own shutdown procedure.

Aside from general software management issues, the *centralised* approach can seem the least complicated and expensive to install. However, this is not the case and such an approach introduces a single-point-of-failure. If the control server hangs and fails to shut down, this can disrupt the rest of the routine, leading potentially to data loss and a system-wide crash. This is not the case in a *decentralised* installation. Here, if one server or PC fails to shut down, the failure is isolated. This approach, therefore, achieves a higher level of overall system resilience. In addition, priority-based load shedding and shutdown is also simpler to achieve with this configuration.

b) Priority-Based Load Shedding and Shutdown

This is a process whereby the load on a UPS is reduced by sequentially powering down specific hardware when the UPS is running on battery power. This reduces the load on the UPS and increases the available runtime for the remaining loads.

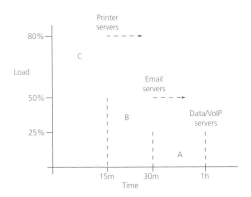

Diagram 8.4 – Typical priority-based shutdown sequence

The loads on a network are prioritised into an A, B and C order in which 'A' type loads must be kept running for the longest time and 'C' type loads the shortest. Priority-based shutdown can be achieved in three ways: programmable output sockets available on some UPS; intelligent power distribution units; or by using UPS monitoring and control shutdown software with each server configured to run for different time periods before shutdown. Load shedding is most common where there are multiple servers or server clusters to protect.

c) Planning

Planning starts by grouping the critical loads by priority, as already discussed. This allows an assessment of those that must be kept running for the longest time on mains power supply failure. Each of the loads can be sized (in VA and Watts) and a battery set sized to achieve a specific runtime.

An important aspect to consider here is how long the shutdown sequences should last and what extra time might be required for manual intervention if a script hangs and shutdown is not achieved. It is best practice to double this time period as most mains power supply failures take place within a few minutes or hours of each other and there may be little enough time to effect a reasonable battery recharge level.

d) Testing

As with any part of the *Power Continuity Plan,* it is important to test the shutdown scripts to ensure that all the systems are safely powered down. This should be done during a controlled rather than a simulated mains power supply failure.

8.3.3 Remote Service Management Software

UPS manufacturers now integrate remote service management within their maintenance plans to provide 24/7 power protection. The UPS are installed with a dedicated modem or connected to the local area network modem. A *Fixed Cellular Terminal (FCT)* is a low cost fixed mobile phone connection which may be used in place of a standard telephone or extension. This can be useful, for example, in remote areas.

Through the modem, the UPS can dial up a specific service centre, report its alarm and initiate a service response script. This can include, for example, automatically dispatching a service engineer to the site, issuing SMS and emails to the relevant personnel or simply requesting a call back facility. Alarms are typically prioritised and where this is the case, each alarm can initiate its own script.

The service centre can also use the connection to:

- poll the UPS they monitor at regular intervals; daily, weekly or monthly to ensure that there is a valid connection and no alarms
- periodically record operating information and interrogate alarm and history logs

An important note is that the dedicated modem (or *FCT*) will require its own source of uninterruptible power as it too is an *ac* powered device.

A UPS service organisation should also be able to remotely monitor third-party UPS in this way using a bespoke monitoring system utilising VFC signals as discussed earlier in this chapter.

8.4 Remote Shutdown

8.4.1 Emergency Power Off (EPO)

Emergency Power Off (EPO) is also known as *Emergency Shutdown (ESD)*, or *Remote Shutdown (RSD)*. EPO may be required in emergencies, for example, the evacuation of a building, to shut down all the systems working within a specific area, including UPS and generators. The process may be controlled from a central EPO push-button, fire alarm panel or BMS and ensures that there is no risk of electrical shock when sprinklers or fire hoses are used to douse a fire within the room. When EPO is initiated, it is common for the systems to require a manual restart. For EPO, the most common approach is to provide contacts on a UPS D-sub or specific EPO port. The EPO circuit is normally closed. When activated the EPO circuit will cause the UPS to shut down immediately, disconnecting power to the loads.

8.5 Monitoring Other Hardware

Within a UPS installation it can be necessary to monitor additional devices and environmental factors to guarantee resilience of the *Power Continuity Plan*.

8.5.1 Maintenance Bypass

Where a UPS has a built-in maintenance bypass, its state can be monitored either through a VFC on the D-sub port or the relevant UPS monitoring and control package. Some external wrap-around bypass panels may also have a built-in communications port (D-sub type) with the capability to provide VFC signals which can be used to monitor its state of operation.

8.5.2 Generator

Most generator manufacturers provide their own AMF panel monitoring packages, which may provide both RS-232 communications and VFC signals.

8.5.3 Environmental

The external environment that a UPS is placed within can dramatically affect its performance, especially the ambient temperature. An environmental monitoring device (UPS powered) can be installed, which has sensors to monitor air-conditioning and fans. It also has motion sensors, for example, with output relays that can be configured for local alarm conditions.

8.5.4 Battery Set

A UPS will test its battery set on a regular basis and report any alarm conditions. Individual third-party battery set monitoring systems can also be installed to supplement this. Such systems can be monitored remotely using VFCs, RS-232 and SNMP with the appropriate hardware and software at local, network or remote levels.

8.6 Summary

Planning how to monitor UPS systems and their associated hardware for alarm signals, and designing appropriate alarm responses is an important aspect of any *Power Continuity Plan*. A range of options is available for this and each one requires careful consideration and attention, especially for larger installations where the UPS may also be operating in parallel configurations.

Attention needs to be given to the cabling and power requirements for remote monitoring and these aspects are now considered in *chapter 9*, together with information for the overall installation.

9. Projects, Logistics and Installation

In this chapter:

- The role of the site survey at the design stage of a Power Continuity Plan.
- Examining the factors that influence where a UPS should be installed.
- Planning the electrical installation including protection and discrimination.
- Final installation, testing and certification.

Introduction

Once a power protection solution has been selected, time needs to be spent planning logistics and any electrical work on site.

Whatever the size of UPS installation, loads will need to be powered down for as long as it takes to reconnect them to the output supply of the newly commissioned UPS. This downtime period will vary with the complexity of the project and type, size and number of loads.

The larger the installation, the more complex the project management required and many *turn-key* systems are installed under the guidance of a dedicated project manager. This person has to be a specialist engineer who can liaise with a number of functions and disciplines, such as a reseller or client, third-party suppliers including mechanical and electrical contractors and logistics companies, consultants, specifiers and potentially public service and local government bodies.

A key difference can exist between UPS suppliers in terms of how they organise their project management function. Some maintain separate sales and project management teams, whilst others integrate them into a job function similar to that of a Technical Energy Consultant (TEC). This is the preferred approach because it gives clients a single-point-of-contact with a multi-disciplined and engineering-oriented person, which shortens communication paths and leads to a more efficient process.

Most UPS suppliers should be able to provide a project manager who can co-ordinate a full on-site installation or work alongside appointed contractors and consultants. Their sole objective is to achieve a first-time installation which is both compliant to the relevant regulations and capable of delivering the intended levels of resilience and power protection. Whilst much of this function can be provided remotely via technical support hot lines and intranets, at some stage a formal site survey is necessary.

9.1 Site Surveys

The complexity of a *Power Continuity Plan* can vary between sites. UPS suppliers generally review a new installation using a set of fairly standard questions, to identify site specific actions and sometimes areas for further investigation. These are usually listed in a formal document known as a Site Survey, *(appendix D)*.

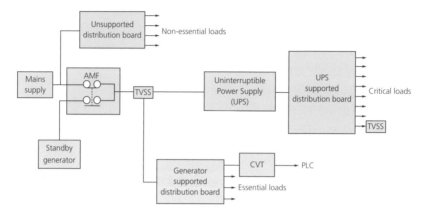

Diagram 9.1 – A typical Power Continuity Plan schematic

A site survey is typically a non-chargeable service provided by a UPS supplier and may require more than one visit to complete, especially where building and electrical contracting works are in progress. Specifically the survey is concerned with:

- **Logistics:** the route the UPS delivery will take including restrictions and obstacles both inside and outside of the building.

- **Environment and Location:** the final installation point for the UPS and its associated system parts including factors that could affect its performance and operation.

- **Electrical Installation:** both upstream to the system and downstream load connections in terms of suitability, protection and discrimination and compliance to the relevant regulations.

9.2 Logistics

By logistics we mean not just delivery of the UPS and associated kit but its positioning, unpacking and the suitability of the final location. UPS suppliers will tend to offer two types of delivery services:

- Kerbside delivery
- Delivery, siting and positioning

Kerbside delivery is (as the name suggests) delivery to a drop off or central point within a site. Once delivered, it is up to the site or commissioning engineer to move the UPS to its final position. This service is generally offered for small UPS (up to 40kg) where the weights involved can be moved safely by one or two people working to a method statement, and/or where the company has its own off-loading facilities such as a forklift.

Delivery, siting and positioning is the more specialised service, where the delivery company uses vehicles with tail-lifts and carries equipment, such as trolleys and stair climbers. Larger UPS systems including battery packs (pre-assembled or in kit form) will be supplied on pallets and require an on-site forklift, normally provided by the client or carrier.

It should be stressed that weight is never an indication of robustness. A UPS is not designed for portability and is sensitive to drops, shock and vibration. Whilst every care is taken to reduce the impact of rough handling, UPS should be treated as sensitive electronic devices, even if the unit in question is an 800kVA module weighing several hundred tonnes. Metalwork panels can all too easily be scratched or bent, a chassis twisted or a PCB become dislodged from mounting pillars when a UPS is poorly handled.

The choice between the two services is dependent to a degree upon the physical size and weight of the systems being delivered, how they are packed (on pallets or not), site off-loading facilities, final location and route.

The project manager will need to walk the entire route, from the off-loading point to the final location. Most sites now have formal booking-in procedures with visitors having to wear ID. On some sites, for example, petrochemical and refinery, health & safety videos may also form part of an induction process. Both aspects should be noted for any project related contractors and service engineers who may have to attend the site.

Along the route, attention needs to be given to obstacles that could prevent access such as low bridges, restricted access, road works and legal parking. For large UPS systems and generators, assistance from local authorities may be required in the form of permits and police attendance. This is especially true for wide loads or if traffic flow has to be policed.

Newbuild sites can generally provide easy access to a dedicated ground floor location. This is not always the case, especially for older buildings. Large sites typically have loading bays with local forklift capabilities. If not, this facility may have to be hired.

Where the final location is not ground floor, but underground or a rooftop, provision will have to be made for steps (up or down), their construction (concrete, metal or wood - spiral, width, turns) and loading. A building lift itself has a maximum floor loading (and weight limit) and may be designed for aesthetic appearance rather than bulk goods handling. There is the risk of superficial damage when used to carry materials such as batteries, cabinets and UPS, even if on pallets.

Where access is not straight-forward a crane may be needed to place a UPS or generator on a rooftop or in an underground location, possibly through a removed window frame or entry hatch. There may even be the need for temporary scaffolding over local obstacles. Other obstructions are also common, such as corners, doorways, steps and so forth. Door widths and heights have to be measured and door frames may have to be removed (sometimes with the surrounding brickwork). Within remote parts of a building, doors may require key or code access. Special fire doors may also have access control mechanisms.

Nothing should ever be assumed. Wherever possible the site survey should be completed with a representative of the site as local knowledge is always important. They should be asked to sign the form on completion and be provided with a copy for their files.

9.3 Location and Environment

Recommendations for final location vary with the type of UPS supplied. Small transformerless UPS up to 10kVA may be installed within an office environment. Systems from 15kVA tend to be installed within a computer room and larger UPS (especially transformer-based) within a plant or switchgear room.

9.3.1 Physical Space

UPS have internal fans for cooling and air may be drawn front-to-back or bottom-to-top. This will mean leaving at least 100-400mm for air flow and heat dissipation around the openings. The more space the better. The UPS will obviously take up floor space and provision has to be made for easy access for maintenance and inspection, and the connection or removal of loads and monitoring cables.

Physical space must also be available for general assembly on site and potentially, future expansion. For example, where a battery set is to be built on site a safe working area will be required. Even if delivered pre-configured inside a cabinet, future battery replacement will normally be completed in situ. Most UPS from 10kVA are capable of expansion using the paralleling techniques discussed in *chapter 5*, and provision should be left for future capacity and battery runtime expansion.

Suitable space and easy access is also an issue for long discharge tests which can run to twelve hours or more. Here an on-site engineer will be expected to set-up measurement equipment and gain access to various parts of the UPS and its batteries from which to take down measurements and record them.

9.3.2 Floor Loading

Some computer rooms tend to use false floors and the UPS and battery cabinets may require extendible false legs, placement on *Raised Floor Pedestals (RFPs)* or a spreader plate to even out the weight distribution. The same can apply when a rooftop or upper floor location is considered with the added issue of weather-proof enclosures and generator acoustic hoods if required. Generators and flywheels also require flat concrete bases to which they can be secured.

9.3.3 Remote and Split Locations

UPS generate a range of alarm conditions indicating an immediate or potential failure if the problem is not addressed. As already discussed in the previous chapter, consideration has to be given as to how these will be monitored and what action will be taken.

Where there is physically not enough room within a designated area, the battery cabinet or stand may be placed in a separate room. This gives rise to the need for extra cables, monitoring and access, as does installing switchgear in another part of the building.

More often, when installed with a generator, the two systems will be split, with the generator housed externally, thus increasing the complexity for alarm monitoring and system management.

9.3.4 Ambient Temperature

As discussed in *chapter 6*, heat kills batteries. Whilst most UPS can operate from 0-40°C without performance degradation, the optimal ambient for a battery is 20-25°C. The larger the UPS, the greater its heat output (Watts, kCal or *British Thermal Units - BTU)* and so the need to assess this impact on ventilation, air exchange and local air-conditioning (if present).

9.3.5 Dust and Humidity

Dust free and low humidity environments are recommended. Dust will be drawn into the UPS, as will any moisture or corrosive chemicals in the air. The potential damage from these can be reduced if fan filters are fitted. If filters are used, they must be placed on a preventative maintenance schedule.

Humidity can also affect performance. Most UPS can operate in environments up to 95% relative humidity. The higher the humidity, the more the chance of corrosion and potential problems from moisture ingress. This can be reduced by using on-site dehumidifiers and/or a 'tropicalised' UPS design.

9.3.6 Piping, Flooding Levels and Sprinklers

UPS should never be placed close to piping, including heating, air-conditioning or fluid carrying drip trays or exhaust gas runs. Fluid carrying pipes can crack leading to droplets that can run into the top or side ventilation slots of a UPS. Siting near sprinkler locations which can be accidentally activated should also be avoided.

Basements and ground floor locations can flood, especially in water treatment works. If this is known to be a potential or actual problem, provision should be made for a plinth and pumping to ensure the UPS remains dry at all times.

Care also has to be taken when a UPS is installed near ventilation slots to ensure there is no risk of ingress from air borne chemicals or salt spray (at a marine site, for example).

9.3.7 Noise Levels

The noise output and frequency of the UPS has to be considered for those working nearby. Noise pressure levels are measured in decibels (dB) and are affected by their frequencies. The human ear is more sensitive to frequencies between one to four kHz. dBA is a more accurate measure as suitable meters use an 'A' class filter to make them mimic human ear sensitivity.

Transformerless UPS use high-frequency switching techniques (around 20kHz) outside the human audible range. Any noise experienced is generally that of cooling fans and the larger the UPS the more powerful the fans. Overall, typical noise levels will, therefore, be around 40-50dBA. Industrial UPS tend to be transformer-based with higher noise levels (up to 80dBA or more). The acoustics of the room can also add to noise pollution problems and any generated resonance.

Generators require further noise level considerations. When powered up they can emit higher noise levels (even when fitted with an acoustic hood).

9.3.8 Lighting Levels

There should be sufficient light around the system for safe working. Often this is not the case when the UPS is placed within a plant room corner and additional lighting may be required.

9.3.9 Health & Safety, and Environmental Standards

The *ISO 9001 Quality Management System* standard is a given within business these days. However, UPS suppliers should also be working to audited health & safety (*OHSAS 18001* or *SAFEcontractor*) and environmental (*ISO 14001*) management systems. They should be able to provide *Risk Assessments* and *Method Statements* for the services to be provided on site. These will include provision for the use of *Personal Protective Equipment (PPE)* and issues such as 'lone worker' arrangements. The latter are particularly important where there is live working (inside or outside working-hours) and the potential for electric shock in remote and/or unmanned locations. If there is an unusual on-site hazard, specific assessments should be generated and made available on request.

From a practical viewpoint, a UPS should be placed where it is not in the pathway of everyday traffic. This removes the problem of trip hazards from associated cabling, and accidental button pressing (if someone stumbles or curiosity gets the better of them).

Rackmount systems provide further issues. There is generally no limit to where a UPS can be placed within a rack cabinet but consideration should be given to safe manual handling, access for maintenance and its effect on the overall centre of gravity of the entire system. For example, a 47U high rack cabinet will require a service engineer to use a small step ladder to get access to its top sections. A UPS on slide out trays near the top of such a cabinet could topple it especially if the areas below are empty.

9.3.10 Permits To Work

Permits, especially relating to site specific health & safety issues may also be required. This is common for work on sensitive military sites, industrial chemical plants and rail infrastructure. Attendance on training courses and security checks (including police) may be required before some permits can be issued, such as for prison work.

9.3.11 Existing Kit and Battery - Removal and Disposal

This can be particularly important where an existing system must be removed prior to the installation of the new one. As discussed in *chapter 6*, batteries are classed as toxic waste requiring licensed removal and disposal.

UPS are not themselves currently covered by the *WEEE* and *Restriction of Hazardous Substances* (*RoHS*) directives. However, most UPS manufacturers are now producing RoHS compliant products and will offer licensed environmentally-friendly disposal of UPS, batteries and standby power systems removed from sites.

9.3.12 Storage and Acclimatisation

It is good practice to allow a UPS to acclimatise to its site prior to switch-on. Usually this takes a short time and can prevent infant mortality. For example, where a UPS has been stored in a low ambient temperature, condensation can arise inside when it is immediately powered up or moved into a room with a higher ambient. Small UPS, like most computer and telecoms products, tend to be packed with hygroscopic crystal bags (to absorb moisture) but this is not practical with larger systems.

9.3.13 Cable Runs, Distribution and Switchgear

A further assessment needs to be given to cable run types and lengths covering:

- supply to UPS system and UPS to load
- switchgear and bypass arrangements
- UPS to battery pack, flywheel or fuel cell
- UPS to generator or alternative energy source
- parallel interface cable runs
- alarm monitoring: remote alarm panel and network access point location

9.3.14 Transient Protection

Where a site is known to suffer from local lightning, it may be appropriate to consider installation of a TVSS. The device will also protect the UPS and the load when it is in bypass from any locally generated transients and spikes. This is not to say the UPS is not capable of protecting itself but the size of a lightning induced transient can be sufficiently large to damage a rectifier or weaken its own built-in protection.

TVSS are normally installed in a 'Zoned' approach which relies on the magnitude of a transient voltage degrading as it passes through a building from main incomer to individual office devices.

- **Zone C:** main and sub-distribution - sized up to 100kA/20kV

- **Zone B:** sub and final distribution - sized up to 10kA/6kV

- **Zone A:** individual devices - sized up to 6kA/400V

TVSS are passive units which lie in parallel with the device to be protected and its mains power supply. They have to react very quickly to a transient surge voltage and divert the energy away from the load. When installed before a UPS system, it is important to also consider any external bypassing routes.

TVSS can also be used to protect communications and signal routes. They can be used to protect communications ports in a UPS, for example, when connected to a local telephone line for remote monitoring as this could provide a transient path for an external lightning strike. Within a building it is always recommended that UPS and their cable runs are separated and placed away from walls to which external lightning rods are attached, to prevent cross-over.

9.3.15 Electro-Magnetic Compatibility (EMC)

Electro-magnetic waves are abundant and vary in their intensity from low to high frequency. They range from background noise from the birth of the universe to the pulses associated with large explosions that can disable electronic equipment. All electronic devices emit electro-magnetic interference and UPS have to comply with a specific standard namely: EN/IEC 62040-2 in order to carry a CE mark.

Some clients, especially in transportation where radio telecommunications are extensively used, may also require additional testing of the UPS, prior to issuing their own approval documentation. Their concern is that UPS themselves use sensitive digital control circuitry which if not well shielded could be disrupted by the electro-magnetic waves emitted by other systems within their field of operation. In addition, cabling runs have to be constructed in such a way as to avoid induction and acting as large aerial receivers for EMC. For example, power and data cable runs should be separated and the cables screened and insulated.

9.3.16 Containerisation

Where installation inside a building is not possible, a UPS system together with its distribution and switchgear can be installed as a containerised system. This is commonly used in remote locations such as oil fields, alongside rail infrastructures, on roof tops or simply where the supply is temporary.

9.4 Electrical Installation

The electrical supplies within a *Power Continuity Plan*, must integrate with those already on site and not interfere with other equipment. Within any building, the electrical distribution system will comprise of an *ac* mains power supply powering a main *High Voltage (HV)* or *Low Voltage (LV)* distribution board within which are conductors feeding load circuits. A large installation may also include further sub-distribution boards. A UPS and generator can be installed anywhere within this system.

The site survey discussed previously will normally identify the scope for any electrical work to be undertaken which must be carried out by certified and registered electrical engineers in accordance with local, national and organisation-specific guidelines. In the UK, the applicable standards are *The Institution of Engineering and Technology (IET) - BS 7671 IEE Wiring Regulations Sixteenth Edition* and *Electricity at Work Regulations 1989*. Further, organisation-specific guidelines may apply on petrochemical or underground transportation sites where there are certain health & safety or electrical considerations.

The complexity of the electrical work required will depend of course on the size of power protection system being installed and its overall design. For plug-in UPS, there may simply be the need for a review of the local electrical distribution system and in particular the protective devices installed, for example, fuses, circuit-breakers and *Residual Current Devices (RCDs)*. For a hardwired UPS, on-site electrical work could include:

- installation of the required cables; from the *ac* supply source to the UPS input; from the UPS output to a distribution system and between the UPS and battery set, generator and any other alternative power sources
- installation of local sockets or fused spurs
- upgrading supply ratings, cables and distribution boards
- installing electrical switchgear panels and maintenance bypasses
- running alarm cables to remote panels or network connection points

In addition, whether the installation is low or higher power rated, it is mandatory that live conductors must be protected from overloads, short-circuits and earth faults. If these occur, they can result in more current being drawn than the conductors are rated for, leading to a dramatic rise in temperature, premature failure and potentially, fire risk.

9.4.1 Harmonics

In the EU, the electricity supply industry is required to meet *EN 50160 - Voltage Characteristics of Electricity Supplied by Public Distribution Systems* and this includes the magnitude of harmonic voltage distortion. In the UK, permissible network supply harmonic levels are also specified in *G5/4-1*, to which consumers must comply for any new building 400V-400kVac three-phase installations. G5/4-1 identifies consumers (domestic, commercial and industrial) by their connection (PCC) to the *Public Electricity Supply (PES)*.

In terms of G5/4-1, the PCC and harmonic limits vary depending on whether the supply is high, medium or low voltage and where the connection is made relative to the site:

- **Consumer terminals:** where a short length of feeder cable is connected to a distributor.

- **Substation low voltage busbars:** from where the consumer has a dedicated supply.

- **High voltage intake terminals:** where the consumer is supplied a high voltage and owns high voltage switchgear, one or more transformers and high and low voltage distribution systems. A high voltage network is likely to have low impedance. Here the electricity supplier will generally allow a large harmonic content load to be connected, much larger than if the PCC was on the low voltage side of the distribution network where the effect is far greater, in part due to the higher associated impedance.

The three stage assessment process applied within the guideline includes:

- **Stage 1:** applies only to 230Vac single-phase and 400Vac three-phase supplies, and therefore, the majority of installations. It covers equipment not exceeding 16A per phase complying with EN/IEC 61000-3-2 and 6-pulse or 12-pulse rectifiers not exceeding 12 and 50kVA respectively. Harmonic current emissions (up to the order 50) from aggregate loads are required to be within specified limits.

- **Stage 2:** applies where the levels of harmonics exceed those for *stage 1* and the PCC is at 6.6 to 22kV i.e. below 33kV. It applies to 400Vac systems where a *stage 1* assessment is not appropriate due to the rating of the equipment, the emission levels or the network characteristics. Harmonic current emissions from aggregate loads are required to be within limits. The voltage distortion caused by the new load is assessed and the effect of adding this to the existing distortion is predicted. The distortion needs to be within specified limits.

- **Stage 3:** applies where the levels of harmonics exceed those for *stage 2* and the PCC is at 33kV or over.

Within *stage 1,* any CE marked equipment with a nominal current draw of 16A or less, for example, a plug-in UPS can be connected without further assessment. Where a number of CE marked items are installed, the aggregate value must not exceed 16A without further assessment.

The process becomes more stringent when examining the connection of new loads to three-phase 400V-400kVac supplies and is therefore applicable to UPS. For example, G5/4-1 sets thresholds for the assessment of 6-pulse and 12-pulse rectifiers at 12kVA and 50kVA respectively and identifies the maximum harmonic current levels allowed for each harmonic order, *table 9.1.*

Harmonic order, h	Emission current, Ih	Harmonic order, h	Emission current, Ih	Harmonic order, h	Emission current, Ih	Harmonic order, h	Emission current, Ih
2	28.9	15	1.4	28	1.0	41	1.8
3	48.1	16	1.8	29	3.1	42	0.3
4	9.0	17	13.6	30	0.5	43	1.6
5	28.9	18	0.8	31	2.8	44	0.7
6	3.0	19	9.1	32	0.9	45	0.3
7	41.2	20	1.4	33	0.4	46	0.6
8	7.2	21	0.7	34	0.8	47	1.4
9	9.6	22	1.3	35	2.3	48	0.3
10	5.8	23	7.5	36	0.4	49	1.3
11	39.4	24	0.6	37	2.1	50	0.6
12	1.2	25	4.0	38	0.8		
13	27.8	26	1.1	39	0.4		
14	2.1	27	0.5	40	0.7		

Table 9.1 – Stage 1 Maximum Permissible Harmonic Current Emissions in Amperes RMS for Aggregate Loads and Equipment Rated >16A per phase, from Engineering Recommendation G5/4-1. These limits are based on a typical fault level of 10 MVA.

The assessment process is complex and a suitably qualified engineer should be consulted if required. Where new installations cannot achieve the permitted planning levels outlined in G5/4-1, the local electricity supplier must be consulted and permission obtained before connection.

9.4.2 Protection and Discrimination

Discrimination is the co-ordination of protective devices within a supply circuit to ensure, for example, that any load developing a fault condition (overload, short-circuit or earth fault) is quickly removed without disruption to those remaining and that its supply conductors are protected.

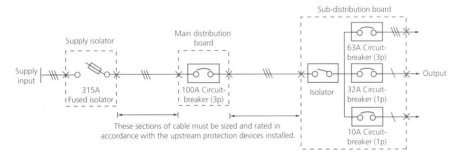

Diagram 9.2 – Shows a simple supply to load discrimination path

Diagram 9.2 shows a simple distribution system, with each of the sections individually protected to ensure discrimination should a fault condition occur within the system.

In a *Power Continuity Plan*, it is vital that a suitable discrimination path is made available for the UPS to protect both it and the critical loads being powered. A UPS installation manual will typically provide information required for protective device selection and rating. The most commonly employed means of discrimination include those shown in *table 9.2*.

Problem	Solution
Overload	Fuse, Circuit-Breaker or Residual Current Device/Circuit-Breaker (RCBO)
Short-circuit	Fuse, Circuit-Breaker, RCBO
Earth Fault	Fuse, Circuit-Breaker, RCD or RCBO

Table 9.2 – Conductor protection methods

The protective devices chosen must be correct for the application, and suitably rated. Fuses and circuit-breakers, for example, have different operating characteristics (namely speed of response) and will therefore react differently when required to disconnect the *ac* supply under fault conditions. Whichever method is used, it is important to note that any failed protective device is replaced on a like-for-like basis to maintain electrical discrimination.

Two time-current curves within *BS 7671 IEE Wiring Regulations Sixteenth Edition - fig 3.4* and *fig 3.6* - show how the typical disconnection characteristics of two circuit-breakers, *type B* and *type D*, differ and in particular their time versus current responses.

For example, a 20A *type B* circuit-breaker requires a current of 100A to disconnect within 0.1-5 seconds. Whereas an identically rated *type D* device will require a current of 400A to disconnect within the same timeframe. This difference in overload capability means that care has to be taken when specifying which type to use, especially within a UPS application, to prevent nuisance tripping at power up.

A *type D* circuit-breaker (motor-rated) can sustain higher overloads for longer periods and is recommended for use with loads with high in-rush currents, for example, some UPS, motor, machinery and transformer installations. A *type B* device (general purpose) has a faster response and is therefore more appropriate to switch mode type loads (computers and telecoms hardware) and general electrical circuits where its use can prevent nuisance disconnection. For most UPS installations a *type C* is the preferred choice.

The actual protective devices used within most installations will comprise of a number of fuses, circuit-breakers or RCBOs, connected in series between the *ac* supply and load. To ensure discrimination under fault conditions, devices are specified to work in a co-ordinated manner so that the correct device trips when intended. Selection starts with the site contractor calculating the disconnection time required, based upon the circuit type installed, its impedance and the protective devices available. The circuit impedance must be low enough to ensure that the necessary currents can be generated when a fault condition occurs, if the protective device is to disconnect the circuit. Measurement is typically performed using an *Earth Fault Loop Impedance Tester*.

For UPS installations there are two types of connection method, each of which dictates the installation and testing required when connecting to their mains power supplies and loads:

- **Plug-in (up to 16A input):** can be installed by any competent person removing the need for a certified electrical engineer if the mains power supply sockets are already available.

- **Hardwired (>16A input):** connected to both the local mains power supply and the load by hardwired terminal connection points. Here, it is mandatory that a certified electrical engineer performs the installation and issues a test certificate.

To specify the protective devices to be used upstream of a UPS it is important to understand the requirements of the particular UPS itself in terms of its connection to the mains power and bypass supplies and the maximum possible input currents that can be drawn from them. The three most common UPS connection type options are:

a) UPS Connection Types

Option 1 - Single-phase input to single-phase output (1/1)

During normal operation, the single-phase load applied to the output of the UPS is indirectly passed onto the incoming single-phase supply via the inverter and rectifier. If, for example, a UPS was supplying a load of 15kVA, then typically a load greater than 15kVA would be applied to the incoming mains power supply. The load connected to the mains power supply is greater than that placed on the UPS due to system losses and the power required for battery charging. If the load was transferred to bypass, the applied load of 15kVA would be directly connected to the incoming mains power supply.

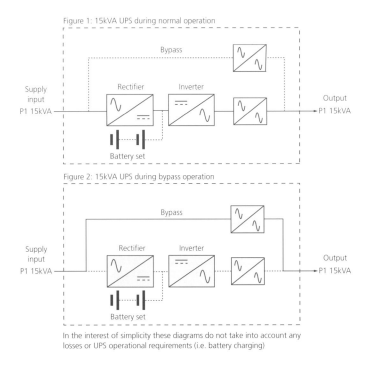

In the interest of simplicity these diagrams do not take into account any losses or UPS operational requirements (i.e. battery charging)

Diagram 9.3 – Single-phase to single-phase UPS connection (1/1)

Option 2 - Three-phase input to single-phase output (3/1)

In this scenario, during normal operation, the single-phase load applied to the output is indirectly passed onto the incoming three-phase supply via the inverter and rectifier. The load is evenly spread across the three incoming phases. If, for example, the UPS was supplying a load of 15kVA then a minimum load of 5kVA would be applied to each of the incoming phases. If the load was transferred to bypass, then the total applied load of 15kVA would be directly connected to the first phase of the incoming three phases.

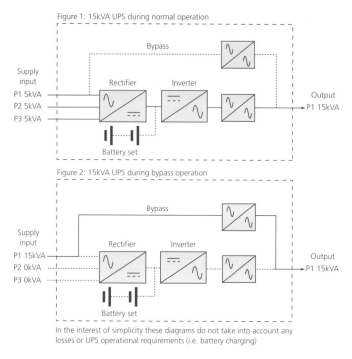

Figure 1: 15kVA UPS during normal operation

Figure 2: 15kVA UPS during bypass operation

In the interest of simplicity these diagrams do not take into account any losses or UPS operational requirements (i.e. battery charging)

Diagram 9.4 – Three-phase to single-phase UPS connection (3/1)

Option 3 - Three-phase input to three-phase output (3/3)

Here, as in option 2 during normal operation, the loads applied to each of the three-phase outputs are indirectly passed onto the incoming three-phase supply via the inverter and rectifier. However, the total load applied is evenly spread across the three incoming phases - even if the output load is unbalanced. Therefore, if the UPS was supplying a total load of 12kVA (2kVA on phase 1 and 5kVA on phases 2 and 3), for example, then a minimum load of 4kVA (12÷3) would be applied to each of the incoming phases.

If the load was transferred to bypass, the 12kVA load would be directly connected to the incoming phases, with 2kVA on phase 1 and 5kVA on phases 2 and 3.

It should be noted that a three-phase output UPS will allow a maximum of one third of the total power available to be applied to each outgoing phase i.e. a 15kVA UPS can only have up to 5kVA load applied per phase.

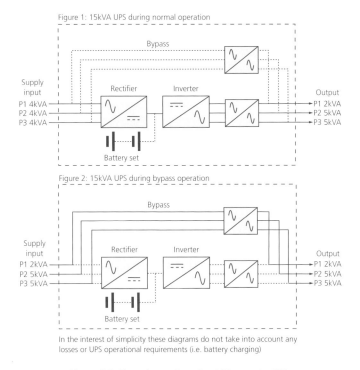

Figure 1: 15kVA UPS during normal operation

Figure 2: 15kVA UPS during bypass operation

In the interest of simplicity these diagrams do not take into account any losses or UPS operational requirements (i.e. battery charging)

Diagram 9.5 – Three-phase to three-phase UPS connection (3/3)

b) Maximum Input Ratings - Rectifier and Bypass

The maximum rectifier input rating defines the maximum input current drawn by a UPS from its mains power supply during a worst case scenario. The value given takes into account battery charging, low mains supply voltage and a 100% loaded UPS output.

The maximum bypass supply input rating defines the maximum input current that can be drawn by the bypass should the UPS need to switch the load to its bypass supply. An incorrectly sized bypass supply can lead to unnecessary nuisance tripping or worst case loss of power to the critical load.

The following two examples demonstrate how to determine protective device ratings for two typical UPS connection types.

Example 1

Here a 10kVA transformerless three-phase input, single-phase output (3/1) UPS is installed. This particular UPS requires a 400Vac three-phase input supply and will provide a 230Vac single-phase output (up to 10kVA@0.8pF). During normal operation the maximum input current drawn by the UPS cannot exceed 18A per phase, *table 9.3*.

However, if the UPS is forced to transfer the load onto its bypass supply the maximum current drawn will increase to 43A. This will be applied to phase 1 of the input supply.

UPS Model	Rating	Connection Format	Rectifier Input (max)	Bypass Rating (max)
MDM 1000	10kVA@0.8pF	3ph (400Vac) in 1ph (230Vac) out	18A	43A

Table 9.3 – Specification table 3/1 UPS

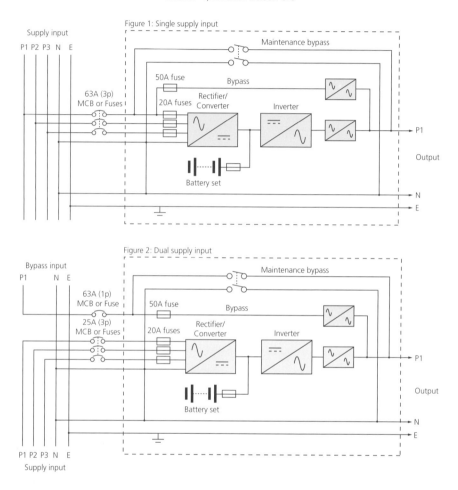

Diagram 9.6 – Typical 3/1 transformerless UPS input connection showing input supply and discrimination

The protective devices must therefore be rated to the same or higher value than the maximum current drawn, which in this case is 43A. The nearest circuit-breaker or fuse size in this instance would be a 63A *type C. Diagram 9.6* shows the input supply and discrimination in both a single input and a dual input system. In *figure 2*, the UPS is a transformerless design and therefore both the rectifier and bypass inputs must share the same neutral. If a completely separate dual input option is required, an additional isolation transformer must be installed.

Example 2

Here, a 30kVA transformerless three-phase input, three-phase output (3/3) UPS is installed. This UPS requires a 400Vac, three-phase input supply and will provide a 400Vac three-phase output (up to 30kVA@0.8pF 10kVA/phase). During normal operation, the maximum input current drawn by the UPS cannot exceed 50A per phase, *table 9.4*.

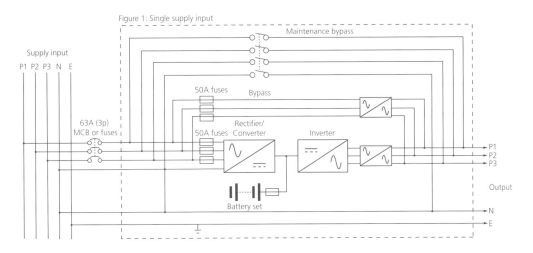

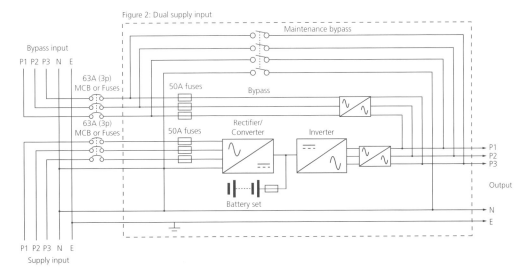

Diagram 9.7 – Typical 3/3 transformerless UPS input connection showing input supply and discrimination

It should be noted that the UPS in *figure 2* is a transformerless type and an additional isolation transformer is required if separation of the rectifier and bypass supplies is desirable.

UPS Model	Rating	Connection Format	Rectifier Input (max)	Bypass Rating (max)
MDT 3000	30kVA@0.8pf	3ph (400Vac) in 3ph (400Vac) out	50A	43A

Table 9.4 – Specification table 3/3 UPS

If the UPS is forced to transfer the load onto its bypass supply, the maximum current will be lower than this (43A). The protective devices must, therefore, be rated to the same or higher value than the maximum current drawn, which in this case is 50A. The nearest circuit-breaker or fuse size in this instance would be a 63A *type C*. The examples demonstrate why matching protective devices to a UPS and its *ac* supply ratings is important. They show that a 30kVA 3/3 transformerless UPS can require similarly rated protective devices to a 10kVA 3/1 transformerless UPS, purely because the second has a single-phase output.

9.4.3 Residual Current Device (RCD)

An RCD monitors energy diverted to the earth from an electrical supply. This can happen, for example, when someone touches a live conductor and receives an electric shock. Under such a condition, the RCD will trip and power is disconnected from the circuit. When any UPS is installed without an isolation transformer, the incoming mains power supply neutral remains directly connected to the UPS output neutral. This means a hardwired UPS does not in any way alter the neutral regime and allows it to be connected into most electrical systems. The electrical systems both upstream and downstream of a UPS are identical whether it is within a parallel installation or not.

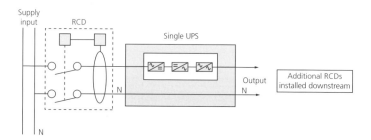

Diagram 9.8 – UPS installation showing RCD implementation

Earth leakage is the measurement of the differential current flowing between the supply phase/s and neutral during normal operation or when an earth fault occurs within a system. For example, if an earth fault occurs within a 230Vac single-phase system, the current flowing through the phase and neutral conductors would not be the same, as some of the current will flow to earth via the fault path. The difference between the current flowing is referred to as the *residual* or *differential current*. To select a suitably rated RCD for a UPS installation, the earth leakage current of both the UPS and its connected loads must be calculated. For a UPS this should be stated in its technical manual.

When installing an RCD on the input side of a UPS, the RCD will trip if a fault occurs on either the input or output of the UPS. If a fault occurs on the output side, the input RCD will trip but this will only disconnect the supply to the UPS input. This will unfortunately, force the UPS onto battery operation and will not disconnect the supply to the downstream circuit where the earth fault is situated. This scenario can be prevented if RCD protective devices are required, by also installing them downstream of the UPS, within its output sub-circuits. This ensures the relevant circuit is disconnected should an earth fault arise.

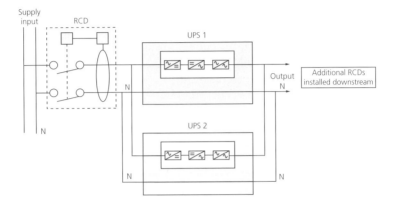

Diagram 9.9 – Parallel UPS installation showing correct RCD implementation

To ensure discrimination is maintained, operation of the RCDs installed either side of the UPS must be co-ordinated. When installing RCDs on the input side of a parallel UPS system, it is important to ensure that only one RCD is installed for the entire system. It is not recommended practice to install one RCD per UPS; if a downstream fault occurs, the leakage current through both devices will be halved (approximately) thus reducing effectiveness.

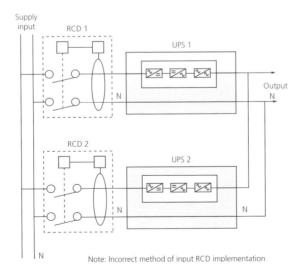

Diagram 9.10 – Parallel UPS installation showing two incorrectly installed RCDs

9.4.4 Cable Sizing and Installation

Within any electrical distribution installation it is imperative to accurately select the correct cable type and size, and the most relevant installation method and routing. For UPS it is always recommended the same cable sizes are installed for both the UPS input and output. The selected cable must be capable of continually carrying the currents required, referred to as its full thermal current rating. If a cable is incorrectly specified, this can result in continuous operation beyond its designed temperature rating, premature failure and potentially a fire risk.

The current carrying capability of a cable is determined by calculating the maximum current (Iz) required and the *ac* supply rating. This calculation is based upon several factors including the design current (Ib) of the circuit and the maximum input rating of the UPS to be installed, the nominal rating of each of the protective devices (In) and the cable rating (It). Cable rating is the value of current for a particular conductor located within a specific environment.

Within *BS 7671 IEE Wiring Regulations Sixteenth Edition - table 4D2A*, shows just how the current carrying capability of non-armoured, multi-core cables (with thermoplastic PVC or thermosetting insulation) is affected by location. As the table shows, current carrying capability reduces under load due to reduced heat dissipation. For example, for a three or four-core 10mm² cable enclosed within an insulated wall, the maximum current carrying capability is reduced to 39A. Whereas in free air their current carrying capability increases to 60A because the cable can more easily dissipate the heat generated.

It is also important to calculate the voltage drop based on the length of the cable and the quantity of current passing through it at full operating load. The greater the load or distance, the greater the voltage drop. For example, the BS 7671 requirements are met for a 230Vac single-phase supply, if the voltage drop between the *ac* supply source and final outlet does not exceed 9.2Vac.

Other factors that have to be taken into account include:

- **Earth fault loop impedance:** as part of the electrical installation it is important to determine the earth fault loop impedance value. A contractor must confirm that the value satisfies the requirements of regulations in force, and that the necessary fault current will be generated should a fault condition or short-circuit occur. Once the level of fault current has been calculated, this can be checked against the time curve of the protective device to ensure that it will trip appropriately.

- **Operating current (Ia):** the operating current is the current required to trip the chosen protective device within the required operating time during a fault condition.

- **Ambient temperature (Ca):** the ambient temperature around the installed cables must be considered to ensure, during operation, that they do not overheat and can dissipate their heat effectively. This is especially important where there are high ambient temperatures and/or direct heat sources, such as solar radiation or heaters.

- **Thermal insulation (Ci):** when cables are installed in an insulated location, the insulation will restrict the cable from effectively dissipating heat.

- **Grouping (Cg):** if several cables are grouped together within one location this will restrict the cable from effectively dissipating heat.

When calculating the cable sizes to be used, correction factors, listed within the relevant wiring regulations, are normally used to address the above issues.

9.4.5 Downstream Protection and Discrimination

To determine the most suitable form of protection and discrimination to be installed on the output of a UPS system, we must first understand just how a UPS system operates should such a fault or short-circuit condition occur.

A fault or short-circuit condition can occur at any time, therefore a UPS must be capable of recovering from such an occurrence without sustaining permanent damage. When a fault or short-circuit occurs, a UPS will react differently depending on its mode of operation at the time of the fault.

a) Normal Operation with a Mains Power Supply Present

During normal operation, with a mains power supply present, any fault or short-circuit on the output of the UPS will lead to the load being instantaneously transferred to the UPS bypass supply to allow the full capacity of the mains power supply to clear the downstream fault.

Once the fault condition has been cleared, the UPS will transfer the load back onto inverter output and normal operation will be resumed.

Diagram 9.11 shows a transformer-based UPS and the current path taken, should a short-circuit occur between one of the three output phases and earth, when the mains power supply is present.

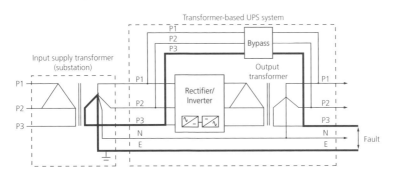

Diagram 9.11 – UPS short-circuit fault current path during normal operation

b) Battery Operation with no Mains Power Supply present

During battery operation (when there is no bypass supply available), a fault condition or short-circuit on the output of the UPS, will lead to a restriction of both the duration and amount of energy available in an attempt to clear the downstream fault. Once the fault has been cleared, the UPS will continue supplying power to the load from the battery set.

If the UPS does not have sufficient power to clear the fault it will automatically shut down in order to protect both itself and the downstream distribution system from permanent damage. This restriction of power is referred to as 'current limiting' and means the amount of current available from the UPS is controlled to typically around 200% (short-circuit current) of nominal for a duration of around 400ms to one second.

The current limiting function of the UPS means that the site contractor must consider the rating and type of the downstream protective devices carefully if they wish to ensure that discrimination occurs during both modes of operation. For example, if a UPS supplies a nominal output current of 100A and has short-circuit capacity of 200% (2In) for 400ms, this means, during a fault condition with no bypass supply present, a UPS will supply a short-circuit current of 200A for 400ms. This will naturally restrict the type and rating of any protective devices used.

Diagram 9.12 shows the current path taken if a short-circuit occurs between one of the three output phases and earth, when no mains power supply is present.

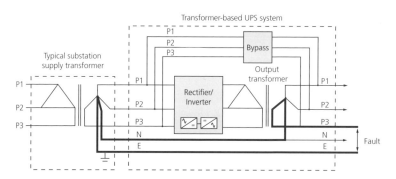

Diagram 9.12 – UPS short-circuit fault current path during battery operation

9.4.6 Galvanic Isolation Options

For those sites requiring Galvanic isolation, there are several installation options depending upon where the isolation transformer is to be installed and with which type of On-Line UPS.

Figure 1, diagram 9.13, shows the simplest installation for a UPS with a single supply and input. Within the installation, an isolation transformer can be installed at point A or point B, or both. As discussed in *chapter 1, section 1.3.3,* care has to be taken when sizing for point A as this transformer must be oversized in accordance with the UPS input supply rating.

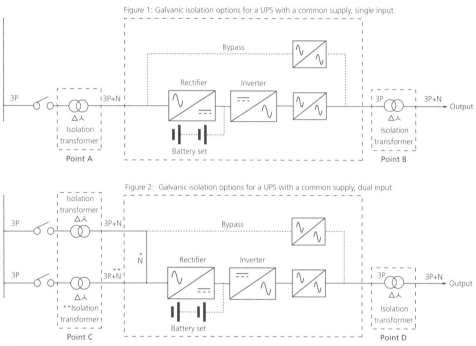

Note:
* transformerless UPS - the rectifier and bypass neutrals are connected and must be common.
** transformer-based UPS - the rectifier input does not require either a neutral connection or the isolation transformer on the rectifier supply.

Diagram 9.13 – Galvanic isolation options for single and dual input (common) supplies

In *figure 2,* the installation is more complex as the UPS has a dual input supply, from a common source. As in *figure 1,* the isolation transformer can be installed at either points C, D or both.

For a transformerless UPS, two isolation transformers are required on the input supplies to provide complete neutral separation, including the bypass supply.

In the final installation option (*diagram 9.14*) the UPS has a dual input supply but from separate sources.

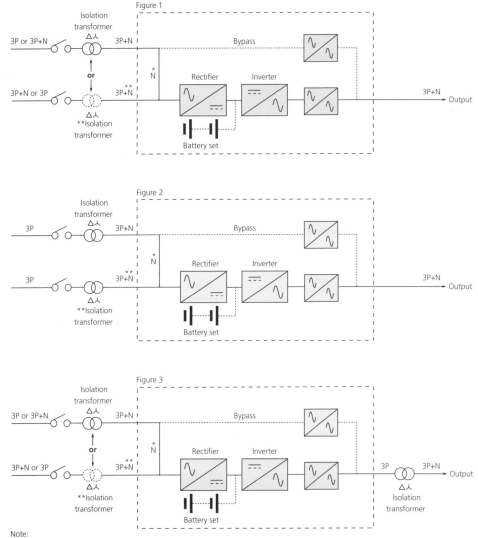

Note:
* transformerless UPS - the rectifier and bypass neutrals are connected and must be common.
** transformer-based UPS - the rectifier input does not require either a neutral connection or the isolation transformer on the rectifier supply.

Diagram 9.14 – Galvanic isolation options for separate dual supplies

An additional benefit arises from the installation of a Galvanic isolation transformer on the input supply side of a UPS. Here, the transformer provides a local and fixed earth-to-neutral connection to assist fault clearance if the mains power supply to the system is completely severed. *Diagram 9.15* shows a fault current path for such a UPS installation.

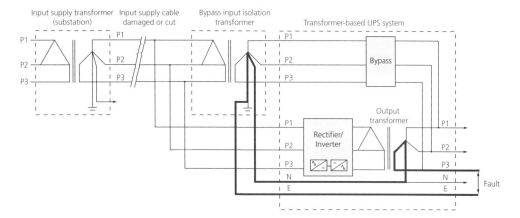

Diagram 9.15 – UPS short-circuit fault current path during battery operation with input transformer

9.4.7 Maintenance Bypasses

There are several different types of maintenance bypass available, including both internal and external arrangements. For UPS below 5kVA, external bypasses are typically available with an additional automatic transfer facility (in case of UPS failure or accidental disconnection). Larger sizes tend to offer manual operation only.

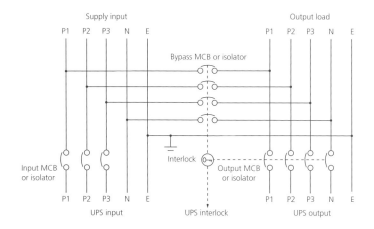

Diagram 9.16 – Circuit-breaker/isolator-based bypass system

Diagram 9.16 shows a typical external circuit-breaker/isolator-based bypass system. The actual number of poles switched will depend upon the type of UPS installed and any applicable site regulations. The bypass switch will typically have three circuit-breakers/isolators: supply in, UPS output and bypass. This allows the UPS to be bypassed using the following procedure:

- switch the UPS into internal bypass - this will depend upon the UPS type
- close the bypass switch - the internal and external bypasses share the load
- open the UPS output switch to disconnect it and transfer the load to the external bypass

At this stage, if the UPS still requires power (during a service visit for testing, for example) the UPS input switch can be left closed. For complete isolation this switch must be opened. At the end of the service period, the procedure is reversed to transfer the load back to the output of the UPS.

The rotary switch-based bypass (*diagram 9.17*) typically has a single three-position switch: normal, bypass/test and bypass.

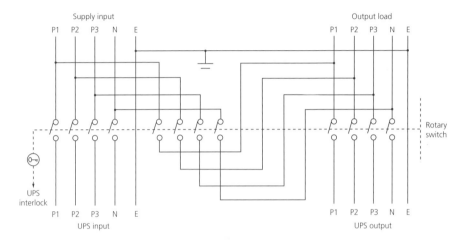

Diagram 9.17 – Rotary switch-based bypass system

This allows the UPS to be bypassed using the following procedure:

- switch the UPS into internal bypass - this will depend upon the UPS type
- turn the switch from the normal position to bypass/test, in which the load is supported by the bypass and the output from the UPS is disconnected

Now, if the UPS still requires power, the bypass switch can be left in this position. For full isolation, it should be moved to the bypass position. As with the first example, at the end of the service period, the procedure is reversed to transfer the load back to the output of the UPS.

Both of the bypass systems discussed provide a seamless transfer and can be typically interlocked (mechanically or electrically) with the UPS system to prevent problems during transfer. The rotary switch-based bypass is generally the preferred method as it is easier to operate than an equivalent circuit-breaker-based one.

Some external bypass switches below 5kVA can also offer automatic transfer of the load to the mains power supply in case of UPS failure or accidental disconnection.

9.4.8 Parallel Systems Connection

Parallel UPS systems can be installed with a single or dual *ac* input supply.

a) Input Supply Rating and Cable Sizing

The overall supply rating for a parallel UPS system must be adequate enough to supply the chosen method of parallel operation, be it capacity or redundancy.

If a parallel-capacity configuration is adopted (*diagram 9.18*) the *ac* supply must be rated to the maximum input current of each UPS module, multiplied by the total number used.

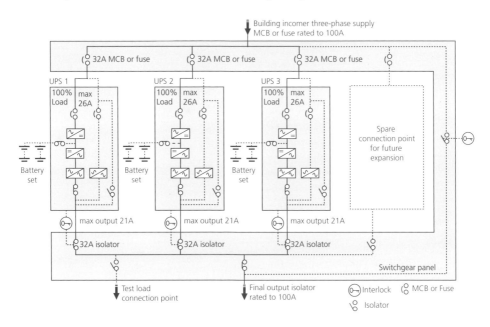

Diagram 9.18 – Typical parallel-capacity system installation schematic

Within a parallel-redundant system (*diagram 9.19 overleaf*) the overall supply rating can be either the same as that used for the parallel-capacity system (preferred) or the total current required by each of the individual UPS modules plus 10% for any redundant modules to cover charging and system losses. In terms of the power cables used within either a parallel-capacity or parallel-redundant configuration:

- the input cables must be sized in accordance to the rating of the supply for each UPS module they are connected to
- the output cables must be rated to either the supply or the maximum output power available from each UPS module (whichever is the greater)
- the input and output cables should be the same length to ensure an even power distribution should the UPS need to transfer their loads to bypass

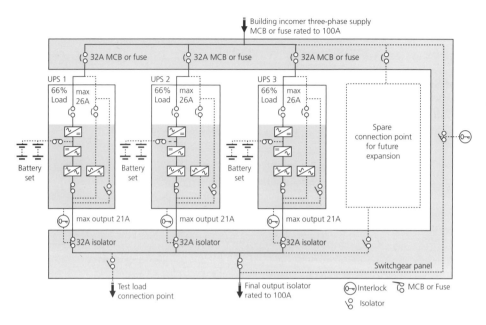

Diagram 9.19 – Typical parallel-redundant system installation schematic

Diagram 9.20 shows the typical cable configuration within a parallel-redundant or parallel-capacity UPS system. Within a correctly installed system, the cable lengths A1+B1 = A2+B2 = A3+B3.

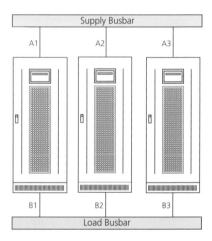

Diagram 9.20 – Parallel system recommended cable lengths

b) Input Supply Isolators and Circuit-Breakers

The use of isolators on the input to each of the UPS provides a means of completely isolating any one UPS module for service, removal or decommission. Circuit-breakers are the preferred means for providing isolation as they can also provide over-current protection (discrimination).

c) Output Isolators

On the output of a UPS (for complete isolation) isolators are preferred to circuit-breakers. This prevents automatic disconnection of a UPS module, which could disrupt operation of the parallel system during use. By interlocking the output isolators, system resilience is increased and unauthorised operation prohibited. The installation of a spare switchgear-set also allows for future capacity expansion of the system.

9.4.9 Dual Input Connection

In order to increase the resilience of a UPS system it is common practice to use a dual *ac* power source rather than rely on a single one. This allows the rectifier and bypass to be supplied from separately derived sources (even from different substations) to mitigate against a single-point-of-failure.

a) Transformer-Based UPS

A transformer-based UPS is generally supplied with a dual input option as standard. This can be selected at installation by simply removing a linking connector from its input terminal. The dual input feature allows the UPS to be powered from two separate *ac* supply sources because the rectifier and bypass supplies of this type of UPS are independent of each other. The typical transformer-based UPS has a rectifier with a three-phase input (delta) and bypass supply that may have either a three-phase or single-phase plus neutral input. Some UPS of this type can even operate without a neutral connection.

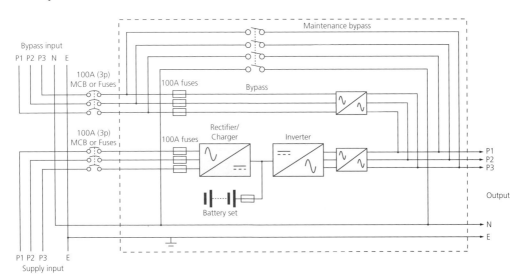

Diagram 9.21 – Transformer-based UPS with dual input

b) Transformerless UPS

In a transformerless UPS, the rectifier and bypass supplies require a common neutral connection, made within the UPS itself. This type of UPS can still be installed with a dual input but with supplies derived from the same source. For such UPS the dual input feature is typically a factory fit option.

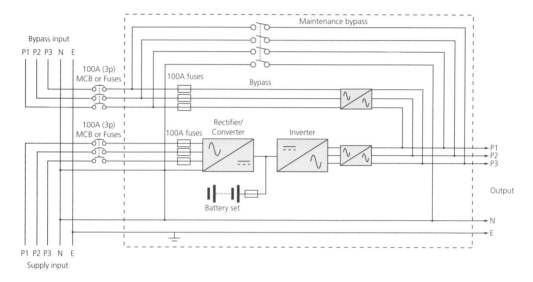

Diagram 9.22 – Transformerless UPS with dual input

9.4.10 Phase Balancing and Neutral Currents

Each of the incoming phases on a three-phase supply should be equally loaded. Where there is an unbalanced load on one or two of the phases the total power demands may lead to current being drawn on the neutral conductor. At its maximum level, the total demand may be 1.73 times ($\sqrt{3}$) the nominal phase currents (including harmonics). The presence of neutral currents can lead to extra demands being placed upon upstream feeders and transformers and overheating. Long-term presence can lead to switchgear failure and in the short-term distortion of the voltage waveform.

9.4.11 Earthing and Bonding

The equipment used within a *Power Continuity Plan* must be electrically earthed to:

- reduce the risk of electrical shocks and fire from overheating conductors
- minimise damage and remove the risk of broken fault return paths
- minimise EMC emissions and susceptibility
- maximise tolerance to the discharge of electro-static energy and lightning transients

For UK electrical installations, *BS 7671, section 4.4* states: 'Every exposed-conductive-part (a conductive part of equipment which can be touched and which is not live but which may become live under earth fault conditions) shall be connected by a protective conductor to the main earthing terminal'.

The earthing (and bonding) of the equipment used within a *Power Continuity Plan* will depend upon the type of electrical supply installed of which there are four common types:

• **TN-C-S systems:** in which the neutral and the earthed protective conductors are combined into a single conductor in part of the system. This is the most common type and uses *Protective Multiple Earthing (PME)*.

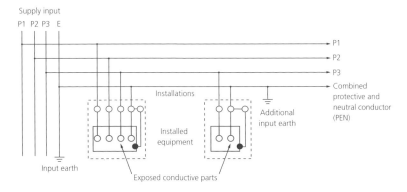

Diagram 9.23 – TN-C-S system

• **TN-C systems:** in which the neutral and the earthed protective conductors are combined throughout the system. Provided that it uses multiple earthing, the same considerations apply as to TN-C-S systems.

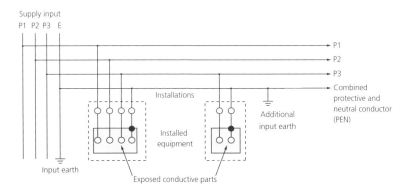

Diagram 9.24 – TN-C system

- **TN-S systems:** in which the neutral and earthed protective conductors remain separate throughout.

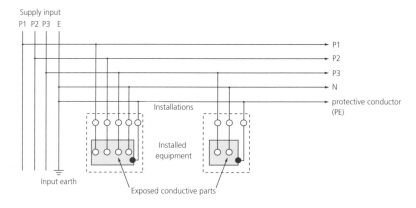

Diagram 9.25 – TN-S system

- **TT systems**: in which the neutral is earthed at the power source but the electricity supplier does not provide an earthed protective conductor.

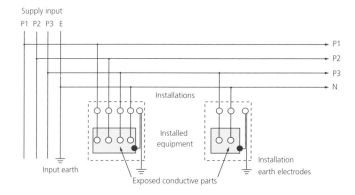

Diagram 9.26 – TT system

9.4.12 UPS Output Neutral-to-Earth Connection

For a UPS installation, it is not advisable to connect the output neutral to the incoming earth because this can result in a share of the neutral current flowing through the supply earth conductor. On some UPS, typically transformerless where the neutral connection through the UPS is filtered, the neutral-to-earth connection point will bridge the filtering which will negate EMC compliance and therefore the CE mark for the product.

If a neutral-to-earth connection is required, an isolation transformer should be installed on the UPS output.

9.4.13 Battery Extension Pack Connection

Selecting the *dc* cables for connection of a UPS to its battery extension pack should follow the same process as that used for *ac* cables.

The size of the battery extension pack is determined by the operational *dc* voltage for the particular UPS and the back-up autonomy time required. The type of connection system used (*2-wire or 3-wire*) will depend upon the type of UPS: transformer-based or transformerless.

A *2-wire* battery set consists of positive and negative (plus cabinet earth) connections. The configuration is used on transformer-based and sub-6kVA transformerless UPS.

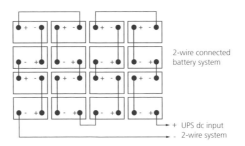

Diagram 9.27 – 2-wire battery set

A *3-wire* battery set consists of positive, negative, mid-point (plus cabinet earth) connections. The configuration is typically used on transformerless UPS above 6kVA.

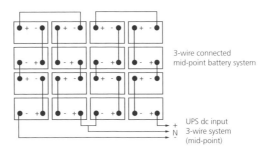

Diagram 9.28 – 3-wire battery set

Regardless of which battery system is used they will all be provided with output fusing intended to protect the cables between the battery pack and the UPS *dc* input. The rating of these fuses will dictate the size of the cables required to be connected between the battery pack and the UPS. As we have seen previously, the rating of any cables must be carefully considered.

9.4.14 Transition Boxes

Extended runtimes typically mean that a UPS must be installed with multiple battery strings. This presents issues as the multiple sets of cables have to be connected to one set of *dc* terminals within the UPS. This is solved through the use of a transition box, *diagram 9.29*. The UPS is connected to two separately fused battery strings. This not only provides protection but also enables each battery string to be individually isolated from the UPS for maintenance or replacement.

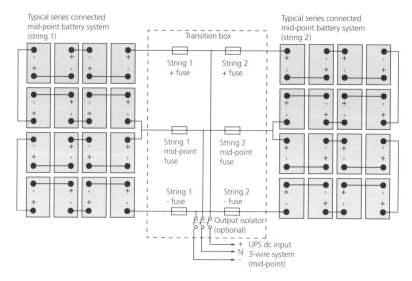

Diagram 9.29 – Multiple battery set transition box

9.4.15 Emergency Power Off (EPO)

An EPO facility (also referred to as *Remote Emergency Power Off - REPO)*, enables the UPS system to be remotely shutdown in the event of an emergency.

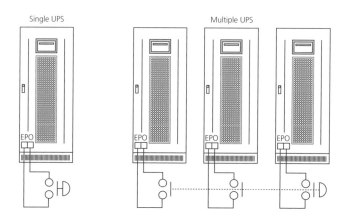

Diagram 9.30 – Single and parallel UPS EPO connection

The EPO is most commonly used in conjunction with an emergency shutdown button or fire control panel. The fire control panel automatically forces the UPS to shutdown to ensure that any fire personnel entering the building are not endangered by the output voltage from the UPS system itself.

The EPO circuit is typically closed and will open to initiate a shutdown. Older systems can however use a normally open circuit and so it is important to check when implementing such a system.

When installing an EPO circuit it is important to ensure that the connection method used is matched to the type of UPS installed. For example, when installing a single UPS module only one switch contact is required. When installing a parallel UPS system it is important to ensure that an individual switch contact is provided for each of the UPS modules.

9.4.16 Remote Monitoring

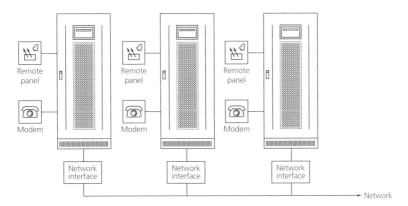

Diagram 9.31 – Parallel UPS remote monitoring

Cabling consideration has to be given to the devices selected for remote monitoring within a *Power Continuity Plan*. These can include, for example: network cards, remote status panels, modems and BMS connections.

In the planning of a parallel UPS system, it is just as important to ensure resilience and redundancy of the communications and monitoring systems. For example, in a parallel system, all of the UPS modules will require their own remote monitoring communication links rather than relying on one overall UPS system connection.

A classic example is the network connection for a parallel UPS system. Here, it is recommended practice for each UPS to have its own network card and connection point. This increases the number of cable runs and points of connection but ensures that resilience is maintained should one or more UPS modules be removed from the system.

In addition, cable routing has to be planned for to avoid the types of transmission problem that can occur due to long lengths, use of unshielded cable and routing through partitions, roof spaces or false floors. For long cable runs, larger cables can be used to overcome resistance and signal loss but multiple cable signal boosters are to be avoided as these introduce single-points-of-failure for the entire UPS system.

9.4.17 Generator - UPS Interfacing

Where a standby generator is installed, both electrical and communications signal cable runs may be required. The specifications for these are generator-specific and should be considered as part of the electrical installation. An example of this is the connection between the UPS, generator and AMF panel (which itself may be remotely monitored).

It is sometimes necessary for the UPS to interface with the generator for control purposes. For example, to de-synchronise the UPS from the generator supply to ensure it provides a stable frequency for sensitive loads or to reduce its battery charging current to alleviate load on the generator when the mains power supply fails.

9.5 Electrical Testing and Certification

For UK installations *BS 7671, section 711-01-01* states: 'Every installation shall, during erection and/or on completion before being put into service, be inspected and tested to verify so far as is reasonably practicable, that the requirements of the regulation have been met'.

The installation of a hardwired UPS, therefore, regardless of whether changes have been made to upstream or downstream circuits, requires the issuing of an Electrical Installation Certificate by a certified electrical contractor. Testing regimes will vary depending upon the UPS size and accessories installed with it.

9.5.1 Earth Fault Loop Impedance Testing

Due to its design, an earth loop impedance test downstream of an On-Line UPS will typically result in high impedance values which will fail to meet wiring and local regulation requirements. Its design, and particularly current limitation when working on batteries, means that a UPS cannot be considered in the same manner as the mains power supply it is powered from.

A UPS simply cannot provide the same quantity of energy which is readily available from a normal mains power supply. When tested, the values returned from an earth loop impedance test carried out downstream of the UPS will reflect the impedance of the UPS inverter. Inverter output power is limited to the size of the components from which it is manufactured; these components are protected to ensure the inverter in particular can continue to operate when overloaded or subjected to a short-circuit. Therefore, the two normal operational states of the UPS (mains present and mains power supply failure) must be taken into account when using earth loop impedance testing to determine fault currents and therefore protective device discrimination.

During normal operation when the mains power supply is present, if a fault occurs downstream of an On-Line UPS, the load and fault condition are transferred to the bypass supply. This protects the inverter and allows the necessary fault current to be drawn from the bypass supply. In this scenario, any earth loop impedance testing must be carried out with the UPS maintenance bypass circuit-breaker closed. This replicates an overload or fault condition when the UPS has the mains power supply available and the values obtained should be normal.

During battery operation when no mains power supply is present and therefore no bypass supply available, the UPS cannot transfer the load and fault condition to the bypass. Now, the UPS must attempt to clear the fault from the inverter which is limited to provide a maximum short-circuit current typically up to 200% (current limited) for a specified time. After this time, the UPS output will fail as the inverter is shut down (to protect itself) and the UPS output will be disconnected. If automatic inverter shutdown fails, the inverter output or battery supply fuses will rupture prior to the thermal limitations of the inverter being exceeded. If its thermal limitations were exceeded, the inverter would be seriously damaged and in particular its IGBT switching components. Once the shutdown has occurred, the unit will remain off until reset.

9.6. Downstream Distribution

The load connection to the source of uninterruptible power must be secure. Provision also needs to be made for power distribution to essential loads. Critical load connection will rely on either direct connection to the UPS output or some form of power distribution unit. The load connection may be socket or hardwired depending upon rating and currents drawn.

The potential installation formats include the centralised and decentralised approaches discussed in *chapter 3*.

9.6.1 UPS Connection

Decentralised distribution typically uses plug-in UPS, which rely on IEC320 socket outputs to provide connections up to 16A in total. Larger currents, of course, require a hardwired connection to the output terminals or industrial-type connector. Where there are multiple hardwired loads, a distribution board will be used.

9.6.2 External Bypass Connection

Where an external bypass is installed, this itself provides the point of connection for the loads; either directly (plugs or hardwired) or via a distribution board. The bypass will have a manual transfer switch or circuit-breakers, and may also include its own automatic transfer switching circuit to provide the installation with additional resilience if the UPS is accidentally removed or fails catastrophically.

9.6.3 Distribution Boards

Distribution boards provide a common point of distribution for the loads and are generally used for centralised systems. Each feed within the cabinet may be individually supplied via a suitably rated circuit-breaker to provide discrimination in case of a load short-circuit. Within a large critical installation, two or more distribution boards may be provided, one for the UPS (critical loads) and one for the generator supporting essential loads.

9.6.4 Power Distribution Units (PDUs)

PDUs cater for power distribution to multiple 'plug & play' loads such as file server clusters. They are available with a number of socket combinations (IEC320, Schuko, UK 'T'), and lengths to accommodate any number of sockets. Each PDU is fused and may also incorporate a Zone-A-rated TVSS. Within a rackmount cabinet the PDU can typically be installed vertically or horizontally.

Intelligent PDUs are now becoming more prominent. These have the facility to be remotely controlled over a network using SNMP or specific software, down to individual socket control. Where more than one PDU is used they should not be daisy chained together. This is because each PDU is normally individually fused and by powering one PDU from another a single-point-of-failure is introduced.

9.6.5 Automatic and Static Transfer Switches

Automatic transfer switches can be used in place of PDUs especially for 'plug & play' loads (as discussed in *chapter 5, section 5.8)*. They are typically relay-based.

Static transfer switches cater for higher power ratings and can be hardwired for either single or three-phase inputs and outputs. They can also be connected in parallel to provide additional resilience and are static switch-based.

Care has to be taken with such devices to ensure that a single-point-of-failure is not introduced on the output side of the UPS. Each device is fused or protected by a circuit-breaker and should this rupture or open, the load could be dropped.

9.7 Summary

This chapter of the *Power Protection Guide* has focused on the importance of planning and in particular the aspects of logistics and installation that need to be covered. The earlier these are considered at the design stage of a new building or data system project, the better. Often this results in a more effective and cost-efficient solution. Its long-term viability however is dependent, like most complex systems, on routine maintenance and this final consideration is discussed in *chapter 10.*

10. Warranties, Maintenance and Services

In this chapter:

- Examining the differences between warranties and maintenance plans.
- Understanding response times in terms of working and clock-hours.
- Details on the general types of maintenance plan available.
- Other typical services provided by UPS suppliers.

Introduction

UPS and generators are complex devices requiring routine maintenance and the replacement of consumable items such as batteries, fans and capacitors.

The nature of such systems means that provision should be made for emergency call-out cover, where the response time may be measured in hours rather than days. There are three aspects to consider for any installation: warranty cover, maintenance plans and additional services.

	On-site Maintenance Plan	No Maintenance Plan
Under Warranty	**Risk Factor 1** All costs covered with a guaranteed response time and additional testing to optimise performance.	**Risk Factor 2** A next day on-site visit, swap-out or return-to-base response.
Outside Warranty	**Risk Factor 3** As above with a focus on consumable replacement.	**Risk Factor 4** The UPS could fail and have to rely on a 'best endeavours' response.

Table 10.1 – Warranty and maintenance risk factors

Table 10.1 demonstrates the risks that a UPS installation runs when it operates without a maintenance plan, especially when out of warranty as there is no guaranteed emergency response time for a call-out.

It is for this reason that maintenance plan provision has to be considered for the power protection systems deployed within a *Power Continuity Plan*. In addition to emergency response, UPS and generators contain consumable parts and will require at the very minimum annual testing and inspection to ensure that their performance is optimised.

10.1 Warranties

Warranty periods vary with UPS size. Typically UPS up to 10kVA are supplied with a two-year warranty and larger systems one-year. These can sometimes be extended to three and fives years where the manufacturer provides this service. These longer warranties are sometimes achieved using ten-year design life battery sets in place of the standard five-year design life. Generators typically have a one-year warranty.

The type of warranty cover is important. Most UPS below 3kVA are covered by a *Return-To-Base (RTB)* warranty where the UPS is returned to a service centre or service agent, repaired or swapped-out. This applies to UPS that can plug-into a mains power supply and with socket outlets for load connection. An on-site warranty provides a higher level of service and is more common for hardwired UPS and generators. For this, most manufacturers provide a next working-day response.

The critical point here is the speed of response. When a UPS is returned there is obviously a delay of several days where the UPS load is unprotected. In addition, without an external maintenance bypass the load must be interrupted when the UPS is disconnected and re-inserted into the supply network. For on-site warranties, a next working-day response for a critical 24/7 system may be unacceptable. This can be the case for critical institutions and service providers who require a four-clock-hour response.

A secondary concern relates to the costs covered under warranty. Most warranties will cover repair labour, carriage and parts but batteries may or may not be included. It is common for the battery set to be supplied with a pro rata warranty passed along from the battery manufacturer. This relates in some part to the way battery performance can be affected by on-site ambient temperatures, mains power supply stability and the number of charge/discharge cycles that can take place, and of course, their duration.

Where the UPS cannot be repaired on-site, it is common for a swap-out unit to be supplied and for this to have a warranty period matching any remaining from the initial sale period.

10.2 Maintenance Plans

These provide more comprehensive cover than a warranty including a 'guaranteed' *Emergency Response Time* which may be defined in either working or clock-hours. *Chapter 5* discussed the methods for increasing UPS system resilience using parallel-redundancy. In such a UPS system, any single module failure can severely degrade the resilience of the entire system, unless it has N+2 or greater redundancy. The faster a failed UPS module can be brought back into service the better. UPS and generator suppliers typically offer three types of maintenance plan ranked in order of their response times:

- twelve-working-hours
- eight-working-hours
- four-clock-hours

When sold by a UPS supplier the plan should be provided on a back-to-back arrangement with the manufacturer or on the basis that the supplier has approved access to manufacturer certified engineers. Both approaches ensure access to the necessary parts, software, firmware, service documentation and technical support.

10.3 Response Times

10.3.1 Working-Hours

Twelve-Working-Hour and Eight-Working-Hour maintenance plans revolve around the working day (8:30 to 17:00 Monday to Friday). The response time is triggered when a call is booked into a service centre and arrangements are made for on-site access. Additional charges can be incurred for response outside working-hours including additional visits for preventative maintenance, for example. Often the decision for outside hours work rests on whether the UPS has been installed with a maintenance bypass facility, and/or in a parallel-redundant configuration that can support a single UPS module being serviced at any one time.

10.3.2 Clock-Hours

As the name implies, *Emergency Response Times* are measured in clock hours. UPS manufacturers typically offer service response on a 24/7 basis and shorter response time plans are available. Four-clock-hours is the norm and any shorter (one or two hours) may require crash kits to be stored on-site or within a local service depot. Crash kits contain first line spares and common assemblies. For UPS below 3kVA it may actually comprise of a full replacement UPS without batteries. This size of UPS tends to have one or two large fully integrated PCBs and it is cheaper to supply them in a replacement UPS chassis as working models. Very short response times on critical application sites (petrochemical or banking) may also require 24-hour on-site attendance by specially trained UPS service engineers.

10.4 Site Access

Site access is a critical aspect within any maintenance plan. On chemical, industrial and rail sites, access can be restricted by the need for on-site health & safety briefings. This can be limited by employing a UPS service partner with the relevant health & safety accreditation such as OHSAS 18001, SAFEcontractor and Personal Trackside Safety (PTS) certification. Where on-site briefings are required, provision should be made for such training prior to any site visits and site-specific engineers appointed for both emergency call-outs and maintenance.

10.5 Costs Covered

A maintenance plan may include all parts, labour and carriage costs but exclude full battery replacement unless specifically requested. These costs will depend on the battery type used and their design life which may be five or ten years or greater. Outside warranty maintenance plans may only allow for labour.

10.6 Remote Monitoring

UPS and generator manufacturers usually supply their own centralised remote monitoring packages which can be combined with a maintenance plan to provide greater system security. Here the kit is remotely monitored via modems and telephone lines (fixed or mobile) by a service centre.

Alarms lead to the UPS or generator dialling the service centre to report any fault codes. The alarms can be generated from self-diagnostic routines or because of a sudden on-site change. For example, a circuit-breaker tripping due to poor load discrimination as a fault occurs. The process guarantees a highly effective, fast speed of response with alarms activating site-specific scripts, dispatch of an engineer and notification to selective personnel via voice, data and text messages.

Under normal operating conditions the service centre can also dial up the UPS or generator to interrogate status and alarm event logs from which regular reports can be generated. As a *virtual engineer,* a service technician can view the current operational status of the kit, download alarm logs for analysis or initiate self-diagnostics. They can also test the communication links with the systems to ensure they are fully operational as an addition to any general periodic testing by the service packages themselves.

In a typical service centre, standalone or networked PCs are used to run the service monitoring packages. These are connected to an internal GSM modem to allow them to send SMS text messages as part of automated response scripts. The packages also provide visual indication of the real-time UPS and generator status and drill down to site specific data.

10.7 Service Level Agreements

A single maintenance plan is essentially a mini *Service Level Agreement (SLA).* It is a contractual document the schedule of which will define all the relevant information:

- service level required
- contact and escalation details
- product details
- spares provision
- replacement system provision
- cost provision

Corporate and multi-site customers may also require an SLA covering the overall service relationship to be provided.

10.8 Other Services

A UPS and generator can require a number of additional services, inside or outside working-hours, which may be included in an on-site maintenance plan or purchased separately as required.

10.8.1 Commissioning

Once a UPS has been installed it will require final power up. 'Plug-in' UPS are user commissionable. As self-contained units with few external connections other than a mains power supply lead, load sockets, remote communications and perhaps an external battery pack, they are designed to be plugged into a local wall socket.

Installing the UPS with an external hardwired maintenance bypass or fused-spur makes the process slightly more complicated and will require a suitably qualified electrician.

Larger hardwired UPS and generators require full on-site commissioning by a service engineer trained to local wiring regulations who will follow set procedures and method statements to power up the UPS and bring it into service.

Most manufacturers will recommend that only their own service engineers or approved service partners provide this service. This removes any problems associated with warranty infringements. These technicians are trained to carry out such work and have access to the latest documentation, communication software, firmware upgrades and spares.

A commissioning service should include:

• inspection of the UPS and associated accessories
• note any environmental or other aspects that could impact performance
• installation and connection of the battery set if applicable
• installation and connection of any auxiliary devices and serial cables
• safety check
• initial switch-on and UPS commission
• UPS configuration set-up
• UPS, bypass and auxiliary device operational test
• UPS discharge test if applicable
• on-site training and handover

Appendix F provides a sample commissioning method statement, whilst *appendix G* provides an example of a commissioning certificate.

10.8.2 Preventative Maintenance (PM) Visits

Preventative maintenance is one of the critical services typically provided under a maintenance plan. Its purpose is to ensure a detailed inspection and service of the relevant kit within the *Power Continuity Plan* and to identify and remove problems. The PM visit may be annual (UPS) or six-monthly (generator).

A sample PM visit method statement is provided in *appendix H*. For a UPS, particular attention is paid to: circuit-breakers, relays and contactors, semi-conductors, fuses, cabling and ribbon assemblies, transformers, PCBs, capacitors, inductors, heatsinks, fans and communication ports.

The age of the individual batteries are checked using the date of manufacture code normally stamped onto their cases, and they are inspected for signs of damage, corrosion and leaks. All terminal connections are checked to ensure they are at the right torque setting and the battery blocks themselves may be individually tested.

A PM visit is also used to *health check* UPS from third-party manufacturers and/or outside warranty for inclusion under a maintenance plan.

10.8.3 Battery Testing, Replacement and Disposal

As discussed in *chapter 6*, battery testing is a fundamental part of any installation because battery sets will require eventual replacement in order to maintain system integrity, whether as part of a UPS or generator starter-circuit. The typical battery testing service will comprise of five stages:

- **Visual inspection:** to check for a variety of battery-specific conditions:
  - VRLAs: distortion caused by plate and pole growth, leakage or corrosion
  - Flooded: plate colour, leakage, corrosion, sediment and electrolyte levels
  - Ni-Cads: leakage and corrosion

- **Measurements:** *dc* float voltage measurements for the battery set, strings and individual blocks will be taken, as well as measuring the Specific Gravity of pilot cells (flooded and wet cells).

- **Mechanical:** clean all batteries, confirm the minimum torque on all connections and top up electrolytes if possible (not sealed VRLA batteries).

- **Environment:** check the suitability of the local environment in terms of ambient temperature and any noticeable environmental matters such as humidity and ventilation.

- **Electrical:** test battery blocks and strings, and load test the full battery set. The method used to test the batteries may involve either impedance or chemical analysis testing, as discussed in *chapter 6*, or load bank testing.

Finally, a site report should be issued with recommendations for future system monitoring or battery replacement. Where replacement is recommended, the original batteries must be replaced according to any regulations and guidelines.

10.8.4 Load Bank Testing

Load banks are typically resistive loads available for either *ac* or *dc* system testing. They can be used to place a load on a UPS inverter or generator, its battery set or alternative sources of power (such as a flywheel or fuel cell). The advantage of load bank testing is it places a direct load on the UPS system or module being tested. This is particularly useful at UPS commissioning and during its working life.

For example, an *ac* load bank can be used to test the entire UPS system or a *dc* load bank the battery set itself. Measurements are taken during discharge from which it is possible to determine battery and system performance. Load testing can also be useful during PM visits, especially for older UPS the battery sets of which may be near to the end of their working life.

Most UPS suppliers will have their own small load banks (up to 100kW) and hire larger sets as required. Logistics problems are similar to those for a large UPS or generator and additional costs will include temporary cable provision and connection, as well as service personnel hours. Load bank testing should be used sparingly though as testing will reduce system resilience, discharge the battery, and could place the loads at risk - should a mains power supply failure occur. For this reason, load bank testing is typically performed outside normal working-hours.

A final consideration needs to be given to the environment on-site. Load banks contain heater elements and generate high ambient temperatures, which may require additional venting. Load banks are also fan cooled and the size of the fan will lead to increased noise pollution on site.

10.8.5 Third-Party Provision

Many customers, who may already have UPS from third-party manufacturers in place, have a desire to standardise on one supplier. This can create problems for UPS suppliers tasked with upgrading legacy systems that may be out-of-warranty or no longer in manufacture. Most UPS service organisations should be able to at least provide an emergency response and PM visit for these systems. The level of service will depend on whether they have access to documentation, communications software (including passwords for each user, engineer and factory levels), firmware and spares.

10.8.6 Full System Tests

Arrangements should be made for a full *Power Continuity Plan* test at least once a year covering both mains power supply failure and restore tests. This will not only test electrical connections but communication links, alarm responses, automatic shutdown scripts and electronic controls. Specific areas of concern will cover UPS and generator start-up and synchronisation, manual start-up routines and contingency plans.

10.8.7 Infrared Non-Contact Measurement

As discussed in this guide, 'hot-spots' are a sign of high connection resistance and component stress caused by high currents being passed through a poorly connected conductor or faulty component. They indicate potential areas for failure within a system that can be easily identified, using infrared non-contact thermal imaging devices and cameras. These are non-invasive and can 'see into' difficult to access areas. They are also ideal where the temperatures could be too hot to touch, assemblies dangerous to access, or there is a risk of contamination in sterile areas.

10.8.8 Hire and Leasing

Most UPS and generator manufacturers will provide elements from a *Power Continuity Plan* on a short-term hire or long-term lease basis. These can be used, for example, to support a specific event or provide power to a site as it attempts to recover its operations from a catastrophic incident. Many of the aspects already considered in this guide will apply to these services.

10.9 Summary

The critical nature of a UPS installation means that maintenance cannot be ignored and systems should be run 'in anger' under controlled conditions to fully flex a site-specific *Power Continuity Plan*.

In terms of long-term management, consumable items such as the battery set in a UPS or generator will require regular inspection and testing. Long-term planning should build full battery replacement into a future budget as the cost for this will usually be excluded from any on-site maintenance plans. PM visits should be made at least annually and where necessary additional testing services carried out on a regular basis.

Power protection itself is as much an art as it is a science, as there are no hard and fast rules to the design of a *Power Continuity Plan*. This guide has attempted to provide information on what the writers consider to be best practice and to help people avoid some of the common pitfalls associated with the topic.

The general caveat of 'if in doubt, ask' therefore applies and the full resources of Riello UPS are at your disposal throughout the world to ensure that you can reach the ultimate levels of power protection and keep your systems running.

Appendices

Glossary of Terms

Active Power
A measure of the actual power (Watts) dissipated by a load.

Alternating Current (ac)
An electrical current whose electrons flow periodically in one direction to a maximum level before dropping back to zero and then flowing in an alternative direction before the pattern repeats itself. The waveform is that of a sinewave.

Amp or Amperes (A)
A measure of electrical current flow.

Ampere-hour (Ah)
A measure of the number of Amps that a battery set can deliver per hour.

Apparent Power
The current drawn by a load at a given supply voltage measured in VA.

Availability
A ratio of system up time compared to its downtime expressed as a percentage.

Automatic Bypass
A circuit within a UPS (or bypass panel) to transfer the load from and to a bypass supply, which may be relay or static switch-based.

Automatic Voltage Stabiliser (AVS)
A device to stabilise the mains power supply voltage to a load. Also known as an Automatic Voltage Regulator (AVR) or Voltage Regulator (VR).

Autonomy (Runtime or Backup Time)
The amount of time (minutes or hours) that a battery set or other power source will support the load.

Battery Block
A self-contained battery consisting of a number of individual and connected battery cells.

Battery Cell
A simple electrical circuit within a battery block consisting of positive and negative electrodes or plates, an electrolyte and separator.

Battery Set
Comprises of a battery string or a number of battery strings.

Battery String
Comprises of a number of battery blocks arranged in series to achieve a set Vdc and Ah rating.

Blackouts
A term used to describe a mains power supply failure, also referred to as an Outage.

Boost charge
A high charge voltage applied to a battery set.

Booster-Converter
An assembly used within transformerless UPS to step up the dc supply from a rectifier or battery set to the level required by an inverter.

Break-Before-Make (BBM) Bypass
A bypass that introduces a break when transferring a load from the output of a UPS to the bypass supply, and vice-versa.

Brownouts
Long duration decreases below nominal (the normal mains power supply voltage), which can last for many cycles or longer.

Building Management System (BMS)
A centralised alarm monitoring system usually providing either a visual status indication board or computer monitoring screen.

Bunding
A method of containing liquid spillage from a system, for example, oil or diesel from a standby generator.

Bypass
A power path arrangement normally providing a secondary power supply path in case the primary one fails.

Capacitance
The ability of a circuit to store electrical energy as a charge. The circuit is known as a capacitive circuit.

Central Power Supply System (CPSS)
A type of standby power system used within emergency lighting, security and medical applications the operation of which is similar to that of a UPS.

Circuit-Breaker
A device inhibiting high surge currents over a set stated figure. Under such conditions the breaker will operate and the circuit is isolated.

Clamping level
The level at which a spike or transient protection device clamps the voltage down to a lower level.

Common Mode Noise

A form of high-frequency electrical noise which results from disturbances between the supply lines and earth (phase-to-earth or neutral-to-earth).

Constant Voltage Transformer (CVT)

A type of ferroresonant transformer.

Crash Kits

Spares kits held on-site to enable a fast emergency response to a system failure.

Crest Factor

The mathematical ratio of the peak to RMS value of an ac waveform.

Critical Loads

Systems which directly affect the ability of an organisation to operate and which must be kept running during a mains power supply failure.

Current (A)

The 'volume' of electricity flowing in a circuit and expressed as Amps.

Current Limit

The restriction of the amount of current that can be drawn from any point within an electrical circuit or UPS output.

Deep Discharge

A battery charge state whereby the battery voltage, (Vdc), has dropped below a safe operating level from which it cannot recover.

Direct Current (dc)

Electric current the electrons of which are flowing in one direction only.

Discrimination

The protection around a device within a *Power Continuity Plan* that will disconnect it, if a short-circuit or overload is applied, to prevent it from damaging other devices, and without interrupting their operation.

Displacement Power Factor

The ratio of Real Power (W) to Apparent Power (VA) at the fundamental frequency.

Distortion

A variation in waveform from a true wave shape.

Distortion Power Factor

The power factor produced by the harmonics generated from non-linear loads.

Dry-Contact

See Volt-Free Contact.

Dynamic Stability
The ability of a device to respond to a load-step change and deliver a stable output voltage waveform.

Earth Fault (Ground)
A connection from the live component of a mains power supply to an earth connection.

Electrical Noise
High frequency noise on a sinewave which may be Common Mode or Normal Mode.

Electro-Magnetic Compatibility (EMC)
The extent to which an electronic or electrical device will tolerate and generate Electro-Magnetic Interference (EMI).

Electro-Magnetic Induction
The production of an electrical potential difference (or voltage) across a conductor, situated in a changing magnetic flux.

Electro-Magnetic Interference (EMI)
A type of electrical noise that causes an electro-magnetic disturbance.

Emergency Power Off (EPO) / Emergency Shutdown (ESD)
A signal contact on a UPS which will initiate a total UPS shutdown.

Emergency Response Time
The speed of response specified within a maintenance plan for an engineer to attend site.

Ferroresonance
A term applied to resonant interactions between capacitors and saturable iron-core inductors. During resonance, the inductive reactance increases to match the capacitive reactance and current flow is limited by the system resistance. The phenomenon is used, for example, within ferroresonant transformers of which Constant Voltage Transformers (CVTs) are a configuration.

Ferroresonant Transformer
A voltage regulating transformer using the principle of ferroresonance.

Fixed Cellular Terminal (FCT)
A communications device that can receive and route telephone calls through a built-in mobile phone capability.

Float Charging
A method of charging a battery set at a steady voltage level.

Flywheels (dc)
A device used to convert Kinetic energy into a standby supply of dc power for a UPS either in place of a battery set or to reduce the initial discharge during momentary interruptions.

Frequency Converter
A device for changing the input frequency to a different output frequency.

Fuel Cell
A device that uses hydrogen as a fuel to generate an ac or dc supply in addition to heat and water.

Gas Discharge Tube (GDT)
An arrangement of electrodes in a gas within an insulating, temperature-resistant ceramic or glass case which switches to a low-impedance when subjected to a spike or transient voltage.

Gas Turbine
A device that converts Kinetic energy generated from combustion into electrical energy to provide an ac standby power source to a load.

Generator
A device that converts Kinetic energy generated from combustion into electrical energy to provide an ac or dc power source to a load.

Harmonic
A variation of a mains power supply sinewave above the fundamental (50 or 60Hz).

Harmonic Distortion or Total Harmonic Distortion (THDi)
Distortion of a mains power supply sinewave from its fundamental frequency and wave shape.

Harmonic Filter
A device to reduce the harmonic distortion generated by a device and enable it to provide a high power factor to its ac source.

Hertz (Hz)
A measurement of the number of complete cycles per second of a waveform. Normal mains frequency is either 50 or 60 (Hz).

Icc
Short-circuit current.

In
Nominal current.

Incomer
The cable carrying the mains power supply into a building from the nearest substation and Point of Common Coupling (PCC).

Inductance
The generation of an electro-motive force in an inductive circuit by varying the magnetic flux through it.

Ingress Protection (IP) Rating
An IP number is often used when specifying the environmental protection offered by enclosures around electronic equipment. The first number refers to the protection against solid objects and the second against liquids.

Insulated Gate Bipolar Transistor (IGBT)
A high power switching device used in inverters and rectifiers.

In-rush
The initial surge in current drawn by loads, for example, to charge capacitive circuits.

Inverter
The circuit within a UPS system which converts dc energy to an ac output.

Isolation or Galvanic Isolation
A separation of the input and output supplies to a device in such a way that energy flows through a field rather than through electrical connections.

JBUS
A communications protocol that creates a hierarchical structure (one master and several slaves) from a single RS-232 communications link, similar to MODBUS.

Joule (J)
An energy measurement unit, determined as one Watt per second.

Maintenance Bypass
A bypass supply which is used to power the load during maintenance and which may be internal or external to the device. It is also known as a bypass panel or wrap-around bypass.

Make-Before-Break (MBB) Bypass
A bypass that makes contact between the primary (UPS output) and secondary (bypass supply) power sources before transferring the load.

Linear Loads
A load in which the relationship between voltage and current is constant, based on a relatively constant load impedance.

Load
The system or systems powered from a device.

Load Shedding
The reduction of the total load placed on a device. For example, in the case of a UPS, load shedding (when the mains power supply fails) reduces the total load on the UPS to increase the amount of runtime available from the battery set.

Mean Time Between Failure (MTBF)
A measure of reliability and the average length of operational time between failures. This can be based on monitoring a field population, or calculated for a system based on the known MTBF values of its components to a defined process and standard.

Mean Time To Repair (MTTR)
A measure of the average time taken to bring a system back to full operation following a failure.

Metal Oxide Varistor (MOV)
A device capable of absorbing very high surge currents without damage to itself.

MODBUS
A communications protocol that creates a hierarchical structure (one master and several slaves) from a single RS-232 communications link, similar to JBUS.

Noise Level
Normally measured in decibels (dB) or (dBA). Noise may also be referred to as electrical noise in a circuit.

Non-Essential Loads
Loads that can be dropped during a mains power supply failure because they are not critical or essential to the operation of the organisation.

Non-linear loads
A load in which the relationship between voltage and current fluctuates based on an alternating load impedance.

Normal Mode Noise
A form of high-frequency electrical noise, that occurs between phase and neutral.

Opto-Isolators
A device that uses a short optical transmission path to transfer a signal between elements of a circuit while keeping them electrically isolated.

Outages
An American term used to describe a mains power supply failure, also referred to as a Blackout.

Overvoltages
Any higher voltage than that agreed as a regulated voltage in a circuit.

Parallel-Capacity System
A type of parallel UPS system where the total load demand is met by operating a number of UPS in parallel without redundancy.

Parallel-Redundancy

A type of parallel UPS system where the total load demand is met by operating two or more UPS in an N+X configuration with all the UPS sharing the load between them equally. If one UPS fails the other supports the load.

Parallel Systems Joiner (PSJ)

A device to join together two independent groups of parallel UPS.

Phase

A single-phase supply consists of a single sinewave at the fundamental frequency. A three-phase supply consists of three waveforms each separated by 120° from each other. Phase is also used to refer to the difference between the voltage and current waveforms when used in relation to power factors.

Phase Power Factor

The ratio of Real Power (W) to Apparent Power (VA) at the fundamental frequency.

Point of Common Coupling (PCC)

The point where a building incomer is connected to the electricity distribution network.

Power Conditioner

A device to stabilise, regulate and filter the mains power supply voltage to a load which may be electronic or transformer-based (Constant Voltage Transformer).

Power Continuity Plan

A plan outlining the methods by which systems that ensure continuity are protected from mains power supply failures and power problems.

Power Factor (pF)

The difference between the actual energy consumed (Watts), and the Volts x Amps in a circuit. Power factor may be lagging, where the current waveform lags the voltage waveform, or leading where the current waveform leads the voltage.

Power Supply Unit (PSU)

The device within a piece of modern electronic hardware that converts an ac waveform into the various levels of dc required to power internal circuits.

Profibus

A type of field bus typically used within control and automation.

Pulse Width Modulation (PWM)

The switching action in an inverter which varies with time, and creates a composite waveform approaching a sinewave.

Radio Frequency Interference (RFI)

Radio waves of sufficient intensity to be absorbed by a circuit and to cause a circuit malfunction.

Reactive Power
A flow of energy (VAr) superimposed back onto the source from which it was drawn.

Real Power
A measure of the actual power (Watts) dissipated by a load.

Recovery Time
The time incurred to obtain a fully regulated voltage after switching loads onto a standby generating set.

Rectifier
An assembly that converts an ac supply into a dc supply.

Rectifier/Charger
An assembly used within transformer-based UPS which converts an ac supply into a dc supply from which to power an inverter and charge a battery set.

Regulation
Control of an ac/dc output voltage to within a set specification.

Resilience
The capacity of a power protection system potentially exposed to hazards to adapt, by resisting or changing in order to reach and maintain an acceptable operational level.

Ripple
An ac element superimposed onto the dc waveform powering a device.

RoHS
Restriction of Hazardous Substances, Directive 2002/95/EC.

Root Mean Square (RMS)
Taking one half of an ac current cycle, RMS is the square root of the average values of all the squares of current and voltage.

Rotary UPS
An Uninterruptible Power Supply that converts Kinetic energy into electrical energy to power a load.

RS-232
A standard interface for synchronous and asynchronous communications up to 20kb/s between two compatible devices (one driver and one receiver) over distances up to 15m.

RS-422
Similar to RS-232 but up to a maximum transmission rate of 10Mb/s-100Kb/s, up to ten receivers from a single driver and a distance of up to 1000m.

RS-485
Similar to RS-422 but with up to 32 drivers and receivers.

Sags or Dips
Short duration decreases, below the nominal mains power supply voltage, lasting several cycles.

Series-Redundancy
A method of providing redundant power to a load whereby the output of one UPS module is used to supply the bypass of another. If one UPS fails the other automatically powers the load.

Silicon Avalanche Diode (SAD)
A device capable of responding quickly to a high-energy surge or transient and reducing its initial surge current.

Simple Network Management Protocol (SNMP)
A communications protocol that allows hardware with a TCP/IP connection on a network to be monitored and controlled.

Sinewave
The waveform naturally produced by a well designed generator, inverter or UPS.

Single-Phase
A single-phase supply consists of a single sinewave at the fundamental frequency.

Slew Rate
The rate at which a UPS can adjust its output frequency in order to synchronise to the frequency of, for example, a standby ac source such as a generator.

Spikes
Large voltage disturbances superimposed onto the normal ac supply with a short duration.

Static Stability
The ability of a device to deliver a stable output voltage waveform under stable load conditions.

Static Switch
A solid state high-speed switching device that can transfer a load between two ac power sources.

Static UPS
An Uninterruptible Power Supply using solid state electronics and therefore no moving parts.

Super Capacitors
A device for storing electrical charge which can be used to provide applications such as small UPS, with a momentary supply of power in place of a battery set or to reduce its usage during momentary breaks in mains power supply.

Surges
Short duration increases in voltage above the mains power supply nominal, which generally last for several cycles.

Switched Mode Power Supply (SMPS)
A type of PSU with a non-linear current draw, most commonly found within computer, telecommunications and electronic devices.

Switching Time
The time it takes to transfer a load between ac supply sources. Also known as Transfer Time.

Three-Phase
A supply consisting of three single phases, each 120° out of phase from one another.

Thyristor
A semi-conductor gate device most commonly used within a rectifier or static switch.

Total Harmonic Distortion (THDi)
A measure of all the harmonics induced in a system compared to a normal sinewave.

Total Power Factor / True Power Factor
The total power factor including both distortion and displacement power factors.

Transfer Time
The time it takes to transfer a load between ac supply sources. Also known as Switching Time.

Transformer
A wound component consisting of windings around a core, with iron sheet laminates that can be used to change voltage levels and provide Galvanic isolation.

Transients
High energy burst voltage disturbances, with a short duration, superimposed onto the normal supply.

Transient Voltage Surge Suppressor (TVSS)
A device using MOVs, SAD/MOVs or GDTs to attenuate a transient or spike.

Triplens (Triple-N)
A multiple of the third harmonic in a waveform.

Undervoltages
A voltage below the set regulated voltage for an extended period.

Uninterruptible Power Supply (UPS)
The terminology used to describe a system (either Static or Rotary) capable of maintaining power to a load for a defined time period irrespective of the state of the mains power supply itself - also known as an Uninterruptible Power System.

UPS Group Synchroniser (UGS)
A device to synchronise the outputs from two seperate groups of parallel UPS.

Valve-Regulated Lead-Acid (VRLA) battery
A type of Lead-Acid battery commonly used within a UPS.

Volt (V or kV or MV)
A measure of electrical force or pressure, which can be expressed as Vac or Vdc.

Volt Ampere (VA or kVA or MVA)
A measure of Apparent Power and the current drawn by a load at a given supply voltage.

Volt-Free Contacts (VFCs)
A pair of contacts that are normally open (NO) or normally closed (NC). When closed they form a circuit through which a current, and therefore signal, can flow for remote detection.

Watts (W or kW or MW)
A measure of the Real Power drawn by a load.

Waveform
A graphical representation of the shape of a wave.

WEEE
Waste Electrical and Electronic Equipment, Directive 2002/96/EC.

World Voltages and Frequencies

Country	Plug Socket Type/s	Single Phase (Vac)	Three Phase (Vac)	Number of Wires	(Hz)
Afghanistan	C,F	220	380	4	50
Albania	C,F	230	400	4	50
Algeria	C,F	230	400	4	50
American Samoa	A,B,F,I	120	208	3,4	60
Andorra	C,F	230	400	3,4	50
Angola	C	220	380	4	50
Anguilla	A	110	-	-	60
Antigua	A,B	230	400	3,4	60
Argentina	C,I	220	380	3,4	50
Armenia	C,F	230	380	4	50
Aruba	A,B,F	127	220	3,4	60
Australia	I	230	400	3,4	50
Austria	C,F	230	400	3,4	50
Azerbaijan	C	220	380	4	50
Azores	B,C,F	230	400	3,4	50
Bahamas	A,B	120	208	3,4	60
Bahrain	G	230	400	3,4	50
Balearic Islands	C,F	230	400	3,4	50
Bangladesh	A,C,D,G,K	220	380	3,4	50
Barbados	A,B	115	200	3,4	50
Belarus	C	230	380	4	50
Belgium	E	230	400	3,4	50
Belize	B,G	110/220	190/380	3,4	60
Benin	E	220	380	4	50
Bermuda	A,B	120	208	3,4	60
Bhutan	D,F,G	230	400	4	50
Bolivia	A,C	230	400	4	50
Bosnia & Herzegovina	C,F	230	400	4	50
Botswana	D,G	230	400	4	50
Brazil	A,B,C,I	127/220	220/380 *	3,4	60
Brunei	G	240	415	4	50
Bulgaria	C,F	230	400	4	50
Burkina Faso	C,E	220	380	4	50
Burundi	C,E	220	380	4	50
Cambodia	A,C,G	230	400	4	50
Cameroon	C,E	220	380	4	50
Canada	A,B	120	600	3,4	60
Canary Islands	C,E,L	230	400	3,4	50
Cape Verde	C,F	230	400	3,4	50
Cayman Islands	A,B	120	208	3	60
Central African Republic	C,E	220	380	4	50
Chad	D,E,F	220	380	4	50

Country	Plug Socket Type/s	Single Phase (Vac)	Three Phase (Vac)	Number of Wires	(Hz)
Channel Islands	C,G	230	400	4	50
Chile	C,L	220	380	3,4	50
China	A,I,G	220	380	3,4	50
Colombia	A,B	110	190	3,4	60
Comoros	C,E	220	380	4	50
Congo	C,D	220	380	3,4	50
Congo	C,E	230	380	3,4	50
Cook Islands	I	240	415	3,4	50
Costa Rica	A,B	120	240	3,4	60
Côte d'Ivoire	C,E	220	380	3,4	50
Croatia	C,F	230	400	4	50
Cuba	A,B,C,L	110/220	190	3	60
Cyprus	G,F	230	400	4	50
Czech Republic	E	230	400	3,4	50
Denmark	C,K	230	400	3,4	50
Djibouti	C,E	220	380	4	50
Dominica	D,G	230	400	4	50
Dominican Republic	A,B	110	190	3	60
East Timor	C,E,F,I	220	-	-	50
Ecuador	A,B	110	190	3,4	60
Egypt	C	220	380	3,4	50
El Salvador	A - G,I,J,L	115	200	3	60
Equatorial Guinea	C,E	220	-	-	50
Eritrea	C	230	400	4	50
Estonia	F	230	400	4	50
Ethiopia	C,F	220	380	4	50
Faeroe Islands	C,K	230	400	3,4	50
Falkland Islands	G	240	415	4	50
Fiji	I	240	415	3,4	50
Finland	C,F	230	400	3,4	50
France	E	230	400	4	50
French Guyana	C,D,E	220	380	3,4	50
Gabon	C	220	380	4	50
Gambia	G	230	400	4	50
Gaza	H	230	400	4	50
Georgia	C	220	380	4	50
Germany	C,F	230	400	4	50
Ghana	D,G	230	400	3,4	50
Gibraltar	C,G	230	400	4	50
Greece	C,F	230	400	4	50
Greenland	C,K	230	400	3,4	50
Grenada	G	230	400	4	50
Guadeloupe	C,D,E	230	400	3,4	50
Guam	A,B	110	190	3,4	60

Country	Plug Socket Type/s	Single Phase (Vac)	Three Phase (Vac)	Number of Wires	(Hz)
Guatemala	A,B,G,I	120	208	3,4	60
Guinea	C,F ,K	220	380	3,4	50
Guinea-Bissau	C	220	380	3,4	50
Guyana	A,B,D,G	240	190	3,4	60
Haiti	A,B	110	190	3,4	60
Honduras	A,B	110	190	3	60
Hong Kong	G	220	380	3,4	50
Hungary	C,F	230	400	3,4	50
Iceland	C,F	230	400	3,4	50
India	C,D,M	230	400	4	50
Indonesia	C,F	230	400	4	50
Iran	C,F	230	400	3,4	50
Iraq	C,D,G	230	400	4	50
Ireland (Eire)	G	230	400	4	50
Isle of Man	C,G	230	400	4	50
Israel	H,C	230	400	4	50
Italy	C,F,L	230	400	4	50
Jamaica	A,B	110	190	3,4	50
Japan	A,B	100	200	3	50/60 **
Jordan	B - D,F,G,J	230	400	3,4	50
Kazakhstan	C	220	380	3,4	50
Kenya	G	240	415	4	50
Kiribati	I	240	-	-	50
Korea, South	C,F	220	380	4	60
Kuwait	C,G	240	415	4	50
Kyrgyzstan	C	220	380	3,4	50
Laos	A,B,C,E,F	230	400	4	50
Latvia	C,F	230	400	4	50
Lebanon	A,B,C,D,G	230	400	4	50
Lesotho	M	220	380	4	50
Liberia	A,B	120	208	3,4	60
Libya	D	127/220	220/400	4	50
Liechtenstein	J	230	400	4	50
Lithuania	C,E	230	400	4	50
Luxembourg	C,F	230	400	4	50
Macau	D,G	220	380	3	50
Macedonia	C / F	230	400	4	50
Madagascar	C,D,E, J,K	127/220	220/380	3,4	50
Madeira	C,F	230	400	3,4	50
Malawi	G	230	400	3,4	50
Malaysia	G	240	415	4	50
Maldives	A,D,G,J - L	230	400	4	50
Mali	C,E	220	380	3,4	50
Malta	G	230	400	4	50
Martinique	C,D,E	220	380	3,4	50

Country	Plug Socket Type/s	Single Phase (Vac)	Three Phase (Vac)	Number of Wires	(Hz)
Mauritania	C	220	220	3	50
Mauritius	C,G	230	400	4	50
Mexico	A	127	220/480	3,4	60
Micronesia	A,B	120	-	-	60
Moldova	C	230	380	4	50
Monaco	C,D,E,F	230	400	4	50
Mongolia	C,E	230	400	4	50
Montserrat	A,B	230	400	4	60
Morocco	C,E	220	380	4	50
Mozambique	C,F,M	220	380	4	50
Myanmar (formerly Burma)	C,D,F,G	230	400	4	50
Namibia	D,M	220	380	4	50
Nauru	I	240	415	4	50
Nepal	C,D,M	230	400	4	50
Netherlands	C,F	230	400	3	50
Netherlands Antilles	A,B,F	127/220	220/380	3,4	50
New Caledonia	F	220	380	3,4	50
New Zealand	I	230	400	3,4	50
Nicaragua	A	120	208	3,4	60
Niger	A - F	220	380	4	50
Nigeria	D,G	230	400	4	50
Norway	C,F	230	400	4	50
Oman	C,G	240	415	4	50
Pakistan	C,D	230	400	3	50
Palau	A,B	120	208	3	60
Panama	A,B	110	190	3	60
Papua New Guinea	I	240	415	4	50
Paraguay	C	220	380	4	50
Peru	A,B,C	220	220	3	60
Philippines	A,B,C	220	380	3	60
Poland	C,E	230	400	4	50
Portugal	C,F	230	400	3,4	50
Puerto Rico	A,B	120	208	3,4	60
Qatar	D,G	240	415	3,4	50
Réunion Island	E	230	400	4	50
Romania	C,F	230	400	3	50
Russian Federation	C,F	230	400	4	50
Rwanda	C,J	230	400	4	50
San Marino	F,L	230	400	4	50
Saudi Arabia ***	A,B,C,G	110/220	190/380	4	60
Senegal	C,D,E,K	230	400	3,4	50
Serbia & Montenegro	C,F	230	400	3,4	50
Seychelles	G	240	240	3	50
Sierra Leone	D,G	230	400	4	50
Singapore	G	230	400	4	50

Country	Plug Socket Type/s	Single Phase (Vac)	Three Phase (Vac)	Number of Wires	(Hz)
Slovakia	E	230	400	4	50
Slovenia	C,F	230	400	3,4	50
Somalia	C	220	380	3,4	50
South Africa	M	230	400	3,4	50
Spain	C,F	230	400	3,4	50
Sri Lanka	D,G,M	230	400	4	50
St. Kitts and Nevis	D,G	230	400	4	60
St. Lucia	G	230	400	4	50
St. Vincent	A,C,E,G,I,K	230	400	4	50
Sudan	C,D	230	400	4	50
Suriname	C,F	127	220	3,4	60
Swaziland	M	230	400	4	50
Sweden	C.F	230	400	3,4	50
Switzerland	J	230	400	3,4	50
Syria	C,E.L	220	380	3	50
Tahiti	A.B.E	110/220	220/380	3,4	60
Taiwan	A.B	110	190	3,4	60
Tajikistan	C,I	220	380	3	50
Tanzania	D,G	230	400	3,4	50
Thailand	A,B,C	220	380	3,4	50
Togo	C	220	380	4	50
Tonga	I	240	415	3,4	50
Trinidad & Tobago	A,B	115	200	3,4	60
Tunisia	C,E	230	400	4	50
Turkey	C,F	230	400	3,4	50
Turkmenistan	B,F	220	380	3	50
Uganda	G	240	415	4	50
Ukraine	C,F	230	380	4	50
United Arab Emirates	G	240	415	3,4	50
United Kingdom	G	230	400	4	50
United States of America	A / B	120/208	277/480	3,4	60
Uruguay	C,F,I,L	220	220	3	50
Uzbekistan	C,I	220	380	4	50
Venezuela	A,B	120	240	3,4	60
Vietnam	A,C,G	220	380	4	50
Virgin Islands	A,B	110	190	3,4	60
Western Samoa	I	230	400	3	50
Yemen, Rep. of	A,D,G	230	400	4	50
Zambia	C,D,G	230	400	4	50
Zimbabwe	D,G	240	415	3,4	50

Notes:

1. Plug types refer to the type of plugs used within a country or region and the nomenclature is a standard international form.

* There is no standard voltage in Brazil. Most regions use 127Vac. 220Vac can be found in northern areas.

** Frequency varies between regions in Japan.

*** Saudi Arabia uses 110Vac. 220Vac can also be found mainly within hotels and some regions.

Type A: Flat blade attachment plug

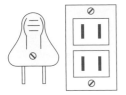

Type B: Flat blade attachment plug with round grounding pin

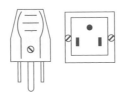

Type C: Round pin attachment plug

Type D: Round pins with ground

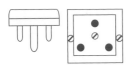

Type E: Round pin plug and receptacle with male ground pin

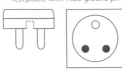

Type F: Schuko plug and receptable with side grounding contacts

Type G: Rectangular blade plug

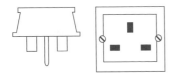

Type H: Oblique flat blades with ground

Type I: Oblique flat blades (inverted V-shape) with ground

Type J: Round pins with ground (off-set)

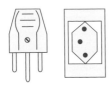

Type K: Round pins with spade ground

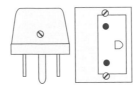

Type L: Round pins with ground (in-line)

Type M: South African plug similar to type D but larger and with one oversized pin

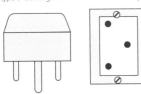

Sample UPS Specifications

500VA-2kVA, IT UPS

Modules	DV 500	DV 800	DV 1100	DV 1500	DV 2000
Power	500VA	800VA	1100VA	1500VA	2000VA
Dimensions (hwd) mm	235x110x383	235x110x383	235x110x383	235x160x425	235x160x425
Weight	7.2 Kg	10.6 Kg	11 Kg	18 Kg	18.4 Kg
IEC mains input plug	1 (10A)	1 (10A)	1 (10A)	1 (10A)	1 (10A)
IEC output sockets	4 (10A)	4 (10A)	4 (10A)	4 (10A)	4 (10A)

Modules	DVR 500	DVR 800	DVR 1100	DVD 1500	DVD 2200	DVD 3000
Power	500VA	800VA	1100VA	1500VA	2200VA	3000VA
Dimensions (hwd) mm	1Ux19"x460	1Ux19"x460	1Ux19"x460	2Ux19"x582	2Ux19"x582	2Ux19"x582
Weight	12 Kg	13.5 Kg	15.6 Kg	15.6 Kg	31 Kg	32.8 Kg
IEC mains input plug	1 (10A)	1 (10A)	1 (10A)	1 (10A)	1 (16A)	1 (16A)
IEC output sockets	4 (10A)	4 (10A)	4 (10A)	8 (10A)	8 (10A)	8 (10A) 1 (16A)

INPUT	
Rated voltage	230 Vac
Voltage range	160 V - 294 Vac
Frequency	50/60 Hz auto-sensing
Frequency range	±5%
OUTPUT	
Rated voltage	230 Vac (+5% -10%)
Waveform	True sinewave
Frequency	50/60 Hz selectable
BATTERY SET	
Type .	VRLA AGM Maintenance-free lead-acid
Recharge time	2-4 hours
ENVIRONMENTAL	
Operating temperature	0-40 °C
Relative humidity	<95% non-condensing
Protection	Overload - short-circuit - overvoltage - undervoltage - temperature - low battery
Noise	<40 dBA at 1m
Communication	USB / RS-232 / slot for interface communication
Compliance	Safety EN 62040-1 EMC EN 62040-2 Directives 73/23/-89/336 EEC EN 62040-3
Performance	IEC / EN62040-3

Dialog Vision

OPTIONS
Netman 102
Battery box (only DVD 2200/3000)
Extended charging current (only DVD 2200/3000)

Note: for individual UPS runtimes refer to the relevant product manual.

3.3-10kVA, Network UPS, transformerless

Modules	DLD 330	DLD 400	DLD 500	DLD 600	DLD 800	DLD 1000
Power	3.3kVA	4kVA	5kVA	6kVA	8kVA	10kVA
INPUT						
Rated voltage	220-230-240 Vac				230 Vac single-phase or 400 Vac three-phase + N	
Minimum voltage	164 Vac @ load 100% 84 Vac @ load 50%					
Rated frequency	50/60 Hz ±5 Hz					
Power factor	>0.98				>0.98 (single/single-phase)	
Current distortion	≤7%		≤5%		≤7% (single/single-phase)	
BYPASS						
Voltage range	180-164 Vac (selectable in economy mode and Smart Active mode)					
Frequency range	Selected frequency ±5% (user configurable)					
BATTERY SET						
Recharge time	2-4 hours					
OUTPUT						
Rated voltage	220-230-240 Vac selectable					
Static variation	1.5%					
Dynamic variation	≤5% in 20ms					
Waveform	Sinewave					
Distortion (linear load)	<3%					
Distortion (non-linear load)	<6%					
Frequency	50/60 Hz selectable					
Crest factor	3:1					
OVERLOAD CAPACITY						
100% <Load <110%	1'				1'	
110% <Load <125%	4"				1'	
125% <Load <150%	4"				10"	
Load> 150%	0.5'				0.5"	
ENVIRONMENTAL						
Weight (kg)	38	40	62	64	80	85
Dimensions (hwd) mm tower/rack	455x175x520/175 (4U)x483x520		455x175x660/175 (4U)x483x660		2x455x175x660/175 (4U)x483x660	
On-Line efficiency	92%					
Line Interactive / Smart Active efficiency	98%					
Operating temperature	0-40°C					

Dialog Dual

Modules	DLD 330	DLD 400	DLD 500	DLD 600	DLD 800	DLD 1000
Power	3.3kVA	4kVA	5kVA	6kVA	8kVA	10kVA
Relative humidity	<95% non-condensing					
Protection	Overload - short-circuit - overvoltage - undervoltage - temperature - low battery					
Communication	USB / RS-232 + communication interface slot					
Colour	Metallic grey (silver)					
Noise	<40dBA at 1m		<45dBA at 1m			
Accessories provided	2x10A cables; 1xIEC-16A plug; software; serial cable; plastic key to release display		2xcable guides; terminal board connection; software; serial cable; plastic key to release display; handles kit			
Compliance	Safety EN 62040-1 EMC EN 62040-2 Directives 73/23-93/86/-89/336 EEC EN 62040-3					
Classification	Voltage Frequency Independent VFI-SS-111 under IEC 62040-3					
OPTIONS						
Extended runtimes	yes (with or without battery charger)					
Maintenance bypass	yes					
Interface cards	yes					
Telescopic rails for racks	yes					

Note: for individual UPS runtimes refer to the relevant product manual.

10-20kVA, 1/1 or 3/1 Network UPS, transformerless

Modules	MDM 10-AF	MDM 15-AF	MDM 20-AF
Power	10kVA	15kVA	20kVA
INPUT			
Rated voltage	230 Vac single-phase or 400 Vac three-phase + N		
Voltage range	±20%		
Rated frequency	45-65 Hz		
Power factor	>0.99		
Current distortion	<4%		
BYPASS			
Rated voltage	230 Vac		
Number of phases	1		
Permitted voltage range	±15% (selectable from ±5% to ±25%)		
Rated frequency	50/60 Hz		
Frequency range	±2% (selectable from ±1% to ±5%		
BATTERY SET			
Type	Lead, flooded and VRLA AGM/Gel;Ni-Cad		
Recharge time	6 hours		
OUTPUT			
Rated power (kVA)	10	15	20
Rated power (kW)	8	12 (3/1), 10.5 (1/1)	16 (3/1), 12 (1/1)
Number of phases	1		
Rated voltage	230 Vac		
Voltage regulation	200-243 Vac		
Crest factor	3:1		
Waveform	Sinewave		
Distortion (linear load)	≤2%		
Distortion (non-linear load)	≤5%		
Static stability	±1%		
Dynamic stability	±5% in 10ms		
Frequency	50/60 Hz (selectable)		
Overload	110% 125% 150% of the rated current for 5h/10'/1'		
ENVIRONMENTAL			
Weight (kg)	from 105 to 243	from 110 to 330	from 125 to 345
Dimensions (hwd) mm	1200x450x750		
Input	Single-phase or three-phase input + neutral		
Remote signalling	Volt-free contacts		
Remote control	EPO and bypass		
Communication	Double RS-232 + remote contacts + communication interface slot		

Multi Dialog

Modules	MDM 10-AF	MDM 15-AF	MDM 20-AF
Power	10kVA	15kVA	20kVA
Operating temperature	0-40°C		
Relative humidity	<95% non-condensing		
Colour	Light grey RAL 7035		
Noise	<56 dBA at 1m		
Protection rating	IP20		
Efficiency	>92% in On-Line / >98% in Economy / Smart Active / Standby-off / AVS mode		
Compliance	Safety EN 62040-1 EMC EN 62040-2 Directives 73/23-93/68-89/336 EEC EN 62040-3		
Classification	Voltage Frequency Independent VFI-SS-111 under IEC 62040-3		

Note: for individual UPS runtimes refer to the relevant product manual.

10-80kVA, 3/3 Network UPS, transformerless

Modules	MDT 10-AF	MDT 15-AF	MDT 20-AF	MDT 30-AF	MDT 40-AF	MDT 60-AF	MDT 80-AF
Power	10kVA	15kVA	20kVA	30kVA	40kVA	60kVA	80kVA
INPUT							
Rated voltage	400 Vac three-phase + N						
Voltage range	±20%						
Frequency range	45-65 Hz						
Power factor	>0.99						
Current distortion	<4%						
BYPASS							
Rated voltage	400 Vac						
Number of phases	3 + N						
Voltage range	±15% (selected from ±5% to ±25%)						
Rated frequency	50 / 60 Hz						
Frequency range	±2% (selected from ±1% to ±5%)						
BATTERY SET							
Type	Lead, flooded and VRLA AGM / Gel;Ni-Cad						
Recharge time	6 hours				4-8 hours		
OUTPUT							
Rated power (kVA)	10	15	20	30	40	60	80
Rated power (kW)	8	12	16	24	32	48	64
Number of phases	3 + N						
Rated voltage	380 - 400 - 415 Vac selectable						
Voltage regulation	346-422 Vac						
Crest factor	3:1						
Waveform	Sinewave						
Distortion (linear load)	≤2%						
Distortion (non-linear load)	≤5%						
Static stability	±1%						
Dynamic stability	±5% in 10ms						
Frequency	50/60 Hz						
Overload	110% 125% 150% of the rated current for 5h/10'/1'						
ENVIRONMENTAL							
Weight (kg)	110-258	115-335	130-350	144-370	160	180	192
Dimensions (hwd) mm	1200x450x750				1400x500x740		
Input	Three-phase + N						
Remote signalling	Volt-free contacts						
Remote control	EPO and bypass						

Multi Dialog

Modules	MDT 10-AF	MDT 15-AF	MDT 20-AF	MDT 30-AF	MDT 40-AF	MDT 60-AF	MDT 80-AF
Power	10kVA	15kVA	20kVA	30kVA	40kVA	60kVA	80kVA
Communication	Double RS-232 + remote contacts + communication interface slot						
Operating temperature	0-40°C						
Relative humidity	<95% non-condensing						
Colour	Light grey RAL 7035						
Noise at 1m	<56 dBA						<60 dBA
Protection rating	IP20						
Efficiency	>92% in On-Line / >98% in Economy / Smart Active / Standby-off / AVS mode						
Compliance	Safety EN 62040-1 EMC EN 62040-2 Directives 73/23-93/86/-89/336 EEC EN 62040-3						
Classification	Voltage Frequency Independent VFI-SS-111 under IEC 62040-3						

Note: for individual UPS runtimes refer to the relevant product manual.

10-80kVA, 3/3 Industrial and Enterprise UPS, transformer-based

Modules	RT 10	RT 15	RT 20	RT30	RT 40	RT 60	RT 80
Power	10kVA	15kVA	20kVA	30kVA	40kVA	60kVA	80kVA
INPUT							
Rated voltage	400 Vac three-phase						
Voltage range	±20%						
Frequency range	45-65 Hz						
Power factor	>0.9 in RT CLEAN version						
Current distortion	<5% in RT CLEAN version						
Soft start	0-100% in 10"						
BYPASS							
Rated voltage	230 Vac three-phase						
Voltage range	±15% (selectable from ±10% to ±25% from front panel)						
Rated frequency	50/60 Hz (auto-sensing)						
Frequency range	±2% (selected from ±1% to ±5% from front panel)						
Standard features	Back-feed protection; separate bypass line						
BATTERY SET							
Type	Lead, flooded and VRLA AGM / Gel;Ni-Cad						
Recharge current (A)	0.2xC10 maximum						
RECTIFIER OUTPUT							
Maintenance voltage	Variable according to temperature (-0.5Vx°C)						
Ripple	<1%						
INVERTER OUTPUT							
Rated power (kVA)	10	15	20	30	40	60	80
Rated power (kW)	8	12	16	24	32	48	64
Number of phases	3 + N						
Rated voltage	400 Vac						
Rated current (A)	14	22	29	43	58	87	115
Voltage regulation	348-424 Vac phase/phase						
Crest factor	3:1						
Waveform	Sinewave						
Distortion (linear load)	≤3%						
Distortion (non-linear load)	≤8%						
Static stability	±1%						
Dynamic stability	±5% in 5ms						
Frequency	50/60 Hz configurable						
Overload	110% 125% 150% of the rated current for 5h/10'/1'						
Frequency stability	±0.05% on mains failure ±2% (selectable from ±1% to ±5%) with mains supply present						

Master Dialog

Modules	RT 10	RT 15	RT 20	RT30	RT 40	RT 60	RT 80
Power	10kVA	15kVA	20kVA	30kVA	40kVA	60kVA	80kVA
ENVIRONMENTAL							
Weight (kg)	210-480	220-490	230-500	230-552	330	450	555
Dimensions (hwd) mm	1200x555x720				1400x800x740		
Remote signalling	Volt-free contacts						
Remote control	EPO andbypass						
Communication	RS-232 + remote contacts						
Operating temperature	0-40°C						
Relative humidity	<95% non-condensing						
Colour	Light grey RAL 7035						
Noise	54 dBA at 1m		60 dBA at 1m		62 dBA at 1m		
Protection rating	IP20						
Efficiency	>90%		>91%		>92%		
Compliance	Safety EN 62040-1 EMC EN 62040-2 Directives 73/23-93/86/-89/336 EEC EN 62040-3						
Classification	Voltage Frequency Independent VFI-SS-111 under IEC 62040-3						

Note: for individual UPS runtimes refer to the relevant product manual.

100-200kVA, 3/3 Industrial and Enterprise UPS, transformer-based

Modules	MP 100	MP 120	MP 160	MP 200
Power	100kVA	120kVA	160kVA	200kVA
INPUT				
Rated voltage	380-400-415 Vac three-phase			
Voltage range	400 V ±20%			
Frequency range	45-65 Hz			
Power factor	>0.95 in the 12MP HC version			
Current distortion	<3% in 12MP HC version			
Soft start	0-100% in 120" (user configurable)			
BYPASS				
Rated voltage	400 Vac three-phase			
Voltage range	±15% (selectable from ±10% to ±25% from front panel)			
Rated frequency	50/60 Hz (auto-sensing)			
Frequency range	±2% (selectable from ±1% to ±5% from the front panel)			
Standard features	Back-feed protection; separable bypass line			
BATTERY SET				
Type	Lead, flooded and VRLA AGM / Gel;Ni-Cad			
Ripple	<1%			
Temperature compensation	-0.5Vx°C			
OUTPUT				
Rated power (kVA)	100	120	160	200
Rated power (kW)	80	96	128	160
Number of phases	3 + N			
Rated voltage	380-400-415 Vac three-phase + N			
Rated current (A)	145	174	232	290
Voltage regulation	348-424 Vac phase/phase			
Crest factor	3:1			
Waveform	Sinewave			
Static stability	±1%			
Dynamic stability	±5% in 5ms			
Distortion (linear load)	≤1%			
Distortion (non-linear load)	≤3%			
Frequency	50 or 60 Hz configurable			
Overload	110% for 60'; 125% for 10';150% for 1'			

Master Plus

Modules	MP 100	MP 120	MP 160	MP 200
Power	100kVA	120kVA	160kVA	200kVA
SYSTEM				
Remote signalling	Volt-free contacts			
Remote control	EPO and bypass			
Communication	Double RS-232 + remote contacts + communication slots			
Efficiency	Up to 94%			
Dimensions (hwd) mm	1900x800x800			
Weight (kg)	600	650	750	800
Noise level	63-68 dBA at 1m			
Operating temperature	0-40°C			
Relative humidity	<95% non-condensing			
Protection rating	IP20			
Colour	Light grey RAL 7035			
Compliance	Safety EN 62040-1 EMC EN 62040-2 Directives 73/23-93/86/-89/336 EEC EN 62040-3			
Classification	Voltage Frequency Independent VFI-SS-111 under IEC 62040-3			

Note: for individual UPS runtimes refer to the relevant product manual.

250-800kVA, 3/3 Industrial and Enterprise UPS, transformer-based

Modules	12RT 250	12RT 300	12RT 400	12RT 500	12RT 600	12RT 800
Power	250kVA	300kVA	400kVA	500kVA	600kVA	800kVA
INPUT						
Rated voltage	380-400-415 Vac three-phase					
Voltage range	±20%					
Frequency range	50-60 Hz					
Current distortion	>4% in CLEAN version					
BYPASS						
Rated voltage	380-400-415 Vac single-phase					
Voltage range	±15% (selectable from ±10% to ±25% from front panel)					
Rated frequency	50/60 Hz (autorange)					
Frequency range	±2% (selected from ±1% to ±5% from front panel)					
Standard features	Back-feed protection; separate bypass line					
BATTERY SET						
Type	Lead, flooded and VRLA AGM / Gel;Ni-Cad					
Recharge current (A)	0.2xC10 Maximum					
RECTIFIER OUTPUT						
Maintenance voltage	Variable according to temperature (-0.5Vx°C)					
Ripple	<1%					
INVERTER OUTPUT						
Rated power (kVA)	250	300	400	500	600	800
Rated power (kW)	200	240	320	400	480	640
Number of phases	3 + N					
Rated voltage	380-400-415 Vac three-phase + N					
Rated current (A)	362	435	580	725	870	1159
Crest factor	3:1					
Waveform	Sinewave					
Distortion (linear load)	≤2%					
Distortion (non-linear load)	≤7%					
Static stability	±1%					
Dynamic stability	±5% in 5ms					
Frequency	50/60 Hz configurable					
Overload	110% 125% 150% of the rated current for 60'/10'/1'					
Frequency stability	±0.05% on mains failure ±2% with mains supply present					

Master Dialog

Modules	12RT 250	12RT 300	12RT 400	12RT 500	12RT 600	12RT 800
Power	250kVA	300kVA	400kVA	500kVA	600kVA	800kVA
ENVIRONMENTAL						
Weight (kg)	2200		2600	3600	4000	5300
Dimensions (hwd)(mm)	1900x1630x850		1900x1630 x1000	1900x1630x850		1900x4400 1000
Remote signalling	Volt-free contacts					
Remote control	EPO and bypass					
Communication	RS-232 + remote contacts					
Operating temperature	0-40°C					
Relative humidity	<95% non contacts					
Colour	Light grey RAL 7035					
Noise	<70 dBA at 1m			<80 dBA at 1m		
Protection rating	IP20					
Efficiency	>93%			<94%		
Compliance	Safety EN 62040-1 EMC EN 62040-2 Directives 73/23-93/86/-89/336 EEC EN 62040-3					
Classification	Voltage Frequency Independent VFI-SS-111 under IEC 62040-3					

Note: for individual UPS runtimes refer to the relevant product manual.

UPS Site Survey

1. Site Details

Site address:	Project:
	Site contact:
	Title:
	Tel or Mobile:
Post code:	Email or Fax:

2. Load Description

Load power supply phases	[ ] Single [ ] Three [ ] Other
Voltage	[ ] 230Vac [ ] 400Vac [ ] Other
Frequency	[ ] 50Hz [ ] 60Hz [ ] 400Hz [ ] Other
Load (kVA)	
Real Power (kW)	
Amps per phase - P1/P2/P3	
Runtime required (minutes or hours)	
Recharge time (hours)	
Installation area (WxDxHmm)	
Preferred UPS format	[ ] Floor standing [ ] Rackmount

3. Environment and Position

NOTE: If YES to any question below please describe in section 6.

Is or will the ambient temperature be below 15°C?   [ ] Yes [ ] No

Is or will the ambient temperature be above 25°C?   [ ] Yes [ ] No

Is there any risk of ingress?   [ ] Yes [ ] No
- from dust, water/fluids, chemicals or gases

Is there anything over the UPS that could leak?   [ ] Yes [ ] No
- water or waste pipes, air-conditioning units etc

Is the air flow restricted (no ventilation)?   [ ] Yes [ ] No

Is there insufficient light in the area?   [ ] Yes [ ] No

Is the floor suspended or an upper floor in the building?   [ ] Yes [ ] No
- what is the maximum floor loading?

Is the final location above/below ground level?   [ ] Yes [ ] No
- which floor will the unit be delivered to?

Is there a lift which we can have unrestricted use of?   [ ] Yes [ ] No
- confirm the dimensions and weight capacity of the lift

Will the equipment have to go up/down stairs or steps?   [ ] Yes [ ] No
- please give details - numbers of stairs and flights, width,
  turns, spiral, weight capacity etc. Note: stair walkers rated
  for 455kgs, safe handling 350kgs

Are there any obstructions along the delivery route?   [ ] Yes [ ] No
- narrow corridors, corners, fire doors, locked offices etc

Is there a loading bay with a docking platform?   [ ] Yes [ ] No

Is there a problem with vehicle access?   [ ] Yes [ ] No
- distance to entrance, legally parked red routes, double
  yellow lines, railings, kerbsides etc

Are there any length, width or height restrictions?   [ ] Yes [ ] No
- narrow roads, low bridges, door ways, overhead beams etc

Are there any time restrictions for access to site?   [ ] Yes [ ] No
- consider lunch hours, opening and closing times etc

Are there any Health & Safety implications evident?   [ ] Yes [ ] No

Is there any hazard that is NOT covered in the standard   [ ] Yes [ ] No
Risk Assessment?
Riello UPS form OHSFMS01

Are there any permits or actions required NOT covered   [ ] Yes [ ] No
in the standard Method Statement?
Riello UPS form OHSFMS11

4. Options

What options are to be considered for the application:

[ ] External bypass [ ] Panel isolation box [ ] Isolation transformer
[ ] Harmonic filter [ ] 12-pulse rectifier
[ ] UPS monitoring software - network [ ] UPS monitoring software - site
[ ] SNMP [ ] Volt-free contacts
[ ] Remote Panel LED [ ] Remote Panel LCD
[ ] Environmental monitoring [ ] Bypass monitoring [ ] Battery monitoring
[ ] Battery extension packs   [ ] On-site standby power
[ ] Remote service monitoring - TeleNetGuard (DDI required or FCT)

5. Electrical Installation Requirements

Mains power supply phases	[ ] Single [ ] Three [ ] Other
Voltage	[ ] 230Vac [ ] 400Vac [ ] Other
Frequency	[ ] 50Hz [ ] 60Hz [ ] 400Hz [ ] Other
Amps per phase - P1/P2/P3	

Is the client (or their contractor) responsible for the electrical   [ ] Yes [ ] No
installation? Riello UPS form OHSFMS01

If yes please ensure the following:

• the client is aware they are responsible for all electrical connections
• the client is aware of the size of the required supply
• the client is sent an installation manual prior to receipt of UPS
• [ ] UPS power point for SNMP and modem
• [ ] Telephone point for TeleNetGuard modem

Is Riello UPS responsible for the electrical installation?   [ ] Yes [ ] No
• if YES please attach Scope of Works

Are building works required?   [ ] Yes [ ] No

Commissioning   [ ] Yes [ ] No

Battery Build   [ ] Yes [ ] No

UPS Removal and Disposal   [ ] Yes [ ] No

Battery Removal   [   ] Yes [   ] No

Equipment Relocation   [   ] Yes [   ] No

To enter site do we need any special form of ID or is there [   ] Yes [   ] No
a booking in procedure?
• if YES please attach detail or describe in section 6

Are site specific Method Statements and Risk   [   ] Yes [   ] No
Assessments required?
Detail items not covered in Risk Assessment OHSFM01 and
Method Statement OHSFM11, in section 6

Are there any Health & Safety requirements required to   [   ] Yes [   ] No
enter site? - PPE hard hats or 'toe protectors' etc

Are there any other special instructions?   [   ] Yes [   ] No

6. Notes

Use this space for special notes or attach further document/s or drawings.

Survey completed:

Dated (dd/mm/yy)	
Riello UPS contact	Signature
Client name	Signature

UPS Sizing Check-List

This check-list may be used to help size UPS for a *Power Continuity Plan*.

General Information		Priority	Input			Current Drawn	Apparent Power	Real Power	Power Factor		Runtime	
Critical Load	Description or Reference		Phases	Voltage	Frequency						Battery	Standby
Yes / No		A / B / C	(3 or 1)	(V)	(Hz)	(A per phase)	(VA / kVA / MVA)	(W / kW / MW)	(pF)	Type	(M / H)	(M / H)
Total												
Add expansion factor (typically 25%)												
Future Proof Total												

Notes:

1. Complete a separate sheet for essential and non-essential loads.
2. For load shedding, group 'A' items must be kept running the longest and 'C' the shortest and therefore groups 'B' and 'C' will be subjected to load shedding if available as an option.
3. State the power factor of the loads if known.

Method Statement - Installation and Commissioning

1. Scope of Work
To install and commission the UPS system including any associated battery extension pack/s, bypass switch/es and auxiliary devices.

2. Customer Actions
The client must supply free, unrestricted and safe access to all working areas and routes. The client is responsible for the health, safety and welfare of Riello UPS personnel including sub-contractors acting on behalf of Riello UPS on their site. The client must ensure all other on-site personnel are made aware of activities to be carried out by Riello UPS as defined in OHSPRO16 - Lone Worker.

Customer Actions - specific - None.

3. Risk Assessment
Ensure that the standard (or applicable site specific) risk assessment covers all risks present on site. If any new or unacceptable risks are identified, carry out a site specific risk assessment. If the risks cannot be eliminated, obtain agreement to proceed.

4. PPE Equipment
The following equipment will be used where appropriate (please tick):
[ ] Safety Helmet
[ ] Ear Defenders
[ ] Eye Protection Glasses
[ ] Dust Mask, Gloves (electrical/carrying)
[ ] High Visibility Vests, (Orange or Yellow)
[ ] Overalls
[ ] Safety Boots
[ ] Other

5. Resources Required
- manpower: please specify
- specialised equipment: please specify
- vehicles: please specify

6. Permit Check-List
Identify and obtain all relevant permits to work, in particular for electrical isolation. Electrical isolation will be requested prior to commencing work from the responsible site representative. The Riello UPS engineer will ensure the isolation is locked out and safe to proceed, testing the isolation using live-dead testing techniques.

Where live testing is required, the engineer will follow the appropriate safe-working practices, including the use of an isolation mat and ensure either a competent person is present, or a person who has been made aware of the procedures in the event of electrocution.

7. Route To Work Area

The route to the work area should be checked for any trip hazards or obstacles ensuring that all equipment and/or parts can be taken to the work area safely using the appropriate lifting/ carrying equipment where required. Parked vehicles will be in allocated parking areas as close to the work area as possible. Recognised pathways and access areas will be used.

8. Secure Work Area

The work area should be made secure to prevent unauthorised access. Where employees/clients or the public have access, a barrier should be erected around the work and identify the risk/s within the work area.

9. Equipment Used

All equipment used will be PAT certified and where power tools are used they will either be battery operated or 110Vac Centre Tapped Earth (CTE) safety tools used with the appropriate safety transformer.

10. Supervision of Sub-Contractors

All sub-contractors will be fully trained and approved by Riello UPS. Sub-contractors will represent Riello UPS and will therefore adhere to procedures as implemented by Riello UPS. Any deviation from that stated needs to be agreed with Riello UPS prior to work commencing.

11. Fire Prevention Requirements

All combustible material will be removed from the immediate vicinity of the equipment/work area. The engineer/s will ensure that they are familiar with fire extinguisher locations and with fire and emergency arrangements. Where 'hot' working is required engineers will carry their own CO extinguisher.

12. Method of Works

12.1 Inspection of the UPS and associated items

Upon completion of the positioning of the UPS system and associated items, the engineer will inspect all of the supplied items for damage and ensure that all of the required components are present to complete the installation or commissioning. Any issues or points raised from this inspection will be brought to the attention of the customer, carrier or supplier.

12.2 Inspection of the UPS location and environment

The engineer will evaluate the suitability of the positioning, location and environmental conditions surrounding the UPS system and associated items. This is to ensure that the proposed location for the UPS will enable the system to continue to operate efficiently under the designed load conditions without causing unnecessary stress upon key components, e.g. the effects of ambient temperature on battery life etc. Any concerns, issues or advice will be brought to the attention of the customer and/or supplier.

12.3 Installation and connection of the UPS and bypass switch

The UPS and bypass system will be electrically installed and connected as required and agreed by the customer. All upstream and downstream electrical work will be carried out in compliance to regulations, guidelines and legislation in force during the time of installation. If required, the electrical installation will also be carried out in compliance with specific customer site electrical regulations and guidelines.

12.4 Installation and connection of the battery set

The batteries will be installed into the proposed battery cabinet using the appropriate lifting/carrying techniques and equipment (refer to OHSPRO01). The installation of the batteries will be carried out in accordance with the applicable battery installation diagrams, data, and battery safe working practice guidelines (refer to OHSPRO17). If during the installation a battery releases acid electrolyte, the acid electrolyte will be absorbed into dry sand, earth or other inert material and will not be allowed to enter any drains. The acid electrolyte can be neutralised using Soda Ash, Sodium Bicarbonate, Sodium Carbonate or Calcium Carbonate powder and the affected area will be washed thoroughly with water. Any neutralisation or absorbing materials used will be collected and placed into a sealed container to await disposal.

12.5 Installation and connection of auxiliary devices and serial cables

Any auxiliary devices, for example, remote panels, SNMP adaptors and modems, will be installed and configured to the basic operational requirements unless specific requirements are requested.

When installing a Master Dialog UPS the communications cable must be connected to both the UPS serial port and the bypass panel serial port park connector facility. If no serial port park connector facility is available or if it is not convenient to use the park facility, the cable will only be connected to the UPS and left coiled neatly in a suitable accessible location (without the need to remove any safety panels).

12.6 Safety check

Upon completion of the installation, all of the previously removed protective panels will be checked and secured, all warning notices cleaned, the area around the system cleared and any safety issue/s raised, brought to the attention of the customer and noted.

12.7 UPS initial switch-on and commission

Once all access panels have been refitted and confirmation that it is safe to switch on, the electrical system supplying the UPS will be energised, and in accordance with the UPS and bypass user manuals the system will be activated and checked to ensure that no permanent alarms occur and operation is correct.

12.8 UPS configuration set-up

Whilst the UPS system is operational, it will be configured and set-up as required, e.g. battery capacity, time, date, operational parameters and method of operation.

12.9 UPS, bypass and auxiliary device operational test

In conjunction with the external bypass switch user manual, the bypass switch will be tested in all switch positions to ensure correct operation as described. This will ensure the bypass switch operates in accordance with the manufacturer's specification.

In conjunction with the specific auxiliary device user manual, the operation of any auxiliary devices will be tested to ensure correct operation as described. This will ensure that any auxiliary devices connected operate as required.

In conjunction with the UPS user manual, the UPS will be tested in all operational states e.g. on bypass, on line and on battery, to ensure that the UPS operates and reports as described. During operation, a full operational check of the display panel will be carried out to ensure that all of the values, status and buttons are functioning and reporting correctly.

12.10 UPS discharge test

If applicable, the UPS system will be discharge tested to ensure that the required battery autonomy time is reached. This will be carried out using either a dummy load or the actual load depending on the site requirements.

The battery discharge test can only be carried out if the battery system has been fully charged; if it is not fully charged then the charge state will be taken into consideration during the discharge. To instigate the discharge test, the mains power supply to the UPS system will be switched off to simulate a mains power supply failure and not be reinstated until the required autonomy time has been met or the connected batteries have been depleted.

12.11 On-site training and handover

If applicable, the customer will be provided with operational on-site training. This will involve a brief description of the UPS and a basic operational overview. This will enable the customer to operate the UPS and understand the system during operation.

Once the customer is satisfied with the work undertaken, the system will be handed over and all relevant installation documentation completed and signed.

13. Generation and Removal of Waste

All waste generated on site will be removed and disposed of in accordance with the local authority environmental policy.

14. Riello UPS References

Reference	Title
OHSSSW01	Safe Systems of Work for Manual Handling
OHSPRO01	Manual Handling Procedure
OHSSSW02	Off-Site Working
OHSSSW03	Safe System Working of Plant and Equipment
OHSPLN03	Electrical Safety Policy
OHSPRO17	Battery Safe Working Practices
H&S File	COSHH Assessments and Data Sheets
OHSFMS48	UPS Installation and Commissioning Certificate

UPS Commissioning Certificate

1. Job Data

Model		Serial number	
Job number		Location	
Environmental conditions			
Condition of connections			

2. Cables and Fuses

Internal breaker rating type		All fuses fitted	[ ] Yes [ ] No
Supply and load cable sizes		Comms cables fitted	[ ] Yes [ ] No

3. Batteries

Internal battery		External battery	
Rating/type		Rating/type	
All battery links secure		Battery date and condition	
dc Volts OK + OK for UPS		Polarity and fuses checked	[ ] Yes [ ] No
Chargers fitted (detail)			

4. Battery Performance Results (with mains power applied)

Float voltage (Vdc)	Measured load (Watts)	Temperature °C

5. Battery Performance Results (without mains power)

Time period						
Volts (Vdc)						
Load (Watts)						
Low battery discharge point reached [ ] Yes [ ] No				Low battery voltage (Vdc)		

6. Refit Covers and Panels

Inner cover	[ ] Yes [ ] No
Outer cover	[ ] Yes [ ] No
Earth terminations	[ ] Yes [ ] No

7. UPS Installation and Set-Up

Instruction	Observation
UPS start-up	
Confirm normal operation	
Confirm battery rating/type	
Confirm reset date/time	
Record any special set-up requirements	
Adjust output to match input	

8. Ventilation Fans and Cleanliness

Confirm fan/s operate correctly	[ ] Yes [ ] No [ ] Attention
Check ventilation slots are clear	[ ] Yes [ ] No [ ] Attention
Check UPS is generally clean	[ ] Yes [ ] No [ ] Attention
Any signs of overheating	[ ] Yes [ ] No [ ] Attention

9. Bypass Test Check (If fitted)

Confirm correct operation of SWMB (if safe to)	[ ] Yes [ ] No [ ] Attention
Confirm external bypass operation in all positions (if safe to)	[ ] Yes [ ] No [ ] Attention
Check supply fuses/MCB	[ ] Yes [ ] No [ ] Attention

10. Operational Data

Input voltage (Vac)	
Phasing	
Rotation checked	
Input frequency	
Battery voltage (Vdc)	

11. Remote Communications

Network interface fitted	[ ] Yes [ ] No [ ] Not required
Remote modem installed	[ ] Yes [ ] No [ ] Not required
Comms cable connected to UPS	[ ] Yes [ ] No [ ] Not required
Comms software CD or web link given to site contact	[ ] Yes [ ] No [ ] Not required

12. Final Considerations

UPS operation	
Generator test	
Alarm logs	
Completion of on-site training and handover	

Job date (dd/mm/yy)	
Arrived on site (hh:mm)	
Left site (hh:mm)	
Riello UPS service engineer name	Signature
Client name	Signature

Method Statement - Preventative Maintenance and Repair

1. Scope of Work
Perform preventative maintenance and/or repair work to the UPS system.

2. Customer Actions
The client must supply free, unrestricted and safe access to all working areas and routes. The client is responsible for the health, safety and welfare of Riello UPS personnel including sub-contractors acting on behalf of Riello UPS on their site. The client must ensure all other on-site personnel are made aware of activities to be carried out by Riello UPS as defined in OHSPRO16 - Lone Worker.

Customer Actions - specific - None.

3. Risk Assessment
Ensure that the standard (or applicable site-specific) risk assessment covers all risks present on site. If any new or unacceptable risks are identified, carry out a site specific risk assessment. If the risks cannot be eliminated, obtain agreement to proceed.

4. PPE Equipment
The following equipment will be used where appropriate (please tick):
[ ] Safety Helmet
[ ] Ear Defenders
[ ] Eye Protection Glasses
[ ] Dust Mask, Gloves (electrical/carrying)
[ ] High Visibility Vests, (Orange or Yellow)
[ ] Overalls
[ ] Safety Boots
[ ] Other

5. Resources Required
- manpower: specify
- specialised equipment: specify
- vehicles: specify

6. Permit Check-List
Identify and obtain all relevant permits to work, in particular for electrical isolation. Electrical isolation will be requested prior to commencing work from the responsible site representative. The Riello UPS engineer will ensure the isolation is locked out and safe to proceed, testing the isolation with tested equipment.

Where live testing is required, the engineer will follow the appropriate safe-working practices, including the use of an isolation mat and ensure either a competent person is present, or a person who has been made aware of the procedures in the event of electrocution.

7. Route To Work Area

The route to the work area should be checked for any trip hazards or obstacles ensuring that all equipment and or parts can be taken to the work area safely using the appropriate lifting/ carrying equipment where required. Parked vehicles will be in allocated parking areas as close to the work area as possible. Recognised pathways and access areas will be used.

8. Secure Work Area

The work area should be made secure to prevent unauthorised access. Where employees/clients or the public have access, a barrier should be erected around the work and identify the risk/s within the work area.

9. Equipment Used

All equipment used will be PAT certified, and where power tools are used, they will either be battery operated or 110Vac Centre Tapped Earth (CTE) safety tools used with the appropriate safety transformer.

10. Supervision of Sub-Contractors

All sub-contractors will be fully trained and approved by Riello UPS. Sub-contractors will represent Riello UPS and will, therefore, adhere to procedures as implemented by Riello UPS. Any deviation from that stated needs to be agreed with Riello UPS prior to work commencing.

11. Fire Prevention Requirements

All combustible material will be removed from the immediate vicinity of the equipment/work area. The engineer/s will ensure that they are familiar with fire extinguisher locations and with fire and emergency arrangements. Where 'hot' working is required, engineers will carry their own CO_2 extinguisher.

12. Method of Works

12.1 Customer comments and issues

12.1.1 Preventative maintenance

Prior to commencement of preventative maintenance work on the UPS system, any comments or issues raised by the customer will be acknowledged and noted to ascertain if any intermittent or erroneous problems exist with the system.

12.1.2 Repair work

Prior to commencing repair work on the UPS system, a clear understanding as to the events leading up to and during the failure will be ascertained from the customer to enable the engineer to understand the nature of the fault and to aid the repair of the system.

12.2 Customer monitoring/control software and systems

12.2.1 Preventative maintenance and repair

Prior to commencement of any work on the UPS system, a clear understanding will be obtained as to any systems that are being used to monitor the operational status of the UPS.

The two main types of monitoring system are:

- software-based via RS-232 serial ports or TCP/IP via a network card
- hardware-based via volt-free contacts

A clear understanding of the monitoring system is required to ensure that the work to be carried out on the UPS will not adversely affect any systems (software shutdown etc).

If either of the two methods of UPS monitoring shown above are in use, then the following will be carried out:

a) Software-based systems

The engineer will ask the customer to confirm that the monitoring software in use is NOT configured to shut down or take emergency action in the event of a loss of communication with the UPS. If it is not configured to do so, prior to any work being carried out the engineer will remove the communications cable/s from the UPS to ensure that no maintenance action will influence the operation of the monitoring systems. If the monitoring system is configured to take emergency action due to a loss of communications with the UPS, the customer will be required to either stop all monitoring processes or reconfigure the system, otherwise the work cannot proceed.

b) Hardware-based systems

The engineer will ask the customer to confirm if the monitoring device in use will be affected or take any emergency action if the operational status of the UPS is altered (i.e. on battery, bypass, off, etc) or if the volt-free contact connection cable is removed (a normally closed system). If it is confirmed that the monitoring device will take action, appropriate steps will have to be taken to prevent or allow for this (i.e. process stopped or monitoring station alerted).

12.3 UPS operation and environment

12.3.1 Preventative maintenance

Prior to powering down the system an inspection of the UPS status will be carried out to ensure that no alarms are present and that all measurements and configuration values are correct. The environment around the UPS will also be inspected to ensure that no problems or potential problems are present e.g. ambient temperature, air flow restrictions, dust or dirt etc, and any other issues that could cause unnecessary premature failure of the UPS or associated items.

12.3.2 Repair work

Prior to powering down the system an inspection of the UPS status will be carried out to determine the type of fault/alarm present. This will enable the engineer to gain a clear understanding of the area of failure and corrective action to be taken.

The environment and site conditions surrounding the UPS will also be inspected to determine if this was a contributing factor to the failure.

12.4 UPS bypass authorisation

Prior to switching the UPS into bypass operation, the customer will be advised that when the UPS is in bypass operation (not applicable to N+1 parallel systems) no battery back-up will be available from the system in the event of a mains power supply failure occurring. Following this brief the customer will be asked to provide a signature to confirm that they have accepted and understood the information provided. If the customer will not allow the UPS to be placed into bypass operation then a full check of the system cannot be carried out and the preventative maintenance visit will continue but with restricted testing.

12.5 UPS bypass

If available, the UPS will be switched to bypass operation in accordance with the manufacturers' user manuals. Once in bypass the UPS will be completely switched off, then isolated and locked off from all sources of supply (including batteries) and confirmed dead using live-dead testing techniques. The UPS will also be left disconnected for the required time to ensure that any internally stored energy is dissipated.

12.6 Detailed inspection and service of the UPS

All necessary access panels will be removed from the UPS and checked to confirm that all energy stored within it has dissipated using live-dead testing techniques. When confirmed safe to do so, the following sections will be inspected for dust and dirt build up, damage, overheating, blockage, failure, leakage or security:

Circuit-breakers, cabling and ribbon cable assemblies, ac/dc capacitors, relays and contactors, transformers, inductors, semi-conductors, PCBs, heatsinks, fuses, current transformers, ventilation fans, display panel, communications ports and auxiliary devices.

If any faulty or potentially faulty components are located the customer will be advised accordingly and the problem noted. Any dust, dirt and foreign objects which could cause failure will be removed and discarded. Once the inspection is complete, all previously removed panels will be replaced and cleaned.

12.7 Detailed inspection of the battery set

With the UPS isolated from the battery set, all necessary access panels and protective screens will be removed from the battery set to gain access to inspect the batteries. The following checks will be carried out:

- all batteries will be visually inspected for signs of damage or corrosion
- all batteries will be inspected for leaks
- all terminations will be checked to ensure they are secure
- the open circuit battery voltage will be checked to ascertain if any voltage imbalances exist. If an imbalance exists, further investigation will be carried out. The nature of the imbalance will be noted and corrective action advised.
- confirm the age of the batteries using the date code stamped on them

The inspection of the batteries will be performed in compliance with the battery safe working practice guidelines (refer to OHSPRO17). If during the inspection a battery is found to have released acid electrolyte, the acid electrolyte will be absorbed into dry sand, earth or other inert material and will not be allowed to enter any drains. The acid electrolyte can be neutralised using Soda Ash, Sodium Bicarbonate, Sodium Carbonate or Calcium Carbonate powder and the affected area will be washed thoroughly with water. Any neutralisation or absorbing materials used will be collected and placed into a sealed container to await disposal.

Once the battery inspection is complete, all previously removed panels will be replaced and cleaned.

12.8 UPS repair and or parts replacement

All necessary access panels will be removed from the UPS and a check made to confirm that all energy stored within it has dissipated using live-dead testing techniques. When confirmed safe to do so, the area relating to the failure will be inspected and replaced or repaired as necessary. All replaced components will be replaced using components of identical rating and type or an equivalent as recommended by the manufacturer only. Once the repair is complete all previously removed panels will be replaced.

12.9 Safety check

Upon completion of the preventative maintenance or repair, all of the previously removed protective panels will be checked and secured, all warning notices cleaned, the area around the system cleared and any safety issue/s raised, brought to the attention of the customer and noted.

12.10 UPS reconnection, restart and check

When safe to do so, all sources of supply to the UPS system will be reconnected and the system restarted in accordance with the UPS user manual. The UPS will be tested in all operational states e.g. on bypass, on line, on battery, etc. to ensure that the UPS operates and reports as described. During operation a full check of the display panel will be carried out to ensure that all of the values, status and buttons are functioning and reporting correctly. If the UPS has undergone repair work, then the system will be tested to ensure the fault has been repaired.

12.11 UPS status history log

Once all maintenance and repair work has been completed, the event history log from the UPS will be downloaded and stored.

12.12 UPS discharge test

If applicable, the UPS system will be discharge tested to ensure the required battery autonomy time is reached. This will be carried out using either a dummy load or the actual load depending on the site requirements. The battery discharge test can only be carried out if the battery system has been fully charged. If it is not fully charged, the charge state will be taken into consideration during the discharge. To instigate the discharge test, the mains power supply to the UPS system will be switched off to simulate a power failure and not be reinstated until the required autonomy time has been met or the connected batteries depleted.

12.13 UPS return to service

Once the engineer is satisfied that the system is ready for operation, the UPS will be switched into service in accordance with the UPS and bypass switch user manuals. A final check will be made to confirm the critical load is connected and protected.

12.14 Customer monitoring/shutdown software and systems

12.14.1 Preventative maintenance and repair

Following completion of all the work, the engineer will reconnect all monitoring systems and confirm normal operation.

12.15 Completion and handover

Once the customer is satisfied with the work undertaken, the system will be handed over and all relevant maintenance or repair documentation completed and signed.

13. Generation and Removal of Waste

All waste generated on site will be removed and disposed of in accordance with the local authority environmental policy.

14. Riello UPS References

Reference	Title
OHSSSW01	Safe Systems of Work for Manual Handling
OHSPRO01	Manual Handling Procedure
OHSSSW02	Off-Site Working
OHSSSW03	Safe System Working of Plant and Equipment
OHSPLN03	Electrical Safety Policy
OHSPRO17	Battery Safe Working Practices
H&S File	COSHH Assessments and Data Sheets
QMSFMS27	Job Sheet

Website Information Sources

www.bifm.org
British Institute of Facilities Management

www.thebci.org
Business Continuity Institute

www.cibse.org
Chartered Institution of Building Services Engineers

www.defra.gov.uk
Department of Environment, Food and Rural Affairs (DEFRA)

www.eca.co.uk
Electrical Contractors Association

www.electricity.org.uk
Energy Networks Association

www.euclid.org
European Cooperation For Lightning Detection

www.gambica.org.uk
GAMBICA Association Ltd

www.itic.org
The Information Technology Industry Council

www.theiet.org
The Institution of Engineering and Technology (formerly The IEE)

www.lpqi.org
Leonardo Power Quality Initiative

www.ofgem.gov.uk
Ofgem

www.riello-ups.com
Riello UPS Manufacturing srl

Standards

BS EN 62040-1-1: Uninterruptible power systems (UPS). General and safety requirements for UPS used in operator access areas.

BS EN 62040-1-2: Uninterruptible Power Systems (UPS). General and safety requirements for UPS used in restricted access locations.

BS EN 62040-2: Uninterruptible Power Systems (UPS). Electro-Magnetic Compatibility (EMC) requirements.

BS EN 62040-3: Uninterruptible Power Systems (UPS). Method of specifying the performance and test requirements.

BS EN 60950 (CE174-2): Information technology equipment safety.

BS EN 60269-1, IEC 60269-1: Low-voltage fuses. General requirements.

BS EN 61000-4-1, IEC 61000-4-1: Electro-Magnetic Compatibility (EMC). Testing and measurement techniques. Overview of IEC 61000-4 series.

BS EN 61000-4-2, IEC 61000-4-2: Electro-Magnetic Compatibility (EMC). Testing and measurement techniques. Electro-static discharge immunity test. Basic EMC publication.

BS EN 61000-4-3: Electro-Magnetic Compatibility (EMC). Testing and measurement. techniques. Radiated, radio-frequency, electro-magnetic field immunity test.

BS EN 61000-4-4: Electro-Magnetic Compatibility (EMC). Testing and measurement techniques. Electrical fast transient/burst immunity test.

BS EN 61000-4-5, IEC 61000-4-5: Electro-Magnetic Compatibility (EMC). Testing and measurement techniques. Surge immunity test.

BS EN 61000-4-6, IEC 61000-4-6: Electro-Magnetic Compatibility (EMC). Testing and measurement techniques. Immunity to conducted disturbances, induced by radio-frequency fields.

BS EN 61000-4-11: Electro-Magnetic Compatibility (EMC). Testing and measurement techniques. Voltage dips, short interruptions and voltage variations immunity tests.

BS EN 61000-6-4: Electro-Magnetic Compatibility (EMC). Generic standards. Emission standard for industrial environments.

BS EN 61000-2-2: Electro-Magnetic Compatibility (EMC). Environment. Compatibility levels for low-frequency conducted disturbances and signalling in public low-voltage power supply systems. Part 2-2 : Environment - Compatibility levels for low-frequency conducted disturbances and signalling in public low-voltage power supply systems.

BS EN 55022, CISPR 22: Information technology equipment. Radio disturbance characteristics. Limits and methods of measurement.

BS EN 60529: Specification for degrees of protection provided by enclosures (IP code).

BS EN 50171: Central power supply systems.

BS 6290-4: Lead-acid stationary cells and batteries. Specification for specifying valve-regulated types.

BS 7671: Requirements for electrical installations. IEE Wiring Regulations. Sixteenth edition (IEC 60364).

BS 7430: Code of practice for earthing.

BS 6651: Code of practice for protection of structures against lightning.

BS EN 50310: Application of equi-potential bonding and earthing in buildings with information technology equipment.

BS EN 50160: Voltage characteristics of electricity supplied by public distribution systems.

BS EN 60896, IEC 60896: Stationary lead-acid batteries.

BS 4142: Method for rating industrial noise affecting mixed residential and industrial areas.

BS EN 60439, IEC 60439: Low voltage switchgear and control gear assemblies.

BS EN 50098-1: Customer premises cabling for information technology. ISDN basic access.

BS EN 50173-1: Information technology. Generic cabling systems. General requirements and office areas.

BS EN 50174-1: Information technology. Cabling installation. Specification and quality assurance.

BS EN 50174-2 : Information technology. Cabling installation. Installation planning and practices inside buildings.

BS EN 50174-3: Installation technology. Cabling installation. Installation planning and practices outside buildings.

BS 2869: Fuel oils for agricultural, domestic and industrial engines and boilers. Specification.

BS 6380: Guide to low temperature properties and cold weather use of diesel fuels and gas oils conforming to BS EN 590 and classes A2 and D of BS 2869.

BS EN 55022, CISPR 22: Information technology equipment. Radio disturbance characteristics. Limits and methods of measurement.

BS EN 60298, IEC 60298: A.C. metal-enclosed switchgear and control gear for rated voltages above 1 kV and up to and including 52 kV.

BS EN 60694, IEC 60694: Common specifications for high-voltage switchgear and control gear standards.

BS EN 60947, IEC 60947: Low voltage switchgear and control gear.

BS EN 60034: Rotating electrical machines.

BS EN 50178: Electronic equipment for use in power installations.

BS EN 50272-2: Safety requirements for secondary batteries and battery installations, stationary batteries.

IEC 60364-4: Electrical installations of buildings.

IEC 60146 (CEI22): Semi-conductor electronic converters.

IEEE 519: Harmonics in power supplies.

IEEE 1459: Standard definitions for the measurement of electrical power qualities under sinusoidal, non-sinusoidal, balanced, or unbalanced conditions.

ISO 2314 BS 3135: Specification for gas turbine acceptance tests.

ISO 3046 BS 5514: Reciprocating internal combustion engines.

ISO 3977 BS 3863: Guide for gas turbine procurement.

ISO 8528 BS7698: Reciprocating internal combustion engine driven alternating current generating sets.

The Electricity supply regulations: 1988 Statutory Instrument 1988 No 1057. HM Stationery Office, London.

Engineering recommendation G5/4-1: planning levels of harmonic voltage distortion and the connection of non-linear equipment to transmission systems and distribution networks in the United Kingdom. The Energy Networks Association.

Engineering recommendation G59/1: recommendations for the connection of embedded generating plant to the public electricity suppliers distribution systems. The Electricity Association of London.

National Standards detailing lightning activity

United Kingdom	BS 6651:1992
Finland	SFS - Handbook 33
France	UTE C15-531 (1986)
Germany	DIN 57185/VDE0185 (1983)
Italy	CEI 81-1 (1990)
Netherlands	NEN 1014 (1991)
Poland	PN-55/E-05003
Sweden	SS 487 01 10 (1978)

Restriction of Hazardous Substances (RoHS) Directive 2002/95/EC.
Waste Electrical and Electronic Equipment (WEEE) Directive 2002/96/EC.

W

Watts, 38, 51
Warranties, 31, 208
Website information resources, 266
WEEE, 137, 175
Weight, 101
Wet-flooded batteries, 125
Working-hours, 209
World voltages and frequencies, 228
Wrap-around bypasses, 46

X

-

Y

Yuasa battery, 125

Z

Zero-crossing, 23, 71
Zone approach, 176

Diagrams

1. Power Quality, Problems and Solutions   Page 15-34

2. UPS Topologies and Design   Page 35-48

3. UPS Sizing and Selection   Page 49-66

4. On-Line UPS Designs   Page 67-102

Tables

Formulae

Apparent Power (pages 51, 53, 56)
Apparent Power (VA) = Volts (V) x Amps (A)

For a linear load:
Apparent Power (VA) = Real Power (W) ÷ Power Factor (pF)
Apparent Power (VA) = $\sqrt{}$(Real Power^2 + Reactive Power^2)

For a non-linear load:
Apparent Power (VA) = $\sqrt{}$(Real Power^2 + Reactive Power^2 + Distortion Power^2)

Availability (page 105)
Availability = (1 - (MTTR ÷ MTBF)) x 100%

Failure Rate (page 104)
Failure rate λ = 1 ÷ MTBF

Power Factor (pages 53, 56)
Power Factor (pF) = Real Power (W) ÷ Apparent Power (VA)*
* including both displacement and distortion components

Real Power (pages 51, 52, 53, 56)
For a resistive load:
Real Power (W) = Amps (A) x Volts (V)

For a capacitive or inductive load:
Real Power (W) = Apparent Power (VA) x Power Factor (pF)

For a linear load:
Real Power (W) = VA x Cos$\varnothing$
Real Power (W) = $\sqrt{}$(Apparent Power^2 - Reactive Power^2)

For a non-linear load:
Real Power (W) = $\sqrt{}$(Apparent Power^2 - Reactive Power^2 - Distortion Power^2)

Reactive Power (pages 53, 56)
For a linear load:
Reactive Power (VAr) = $\sqrt{}$(Apparent Power^2 - Real Power^2)

For a non-linear load:
Reactive Power (VAr) = $\sqrt{}$(Apparent Power^2 - Real Power^2 - Distortion Power^2)

Note: please refer to the relevant page number/s shown to ensure that the formulae are used in context.

UK
RIELLO UPS Ltd
Unit 68 - Clywedog Road North
Wrexham Industrial Estate
Wrexham LL13 9XN
Tel: +44 (0)1978 729 297
Fax: +44 (0)1978 729 290
www.riello-ups.co.uk
sales@riello-ups.co.uk

FRANCE
RIELLO ONDULEURS s.a.r.l
Siège, Parc d'Activités de Limonest
Bâtiment 2 - Hall A - 1, Rue des Vergers
69760 Limonest
Tel: +33 (0)4 72 17 71 08
Fax: +33 (0)4 78 35 14 22
www.riello-onduleurs.com
contact@riello-onduleurs.com

Sales Products Direction
17^19 impasse Alexis Trinquet
91030 Evry cedex
Tel: +33 (0)1 60 87 54 54
Fax: +33 (0)1 60 87 54 50
www.riello-onduleurs.com
ventes@riello-onduleurs.com

Sales Projects Direction
18, Rue du Parc 67205 Oberhausbergen
Tel: +33 (0)3 88 56 87 70
Fax: +33 (0)3 88 56 28 88
www.invertomatic-france.fr
direction@invertomatic-france.fr

ESPAÑA
RIELLO TDL s.l.
c/Terra Alta, 88 - P.I. "Can Carner"
08211 Castellar Del Vallès, Barcelona
Tel: +34 (0)93 74 71 210
Fax: +34 (0)93 71 46 562
www.riello-tdl.com
comercial@riello-tdl.com

RIELLO ENERDATA s.l.
P.l. Prado del Espino c/Vidrieros c/v Labradores
28660 Boadilla del Monte, Madrid
Tel: +34 (0)91 63 33 000
Fax: +34 (0)91 63 21 793
www.enerdata.es
enerdata@enerdata.es

DEUTSCHLAND
RIELLO UPS GmbH
Siemensstr. 12
21465 Reinbek Bei Hamburg
Tel: +49 (0)40 727 57-06
Fax: +49 (0)40 727 57-189
www.riello-ups.de
info@riello-ups.de

ASIA
RIELLO UPS
Sales Office
Riello UPS (Asia) Co., Ltd
28F, No. 500 Fute Dong Er Road
Waigaoqiao Free Trade Zone
Shanghai 200131, CHINA
Tel: +86-21-50464748
Fax: +86-21-50464648
www.riello-ups.com
edmund@rielloups.com

Technical Support Centre
Unit 416B, Wack-Wack Twin Towers,
Wack-Wack Road
Mandaluyong City - 1555 Manila
PHILIPPINES
Tel: +63 2 7250070
Fax +63 2 7275208
www.ups-service.net
mary@rielloups.com